THE
CHURCH AND MODERN SCIENCE

THE CHURCH AND MODERN SCIENCE

by

P. J. McLAUGHLIN, D.Sc.

DUBLIN: CLONMORE AND REYNOLDS, LTD
LONDON: BURNS OATES AND WASHBOURNE LTD

First Published 1957

NIHIL OBSTAT : MICHAEL O'HALLORAN, P.P., D.D.,
CENSOR THEOL. DEP.
IMPRIMI POTEST : ✠IOANNES CAROLUS,
ARCHIEP. DUBLINEN, HIBERNIÆ PRIMAS.
MAY 28, 1957.

MADE AND PRINTED IN THE
REPUBLIC OF IRELAND BY
CAHILL AND CO., LTD., DUBLIN
FOR CLONMORE AND REYNOLDS LTD.

PREFACE

THE key-field of modern thought, where perhaps the survival of Western culture is being decided, lies in the border country touching on science, philosophy and religion—at present art has no territory in this region. The great problems of our time are three-dimensional and involve the true, the wise and the good. Tensions exist not because there is ill-will among the land-owners but rather for lack of a common language. The object of this book is to promote good communications and try to help neighbours to understand one another. For this purpose we present some science for the philosopher and some philosophy for the man of science The standpoint taken up in philosophy is that of the critical realist, because we think his point of view can be helpful to the modern scientist who now feels that his subject cannot live healthily in isolation.

The second part of the book consists almost entirely of addresses delivered by H.H. Pope Pius XII to scientific and other professional bodies. Their value for our age we refer to elsewhere. Where we translate the discourses, our aim has been to assist the student and at the same time follow the advice of St. Jerome quoting Horace's golden rule against literal renderings: "*Ne verbum verbo redderes, fides interpres.*" We have accordingly made an effort to present in plain and readable English a faithful interpretation of the Sovereign Pontiff's mind. Some allowance has been made for the differing qualities of the Latin and English temperaments, the one restrained, the other copious.

Besides the difference of style and genius in the languages, one has to remember that papal documents deal with problems that are in themselves difficult and often highly abstract. To induce as many as possible to consult these immensely important papers, we have inserted cross-heads or sub-titles generously. Our translations are, of course, in no way official. For the convenience of anyone desirous of reading the original texts, we have provided numerous references in the list of sources.

P. J. McL.

Maynooth,
29th June, 1957.

TAIL-PIECES. The tail-pieces reproduce the impressions which the artist, Sr. M. Berenice, O.P., received from photographs by Rev. Dr. Casey, O.P., Newbridge, of exhibits in the Maynooth Museum of Science (except item 11, which is in Trinity College, Dublin).

They represent : 1. an early Dublin microscope (eighteenth century) (p. 9) ; 2, Joly's calorimeter (p. 72) ; 3, 4, 5, 6, Callan's galvanometer (p. 99), induction coil (p. 131), electric motor (p. 177), and rapid contact-breaker (p. 183) ; 7 and 8, sextant (p. 207) and telescope (p. 259) by Yeates ; 9, theodolite (p. 281) ; 10, differential thermometer (p. 350) ; 11, the " P.M." dynamo (1832) (p. 360) ; 12, Hartley's spectrometer (presented by University College, Dublin) (p. 366).

CONTENTS

ACKNOWLEDGEMENTS

I wish to express my gratitude to Father Stephen Browne, S.J., for facilities at the Catholic Central Library, Dublin; to Rev. Denis Faul of the Dunboyne Establishment, Maynooth, for help in checking and tracing sources; to P. Walsh of the staff of the Dublin Institute for Advanced Studies for invaluable secretarial assistance; to the publishers and printers for unfailing courtesy at all times; and to those responsible for the tail-pieces.

For permission to quote or make use of their publications, I gratefully acknowledge the courtesy of the following publishers, periodicals and individuals: the Pontifical Court Club, Salesian Press, London (*Catholic Documents*); the Catholic Truth Society, London; the Tablet Publishing Company, London (*The Tablet*); Maison de la Bonne Presse, 5 rue Bayard, Paris (*Documentation Catholique*); Very Reverend Dean Mulcahy (*The Hymns of the Roman Breviary and Missal*) and Sir Edmund Whittaker (*Space and Spirit*).

PART ONE

THE NATURE OF SCIENCE

I *THE THEORY OF SCIENCE*

1. *The Philosophy of Science*

T HOUGH historians and scientists have gone into the question, it must be admitted that the unique development of modern science in Western Europe is a fact still calling for an adequate explanation. It is not enough to say that science grew out of its swaddling clothes because natural philosophers deserted the library and the cloister and gave up theorizing for empiricism. Bacon's view that " the true and lawful goal of science is the endowing human life with new discoveries and powers " was the aim of other very intelligent civilizations, such as the Chinese, Islamic and Byzantine; yet not one of them succeeded in anticipating the scientific revolution of the 16th and 17th centuries in Europe. The Byzantines were eminently practical as a people, but their culture was sterile. The late medieval and renaissance criticism of Aristotelian physics was primarily due to men who were neither pure scientists nor pure technologists, but understood both and were philosophers of science besides. An interest in the theory of science, curiosity about its basic principles, would appear to be an indispensable factor in the development of science itself. This opinion is sufficient to justify an enquiry into the philosophy of science, as the subject is now commonly called.

But what exactly is to be understood by the philosophy of science? According to G. J. Whitrow (*British Journal for the Philosophy of Science,* Nov., 1956) it is " the critical study and systematic elucidation of the processes of scientific method, discovery and explanation, and of the particular habits of thought which the practice of science tends to encourage ". Its connection with studies in the history of science can be close and can prove profitable to both disciplines. W. P. D. Wrightman in his book, *The Growth of Scientific Ideas* (Edinburgh, 1951) believes that " a historical study undertaken in a critical spirit provides a better introduction to scientific method than any abstract discussion ". Renoirte in his *Éléments de Critique des Sciences* (Louvain, 1945) outlines the relation between epistemology, the general theory of knowledge, and the philosophy of science, which he describes as scientific criticism in no carping spirit but as a department or prolongation of epistemology. It attempts to see and say what exactly science is, and what it does. It should study how scientific method has been progressively formed down the centuries. The philosopher of science does not tell the man in the laboratory what he should do, and how he should do it. But as we pass from a securely established discipline like physical science, to say, the social sciences and to other fairly recent additions to the scientific spectrum, these new departments are seen to find in philosophy some central guidance.

In the present section, keeping a close eye on historical developments, we seek to examine and clarify rapidly, without too much detail or profound study, the outstanding elements in the structure of any science, but especially as typified in the physical sciences. In view of their importance for many fields of knowledge and human activity, we refer especially to physical law, physical theory, scientific method and the notions of chance and frequency in statistics. The precise nature of physical law is a big question. Few thoughtful readers but will find the Papal address on the relation of natural laws to the source of all law, the divine eternal law, invaluable for its breadth of view and depth of analysis. A few notes are added to elucidate what may be strange or technical to some of our readers. It has been thought it would help to say a little about other forms of law, including moral and civil law, and how they differ from each other as well as from physical law. The latter is always a generalization, while moral law is an imperative.

Many streams join to form the swelling current that is now the philosophy of science. Amongst the various and widely spread tributaries we may mention French elements represented by Poincaré, Duhem and the Louvain school. Germany had a strong representative in Ernest Mach who influenced English thought through his disciple Karl Pearson, author of the *Grammar of Science*. Apart from the purely formal school of mathematical logicians to whom we refer elsewhere, a native British flavour was provided in N. R. Campbell whose *Physics: The Elements*, benefited greatly through being introduced in a French dress to continental readers by Émile Borel. A new outlook is being produced in Britain by writings like those of F. Sherwood Taylor and E. F. Caldin, and by bodies like the Aristotelian and Aquinas Societies of London. An account of the efforts of the Viennese school and its logical positivism will be found in *Modern Science and its Philosophy* by Phillip Frank (Harvard University Press). There is considerable evidence of a steadily growing scholastic contribution. In Ireland, Dr. Alfred O'Rahilly's *Electromagnetics* is notable, and sound criticism also appears in Henry Gill's *Fact and Fiction in Modern Science*. The scholastic movement shows itself likewise in America where V. E. Smith's *Philosophical Physics* (Harper, New York, 1950) was a harbinger of the activity now going on in Notre Dame University. Several publications have appeared as a result of the work that is being done by the Albertus Magnus Lyceum for Natural Sciences, River Forest, Illinois, where the aim is to integrate the sciences through a dialectical approach. The publications of the New York Philosophical Library represent a variety of viewpoints.

2. *Physical Law*

Modern science is " in method an interaction of induction and deduction, while in purpose it is an interplay of the comprehension and conquest of nature ".—S. Sambursky: *The Physical World of the Greeks.*

In our everyday experience we notice regularities in the world around us. We see the sun rise in the east and set in the west. We note that clouds from a certain quarter bring rain. We observe there are substances possessing identical properties—the same lustre and taste, the same hardness and density, the same melting point. Like Adam naming the animals, we then speak of iron, copper and silver; and, later on, we talk about metals. Passing over the question of how we arrive at classes and universals (it is quite a big jump from ' this cloud ' to ' clouds ', or, from ' this bit of silver' to ' silver '), we admittedly tend to correlate facts of nature, and to generalize, perhaps illicitly. At their various levels, the generalizations constitute laws of nature or natural laws. The primary aim of physics is to discover such laws. As one man has put it: " It is the chief function of science to trace the causes of events and build up a system of general laws."

Physical laws are of two kinds, qualitative and quantitative. A qualitative law isolates out of the rich manifold of experience a relatively few significant facts and describes the procedure or recipe to be followed in order to bring them into correlation by a causal series, a cause and effect relation. The full law would state what exactly has to be done to produce such and such a result. But a great mass of detail is never put into words or symbols, and is only learned in the laboratory. Scientific description is by its nature a simplified description of what happens and of its relation to other parts of the universe, and is far from complete. A descriptive law is a qualitative law, and it is important for focussing attention on significant ideas as well as on significant facts. The law " like charges of electricity repel each other ", expresses a significant fact only for those who through experience and reflection have grasped the idea of an electric charge. Ampère's notion of an electric current and his ' swimming ' rule for finding its direction were both of tremendous importance in the development of electrical science, though neither is a quantitative law.

In recent decades there has been a tendency to belittle, and even ignore, qualitative physical law, perhaps because of the dictum of Kelvin:

> " When you can measure what you are speaking about and
> express it in numbers, you know something about it; but when
> you cannot measure it, when you cannot express it in num-
> bers, your knowledge is of a meagre and unsatisfactory kind."

It is too often forgotten nowadays that qualitative laws (they include descriptions, definitions, classifications, recipes, models and all manner of generalization) are the indispensable forerunner of quantitative law. If men had not first noted how in various circumstances a beam of light is reflected, refracted or absorbed, there would never have been the quantitative laws of Snell and Brewster. Descriptive laws like ' hot bodies radiate heat ' and ' iron is a better thermal conductor than wood ', whether discovered by induction or deduced from theory, are necessary, not only for practical ends, but also for carrying out experiments and for furthering knowledge and making fresh discoveries. Physical science has its origin in purely qualitative observations, in the study of physical changes such as water turning into ice or steam, lightning flashing, in remarking the changes in things which are perceptible to the senses. Physical science would never begin if we waited to replace our sense impressions by measurements. Through reflection on these sense impressions we become familiar with physical causes and effects, with physical events or phenomena.

There are two sources of confusion to which it is well to advert at this stage, though we shall not discuss them until later (§ II). They concern the existence of physical cause. On the one hand, its very existence is denied by some philosophers who hold that cause and effect relations do not occur in physical laws. They hold that physical laws are only mathematical and express purely formal relations. I fear the holders of such views would fare ill in a laboratory if they tried an experiment without knowing what caused what. At the other extreme are those who confuse physical cause with ontological cause. We shall return to this question in due course.

Discovery of quantitative laws consists in perceiving (and sometimes in inventing new ideas and new mathematics to express) a constant relation between the measures obtained in a set of precise and controlled experiments. The scientific way of discovering laws is to study what actually happens. Fourier's analysis, Fresnel's integrals and Heaviside's operators had their origin in experimental studies of heat, light and electricity. We may sum up the results of experiments in an algebraic relation, but this general relation or formula is no more the physical law than a coded telegram without its dictionary is a message. The key to a physical law is in the laboratory. The physicist studies states and changes of matter, not the silent symbols of mathematical equations, which may mean anything or nothing.

Physical law is based on two important assumptions which are not infrequently taken for granted and are not made explicit. Physical law assumes the uniformity of nature, that what happened yesterday can happen to-day and to-morrow. It also assumes the validity of inductive generalization, which is to say, that it is valid to pass from the individual physical fact in the laboratory and connect it up with the big wide world's multiplicity. We shall defer consideration of these matters for the present.

Experimental laws are the expression of real factual relations. In formulating them, the physicist takes every care he can to eliminate or allow for subjectivity, and to study only the objective fact; he *depersonalizes,* but he can never be sure he has perfectly succeeded. He can never know if he has allowed for all the factors, subjective and objective, influencing a measure. Hence he can never be certain that his law will not be modified by future discoveries.

Physical law is thus *progressive* and *corrigible.* The man of science no longer claims finality for his laws (as did some of his predecessors last century) but he claims he attains an ever closer approach to truth as his law grows by accretion and emendation. His law is provisional, and in this lies its strength, for it can always be improved so as to admit fresh facts and triumph over an additional decimal.

Again, physical laws are *schematic,* that is, they are sketchy outlines and incomplete, because in framing them we find it impossible to include in one formulation all the pertinent factors even if we know them. Like jugglers, we are limited in our powers to deal with a variety of entities at one and the same time. In our physical laws we take nature piece-meal; we leave out a lot and introduce arbitrary simplifications.

Even if the law is formulated in precise terms, it may be illusory to apply it or to attempt to verify it with exactitude. Consider, for instance, an application of the Newtonian law of gravitation. To find the period of a planet's rotation round the sun, the computer first takes account of the solar and planetary masses and the distance between them. This he improves by considering and allowing for the influence of other planets. But since all bodies affect one another, the exact calculation would involve every body in the universe. It is not practical to make such a calculation, but in principle and with the expenditure of sufficient labour one can attain any given degree of precision. This method of successive approximations is characteristic of science which constantly gets closer to its objective but without ever reaching it.

INEXACTNESS OF PHYSICAL LAWS. As has been pointed out by Duhem and others, for the above reason physical laws are never really exact but only approximate. There are additional reasons for the inexactness of physical law. There are natural defects and limitations in all measurements. Some arise from the side of the equipment, others have their source in human imperfections, while others again spring from defects in theory. The use of an instrument itself generally depends on theory, a theory which is perfectible and only approximately accurate at any given stage of its history. Progress in thermometry, it is well known, was dependent on developments in the theory and laws of gases.

Sometimes, too, the theory on which a measure is based, needs interpretation before a measurement can be made. Not infrequently, there is ambiguity of interpretation, and the measures suffer accordingly. Modern theoretical physics, as we all know, abounds in such ambiguities.

Again, there may be a fundamental ignorance of the exact law. According to the principle of indeterminacy, exact laws are unknowable in the atomic domain.

Even if law and theory are precise and unambiguous, their application and verification must be inexact on account of the natural limitations of instruments and observers. Instruments are coarse. No instrument or apparatus is indefinitely sensitive, but each has a threshold below which its indications are illusory. (In physics, zero does not mean absence of a property.) Since instruments are perfectible, endlessly so, no actual instrument can ever be perfect, but must retain some degree of coarseness and insensitivity. From the time of the Renaissance, the power, penetration and precision of our senses have prodigiously increased because of apparatus that daily becomes more perfect, but while coarseness is diminished, it can never be completely removed.

Besides the natural defects of instruments, there is personal error in reading and using them. The combination of personal and instrumental inexactitudes produces an unavoidable amount of experimental error which is necessarily present in every physical measurement. Statistical studies of experimental errors can be made and the results compared with the mathematical theory of random errors. This may lead to the detection and elimination of systematic error, but it is doubtful if statistical and mathematical theory are strictly comparable in such a matter, as we hope to show later.

Some phenomena cannot be measured in any strict sense of the word, for example, smells, tastes, and in general the intensive character of properties, e.g., temperature. We can add a foot to a foot and produce a length of two feet; but adding a gram of water at $1°$ C to a gram of water at $1°$ C does not result in water at $2°$ C. Quantities are measured, but intensities are only marked.

Finally, let us mention two fundamental difficulties that produce uncertainties, and may therefore militate against the ultimate exactness of physical law. First, there is a vicious circle in the measurement of time and duration. Time is measured by uniform motion, and uniform motion is measured by observing that equal intervals of space are traversed in equal time-intervals. Lastly, we are always faced with the basic problem; how assure that measuring scales keep constant. We never can really do so. We can never attain to certitude in this matter.

LAW AND PRINCIPLE. A physical principle is sometimes confused with a physical law, but there is a clear enough distinction between the two. A principle is more stable than a law. Once it is accepted, a principle cannot be upset by experiment, whereas a physical law is invariably modified by fresh experience. A principle is conventionally stable, much as the standard yard or metre is by agreement defined to be a yard or a metre long and may not be modified by the results of new researches. Newton's so-called laws of motion are really principles. The first, the principle of inertia, is in flat contradiction with experience. Three centuries ago, this bold powerful concept changed the face of science and swept away the two thousand year old Aristotelian physics. The second is a pure physical definition, an operational one; while the third has pragmatic or methodological value. We return to this again.

Physical principles are of two kinds, the one *a priori* in character includes axioms, postulates and basic ideas, while the other is rather pragmatic and has been adapted from experimental laws.

Experimental laws, as we have already seen, are provisional. When a scientist is confronted with a discrepancy between a physical law and some new experience, he may do one of two things. He may modify the law to make it conform with the fresh experience; and in this way, he would make the law less provisional and nearer to reality. The ideal gas law was found by experiment to be only approximately true for real gases, and Van der Waals introduced two new factors into it to make it do better service—he modified the law. Or, a scientist may refuse to alter the old law, to which he accords an absolute character. This is to erect the law into a principle. A perfect or ideal gas law is then defined as one for which the old law holds. No such gas exists. So we get an ideal gas by definition, an ideal " object " defined by a principle. (Such an ideal has its uses in facilitating the study and further investigation of actual gases—it has pragmatic value.) A principle partakes of the logical rather than the factual order.

In general, between the ideal objects defined by principles and real objects there is a difference which experiment can always make more precise.

The danger of confounding laws which are experimental and corrigible with principles which are regarded as absolute is ever present. Thus a distinguished physicist like Sir Arthur Eddington looked on *entropy* as an *a priori* conventional symbol, and failed to see it was a mathematical construct based on experience. The law of entropy states only a fact without giving a reason. It is a pragmatic principle adapted from the experimental law that heat processes are uni-directional, that heat of itself passes only from a hot to a cold body, and not *vice versa*. The principle of entropy is, so to speak, a mathematical physicist's expression of the one-way traffic law of the universe.

HYPOTHESIS AND LAW. All hypotheses are working hypotheses until they are fully checked by experiment. When thus tested and proved, they have the same value as other experimental laws, no more, no less. The hypothesis is said to have been verified. It is now a law, an experimental law, based on induction; it is a statement in less or more precise terms of fact in the physical world.

PHYSICAL CAUSE AND LAW. The subject matter of physical science is not ideas and abstract truths as in mathematics, but concrete, contingent facts. There is, however, no science of the particular. So the variable passing fact itself is not the proper object of these sciences. Rather, we seek to find the *cause* that produces it, and we search for the general and enduring or permanent *law* that governs it. Yet, though the fact is not the object of science, it is the necessary means. Unless one studies and observes the fact, one cannot penetrate to the *cause* and the *law*.

What precisely is meant by cause and law here? We have to take them in an empiric, phenomenal sense, not in a metaphysical sense. A physical cause is any phenomenon or event which is necessary and sufficient to determine the appearance of another event or happening, the latter being called the effect of the former, which is then called the cause. A physical law is the constant relation linking a physical cause to its effect, so that the former being placed, the latter follows. Thus the hammer strikes and the gong sounds; fire heats and the metal expands. Neither physical cause nor physical law explains itself, and each therefore requires a sufficient reason. The latter necessarily consists in a *metaphysical cause*, i.e., a real and concrete being that exercises an effective influence on the production of the phenomenon.

At first sight it would seem that natural science has no need of metaphysical causes. But this would be a grave mistake. Without them, *induction* would be inexplicable. If one had nothing but phenomenal or physical causes and laws, generalization would be impossible, and physical law would be no more than an empirical statement, a dumb witness of a constancy of *fact* in the succession of events.

Positivists confuse the two orders, the physical and the metaphysical, and they abuse the process of abstraction. Their assertion that " the order of nature is produced by the regularity of phenomena " is an evident sophism. In a machine, the regularity of movement does not stop us from looking for a power which causes and explains its action.

A law of nature merely describes regular behaviour, and such behaviour requires a metaphysical cause or agent to explain it.

STRUCTURE OF A SCIENCE. It may be helpful at this stage to outline the structure of a physical science. One may represent the basic features as follows: —

    I. Significant facts and ideas.

    II. Laws:
        (*a*) Descriptive;
        (*b*) Quantitative.

    IIa. Principles:
        (*a*) *A priori;*
        (*b*) Pragmatic.

IIb. Hypotheses:
    (*a*) Working;
    (*b*) Confirmed.

III. Theories:
    (*a*) Concrete;
    (*b*) Abstract.

IV. Syntheses of Theories, or Systems.

We note there is constant interplay of fact and idea under heading I. We note too that laws generalize the facts, and theories generalize the laws and the great syntheses subsume the healthy theories. This is the characteristic of the inductive method, a continual ascent from the particular or less general to the more general.

INTERPLAY OF IDEA AND FACT. The fact suggests the idea, the idea directs the investigation and the investigation checks the idea, said Claude Bernard, referring to the three essential movements in the experimental method.

The experimental method reproduces the circumstances surrounding a happening in various ways and combinations, but always under experimental control (i.e., factors can be varied in a known way at will). The art of the method lies in the best choice of combination of circumstances, and in the craftsmanship of exercising the required control.

It is easy to appraise the results, but usually great acumen is needed to weld them into a coherent system or theory.

We can never be sure of re-establishing all the circumstances that led to the result. Moreover, not all of them are essential. Without some enquiry into the causes that operate, we may repeat some trivial circumstances and omit essentials.

Ideas interpret facts and give them their significance, but ideas must be checked by facts. This has not always been understood. The hypothetical or *a priori* method has neglected facts and exaggerated the part of preconceived ideas. Taking a charitable view of the Master's inconsistencies on the subject, we may say this is what Newton was referring to when he said: " *Hypotheses non fingo*—I am no theorist," meaning he was not a spinner of idle, extravagant and fantastic theories.

At the other extreme is the empirical method which rejects all original ideas and attends only to facts. The empiricist sees that certain results follow from a stated or given set of facts; so, in order to repeat the result, he repeats the circumstances, slavishly, dully and unintelligently, without understanding, in a brutish way. The experimental method avoids both extremes and achieves the golden mean. With the theorist, it admits the capital importance of the idea, but taking it as a starting point only, it seeks a sanction for it in experience. With the empiricist, it appreciates the supreme value of facts, but understands also that they have to be interpreted by some theory and tested further by reasoned fresh experiment. In this way it escapes the extravagance of the one and the insufficiency of the other. From this intimate linkage of experience (which provides the particular) and reason (which seeks to probe experience and find in it the general)—from this harmonious concourse of fact and idea there results science. *Connubium mentis et rei*—science is a marriage of mind and reality, as Bacon said. Yet we keep in mind that science and empiricism differ only in degree; even though we regard scientific knowledge as the opposite of empirical knowledge. This is the method practised by the great scientists. It has led to the great discoveries. Its judicious use supposes the two great qualities that constitute scientific acumen. On the one hand a powerful imagination which conjures up and anticipates what must be; on the other an exactness and rigour in the study of things which excludes every iota of bias or illusion.

In the *Novum Organum,* Bacon has described the three methods in one of those picturesque figures of which he had the gift. The empiricists, said he, are like the ants that gather together material without any cohesion. The theorists resemble the spider that spins out of its own body beautiful and delicate webs without solidity or value. The experimentalist is like the bee that extracts from flowers the material for its honey; then by its own art turns it into nectar.

FRUITFUL IDEAS. The most fertile ideas in physical science have been, perhaps, the root notions which correspond to discrete and continuous quantity in mathematics, namely, the concepts of particle and wave, employed as models or as analogies or even literally and with crude realism at different times in the history of science. The particle of matter appears as mass-point, star, material body, or corpuscle in various disciplines from studies of gases to astronomy; as molecule with marked shades of difference for the chemist and the physicist; as atom, electron and various " ultimate " entities; as quantum of energy, even—discrete supports for energy all. The wave, a symbol of continuity, representing a mode or vehicle for continuous exchange of energy, has appeared implicitly or explicitly in connection with a variety of media, including various æthers of both ancient and modern times, an endless number of fluids invented to explain phenomena in electricity, magnetism, heat and light, and all manner of radiation and vibratory happenings. Sometimes the fluid is imponderable, as in the caloric theory of heat, or even turns up with a negative weight as in the case of phlogiston. The prevailing theory of wave mechanics continues the tradition wholeheartedly and is inspired by the dual analogy of wave and particle, drawn from the seaside breakers and the sportsman's football, or other equivalents.

Many sciences spend centuries seeking to find, clarify, and define their fundamental ideas, their seed or germinal notions. It has taken upwards of two thousand years to evolve the present concept of a chemical compound, and the idea is still being modified and refined as the domain of chemistry is extended by fresh experiment and discovery. Like scientific law, the seed ideas of a science are themselves progressive and corrigible, never final, never static unless the science is dying. Modern science is very much alive; and life, growth and change—constant, bewildering, energetic, dynamic change—are notable among its characteristics and signs.

THEORIES. Theories play an important part in the growth and development of a science.

In the history of physics, we can distinguish two kinds of fruitful theories which we may call the concrete and the abstract types. Concrete theories would include all manner of models and analogies that can be imagined, various effluvia and fluids, the " hard glassy spheres " of Newton's atoms and the " elastic strings " of Faraday's magnetic and electric " lines of force ", the quasi-elastic solid of MacCullagh and the vortex-sponges of W. Thomson and Fitzgerald, imagined and conceived in order to explain the " æther ", along with electro-magnetic phenomena. The early experimenters had often a naïve but robust belief in the literal reality of their models with exact correspondence at all parts between nature and the behaviour of the model. Later more sophisticated workers supposed that phenomena occurred " as if " the scheme of things were as imagined in the model, but not really so. They belonged to the " als ob " school. The movement of sophistication seems to have moved perilously near scepticism in recent decades. Even atoms are now looked on by some as only models, while a sober review of the evidence would suggest they are as real as tennis-balls though the structure of light is too coarse ever to allow us to see them.

The analytic theory of heat developed by the great mathematician, Fourier, is the prototype of the abstract theories. To the experimenter, Fourier's theory of heat conduction is a mathematical model which exhibits the same essential features as a mechanical or concrete model; as, for instance, the kinetic theory of gas. At every point, from postulates to suppositions, from verifications to conclusions there is parallelism. The great difference is that abstract theories emphasize *logical,* and the concrete theories stress *analogical,* considerations. Otherwise the resemblance is formal and complete.

Following Poincaré and Duhem, mathematical writers try to insist that the abstract type of theory is the only valid kind of physical theory. They attempt to provide a logical synthesis of the laws that have been verified by experiment. According to Duhem, the mathematician or theoretical physicist constructs by means of signs and marks borrowed from arithmetic and geometry a symbolic representation of what our senses—aided by instruments —tell us. Once got, the representation lends itself to reasoning processes that are easier, surer, and quicker than the purely experimental data they replace. By this artifice, physics assumes a scope and precision it could never attain without the schematic form we call theoretical or mathematical physics. (Duhem: *Le Mixte.*)

The experimental physicist and the critical realist do not accept such a view in its entirety. They hold it is in essentials in contradiction with experience and with the whole history of science. They point out that throughout history, abstract and concrete theories have reflected the two kinds of outlook that have at different times been ascendant in physical science. There is the mind, like the mind of Boys and Kelvin, with strong intuitions of concrete reality. This type of mind is at home with mechanical models and elastic springs and feels happy with them: a big-end or a gyroscope is as simple to it as the concept of a point or a line is to a mathematician. This mind is suspicious of the abstract idea that is many removes from reality. Darwin, for instance, would not chop-logic with his critics; instead he crushed them by pounding them with facts. By contrast, the severely logical mind loves refined theories and aims at simplicity and unity through high-power economical concepts such as the " potential-function " in gravitational theory, or the " characteristic-function " of Hamilton's optics and dynamics. These two kinds of mind are reflected in the two classes of theory we mention. The one gives us a picture-gallery to excite the imagination, the other a chain of elegant arguments to convince and enchant the reason. The one stimulates the experimenter to search for new phenomena, the other tempts him to philosophize and try to rationalize the empiric, and bring the multiple facts of the universe all under the single wing of law and order.

FUNCTION OF A SCIENTIFIC THEORY. In practice, scientific theories serve three main ends. First, they are usually designed to provide in whole or in part a more or less logical or analogical synthesis of experimental laws and facts. Next, it is a very important part of their function to help the physicist to discover new laws. This it does chiefly by suggesting and predicting new phenomena through analogy of the model or a new set of equations, deductively derived from the basic assumptions of the theory and leading to new experiments for verifying the suppositions of the theory. Finally, a theory provides images and terms useful to the physicist for conversing in a human way with his fellows and discussing and appraising the experimental findings.

A good theory is a fruitful theory and evokes new ideas, but it need not be literally true; i.e., it corresponds but need not conform rigorously with reality. It need not even be consistent, that is, free from contradiction. The æther theory of light was a mass of contradictions long before it was abandoned. The Rutherford-Bohr atom formally contradicts the laws of electro-dynamics. The biological theory of evolution is diametrically opposed to the physicist's second law of thermodynamics. The molecule of the chemist is a very different affair from that of the physicists in statistical mechanics.

IMPERMANENT NATURE OF SCIENTIFIC THEORIES. The history of science shows that scientific theories are to be regarded as large-scale hypotheses which are rarely confirmed in the long run except in part. A theory is justified and retained in so far as it serves as (a) a substratum for a host of facts and laws, and (b) impels the scientist to the fresh experiments or observations which it suggests. A theory in science is thus good or bad, elegant or unattractive to the mind, but it is never true or false. It is a working hypothesis at all times until and in so far as it is confirmed by experiment, and it is a good theory as long as it makes a scientist reflect and work. The history of natural science from Thales to Einstein makes it clear that few scientific theories have any more permanence than fashions in hair styles or medical treatments. Like hypotheses on the smaller scale, they are retained only in so far as they are confirmed by experiment and have a utility as satisfying and suggestive models. Like hypotheses also, that part of theories endures as true knowledge concerning the physical world which has been confirmed by experiment.

CONFLICT OF THEORIES. When there is conflict between two theories, as for instance, between the relativity theories of Einstein and Newton, there may be other considerations.

From the practical standpoint, there was little to choose between Einstein and Newton. For theoretical and methodological reasons, however, Einstein's theory is preferred to Newton's because it obeys the fundamental guiding principle (not always followed) of mathematical physics that " whatever is expressed other than the relations between measurements is foreign to the pure method of theoretical physics ". This does not hold for experimental physics, either in practice or in theory.

How a scientific theory is constructed, functions and is replaced by a new theory is well illustrated in the history of the corpuscular and wave theories of light of which a full account has been given in Whittaker's *History of the Theories of the Aether and Electricity.*

The history of theories in physical science frequently illustrates how from false premises either true or false conclusions can come. For example, Descartes deduced correctly Snell's law of refraction of light from a theory containing one false premise, namely, that light travels faster in a dense than in a rare medium. His was the error of affirming the consequent, the common fallacy in inductive science.

SPIRAL PROGRESS OF SCIENCE. Starting from ordinary sense experience and qualitative generalizations, the scientist translates some of them into quantitative facts, that is, linked sets of numbers furnished by definite measuring instruments used in prescribed fashion. Between the numbers he discovers functional relations called laws which 'explain' his facts. He explains the laws by a system of more general linked equations called a theory. By pure deductive reasoning or by analogy, he draws from the theory suggestions for fresh experiments and for new and more precise measuring equipment (this is a function of the theory to some extent). All this results in the discovery of new laws and in the more precise formulation of old ones. Sometimes the new discovery cannot be explained (i.e., reasonably inferred) from the old theory, and then a modification or a new theory is required. (This is a trait of science: a single new fact can demolish an elaborate theory centuries old.) This in turn suggests new postulates and new equations and better instruments, and so the spiral continues. Equations which have definitely been acquired under one theory are retained, though the supporting images of the old theory are or may be discarded.

REALITY OF SUPPORTING IMAGES OR MODEL. The model consists of a few elements (e.g., atom, electron, particles and local motion) which usually are not data of experience but postulates of the physicist. Thus, no one has ever experienced æther or its waves, corpuscles or their swift motion in straight lines, molecules or atoms or the host of entities that are now supposed to populate the sub-atomic world. These were all posited by their inventors, Huyghens, Fresnel, Descartes, Newton, Higgins, Dalton, Avogadro, Ampère, Rutherford, Bohr, Einstein, Planck. They cannot be assumed *a priori*. The meaning of such concepts must be justified by experiment. Sometimes they are open to test, and their existence can be verified. Until recently it was hoped that with constantly improving apparatus this could be done for all entities however small. According to present ideas, however, it is considered in the domain of atomic physics that the elements entering into the model are not subject to strict experimental check, and so they must remain in the realm of unverified hypothesis.

INTERPRETATION OF A MODEL. Up to some 30 years ago, most if not all leading scientists believed a model expressed the inner constitution of things: that is, they considered that material things not only acted " as if " they were composed of atoms, but were actually composed of atoms; light was not just analogous to waves in the æther but was waves of æther. To-day, there is a tendency to go to the other extreme. Models are regarded as having their uses but not as valid representations of the material world. They are imagined rather than experienced. One of their functions is to provide us with an image and language to help us converse intelligibly on the subject-matter of science. Moderate realists would hold there is some sort of correspondence between the model and the material world, quite good correspondence in so far as conclusions are soundly based on experience and inferences from experience. The epistemological questions, however, do not fall within the province of physical science unless in so far as they involve physico-chemical facts.

SCIENTIFIC EXPLANATION. To the philosopher, explanation is satisfying only when it is in terms of ultimate causes. The physicist is content with explanations in terms of secondary causes and physical laws or theories.

In everyday life, one explains by giving *causes,* efficient causes or *agents,* in answer to questions such as: Who did it? Why did he do it? How (When, where, with what . . .) did he do it? If we ask: Why does a body fall? and we are told: Because of gravitation, it brings about the fall. We still ask, Why? and we can keep on asking Why? without ever getting a final answer. The physicist may say: Gravity is a force, and a force accelerates matter. This is a more general explanation, but it is not final, it does not put a stop to questioning as does the answer: ' John,' in reply to the question: "Who did it?" The physicist may explain facts by showing they can be deduced or analogically inferred from laws. Laws are similarly explained by deduction or inference from theories. Such an explanation is not in terms of ultimate causes, but it shows the law is a particular instance of a more general law, or is what you might expect from the nature of the model.

As a support for the more general laws or theories, the scientist may imagine a mechanism or model so constructed that it parallels the phenomena observed. He may then make use of the model to explain that objects in the real world act " as if " they were constituted after the manner of the model. So Newton made use of the corpuscular theory to explain optical phenomena, while Fresnel employed the wave model for the same purpose.

EINSTEIN'S THEORY OF RELATIVITY. Many of the foregoing points are illustrated in the supersession of Newtonian mechanics by Einstein's theory of relativity. It is perhaps unfortunate that the theory is called relativity, since actually it was designed to express the *absolute* character of physical laws, that is, their invariance or constancy.

Up to the beginning of the century it was considered by physicists that light was propagated in a special stationary and immobile medium, the æther. In these conditions the earth should at some season of the year or other betray motion relative to the æther, but the very precise measurements of Michelson failed to detect any such motion. It became a problem how to explain or even understand this nul result if the Newtonian idea of relative motion and its effect on physical laws held true.

According to Newtonian mechanics, the ordinary laws of physics do not change when you jump from the ground on to a uniformly moving vehicle (an unaccelerated vehicle), but the laws of electrodynamics—Maxwell's equations—do change, and are different on the ground from what they are on the steady-moving vehicle.

(1) In his special theory of relativity (1905), Einstein supposed that all physical laws, whether mechanical or electrodynamic, keep exactly the same on all systems in uniform relative motion to each

other. In his *general* theory of relativity (1919), he extended this *principle* to accelerated systems.

(2) Einstein's second principle was: The speed of light is the same for all systems in steady motion relative to one another. A beam of light has the same velocity relative to us whether we move or not (as long as we move without acceleration). This is in flat contradiction to the Newtonian principle. It is a plain acceptance of the physical result that no motion has been detected of the earth relative to the æther, that in all circumstances and experiments the velocity of light is constant in a given medium.

Once these two principles are admitted, the electrodynamical laws are expressed in exactly the same fashion for all systems in unaccelerated motion relative to each other. Further the nul result of Michelson's experiment is " explained ", as well as other physical and astronomical facts formerly hard to understand or interpret. The new principles, however, demand a recast of New-tonian " laws " or principles of motion, and those of us who are set in our ways, or whose ' common sense ' knowledge is based on the science of the past generation, find it naturally enough rather bewildering.

Einstein's theory is a physical theory and has nothing to do with metaphysics. No matter how certain the formulæ of Einstein may be, they are capable of being interpreted in an infinity of ways. The physicist chooses the interpretation which is the most com-prehensive or the most convenient (i.e., which establishes most order and unity in his science). This does not mean that the theory is ontologically true. The interpretation is hypothetical, " as if " or " als ob ", by analogy.

The physicist will not hesitate to drop an elegant and beautiful synthesis once he finds another that appears preferable. Stalin put this in his own way when he told the Conference of Stakhanovites in a memorable speech on the need of his country for modern science:

> " Science is called science because it recognizes no fetishes and does not fear to raise a hand against that which is dying and old, because it listens attentively to the voice of experience and practice."

NEWTON'S LAWS OF MOTION. For two thousand years men fol-lowed Aristotle and believed that the all-important distinction in mechanical science lay between rest and motion. Newton showed it was far better to attend to the difference between steady and unsteady motion. Einstein's contribution was to show that the Newtonian conception requires modification in the case of bodies moving with very high speed.

In Newtonian mechanics, rest is a particular instance of steady motion, namely, the case where a body's speed is too small to be measured. To-day we are well aware that rest and motion are relative terms. Seated in my chair at my desk I am at rest—relative to the earth. But I move since I partake of the earth's various motions. I share in the daily rotation that gives day and night, I move with the earth in her annual journey round the sun which produces the seasons, I voyage with the solar system as it sails towards a distant constellation, I speed through space with the home galaxy, the Milky Way, as it recedes from other nebulæ. But all these motions, swift as they are—20 miles a second or more, some of them—are sensibly rectilinear and uniform. They are steady or unaccelerated, and I sense no difference between rest and steady motion. Both are the same to me, both are the same in Newtonian dynamics. Mechanical laws are the same for all observers in steady motion, whether their movement is slow or fast.

Steady motion is the natural state of matter, said Newton. This is the principle of inertia, Newton's first law of motion. A body at rest or in uniform motion in a straight line perseveres in that state indefinitely unless it is interfered with. The natural condition of a lump of matter is, once started it just keeps moving steadily and forever in the one direction. This is what is meant by the inertia of matter, its inability to change its state, its inability to accelerate itself.

This idea of the inertia of matter has been called the greatest revolution in history because it brought humanity over a long-standing hurdle. Aristotle, reflecting on the instance of a horse pulling a cart, had argued that a body in motion needed to have something pulling or pushing it all the time it moved. Take away the push or the pull and the motion will stop, he said. No motion without a mover in attendance. ("*Quidquid movetur ab alio movetur.*") Rest and motion were put on mental pedestals, if not on altars, and inordinately reverenced. So, up to the 17th century, physicists beat their heads against prison bars and made a futile distinction between absolute rest and absolute motion (not adverting to the fact that if the material universe consisted in a single particle, neither rest nor motion would have any meaning). No one could say plainly and convincingly how an arrow sped to its mark when it had lost contact with the bow string. No man could explain the movement of projectiles. A ball rolling down a plane and up a slope was another puzzle. For the sacred teaching was that everything in motion required to be attended all the time by a mover.

So long as you believed in the Aristotelian physics, there was little chance of chasing the spirits from the rivers or the winds. Intelligences would continue to preside over the movement of the spheres. The seas and mountains would be animated. Myth would be a substitute for natural philosophy. It would be impossible to turn alchemy into chemistry, astrology into a science (Newton himself, in tune with the scientific temper of his time, spent more hours on alchemy than at mathematics).

Newton's second law of motion deals with accelerated matter, and defines force in terms of inertia and acceleration. The law is a pure definition, and is of great historical importance since it marks the beginning of the mathematical physics method, which affords modern science the great powers referred to by Duhem (Cp. p. 22). The definition is operational. Newtonian force is a construct, a mathematical construct, and has no relation with muscular force or physiological sensation, with tension, push or pull, or any other anthropomorphic concept. Force is a name for a product of inertia and acceleration, a portmanteau-term, neither more nor less. It is operational because it states how force is got by carrying out two specified measurements. There is no reference in Newton's second law to the nature of force, to the 'occult' property that overcomes the inertia of matter. There is no attempt to say what it is exactly that produces or causes acceleration in matter.

Newton's third law, the principle of equilibrium for both steady and accelerated matter, is purely methodological, and is merely a guiding principle for working out problems in statics and dynamics. In stating that 'action and reaction are equal and opposite' it prescribes a mode of conceiving dynamical questions, it does not create a reaction or assign physical reality to it. The concepts of action and reaction provide an economical method and useful framework for dealing with, and for understanding, problems.

Newton crystallised the laws of motion but he did not originate them in their entirety. Their power and beauty are almost incredible, and one never ceases to wonder at, and delight in, their content and extent. For all practical purposes, in engineering and in most departments of physics, they are still fundamental. It is only in certain sections of atomic physics and astronomical science, when there is question of high speed phenomena, that Einstein's refinement of them must be taken into account.

We see from the foregoing outline that Newton's so-called laws are in the nature of principles, axioms or postulates. Newton's way of looking at things produced simplification, power and elegance, and strengthened the faculties of man. Einstein's refinement of Newton enhances our powers still further.

3. *Papal Address on Natural Law*

[This is the address " Nel ritrovarCi qui in mezzo a voi " delivered by His Holiness, Pope Pius XII, February 8, 1948, to the members of the Pontifical Academy of Science.

After a tribute to his illustrious predecessor, founder of the present Pontifical Academy, the Sovereign Pontiff spoke on the subject of natural law and its relation to the eternal law and the divine government of the world.

We give a translation of the full text except for the introduction].

NOTION AND IMPORTANCE OF NATURAL LAWS. On this our earth it is plain that man is master and holds sway over all other living creatures. To him it was given to multiply and populate the earth; and, with toil, to win his daily bread. We do not wonder, then, that the Stagirite, the mighty Aristotle, compared the mind and spirit of man to the hand, which is the ' instrument of instruments '. Every artefact indeed owes its existence to the hand of man—cities, forts, public buildings; monuments of wisdom and of science, of art and poetry; all the inheritance and patrimony preserved in museums and libraries; and the monuments of civilisation generally. Similarly, the soul was given by God to man, one might say, to cope with the different natures of things—since through sense and understanding the soul of man receives within itself the multiple images of reality.

Allow Us, therefore, gentlemen to express admiration for your work as students of nature whether in the class-hall, laboratory, workshop or factory.

You are designers as well as teachers. You design and construct all sorts of instruments—telescopes, microscopes, spectrometers and a thousand others—for manipulating and controlling the forces of nature. Yet, you do not create the matter which you handle. Rather, you mould it and control its activities and energies according to the laws you discover and study. Thus you combine practical and technical knowledge with speculative knowledge of things.

THE TRUE LAW OF NATURE. The true law of nature, patiently and diligently investigated in the laboratory before it finds form and expression in symbols or words, is something more than a mere description or a formula: such deal only with appearances and not with the essence and fundamental properties of things. A genuine law of nature does not stop short at the surface of an object, nor is it content with no more than sense images. It goes deeper: it penetrates into reality, searches and discovers the intimate and hidden forces behind phenomena, and lays bare their activity and interaction. In this way it is easy to see how knowledge of natural laws makes it possible for man not only to master the forces of nature, but, through progress in technology, to press them into his service. Thus, we come to understand, for instance, how the regular order exhibited by spectral lines and detected in the laboratory may one day afford the astrophysicist, in addition to a wider knowledge, a deeper insight into the puzzling constitution and evolution of the heavenly bodies.

So, basing himself on natural law (especially as it is known in the physico-chemical sciences), and fortified with the powers of modern technique, the research worker defies obstacles and proceeds to fresh discoveries. Once started on an investigation, he has put his hand to the plough and he does not turn back.

THE ATOMIC AGE. Perhaps the most spectacular result of such intense activity and constant effort is, that it has been found possible to arrive at a deeper understanding of the laws relating to the structure and disintegration of atoms. It now seems likely that we can to a considerable extent control the release of atomic energy (so as to dispose of enormous quantities and not mere trifling amounts). The use of energy locked up in the uranium nucleus was mentioned by Us in Our address to this Academy on February 21, 1943. At that time We had in mind what the great physicist, Max Planck, wrote on the subject. Deliberate release of energy has now become a reality in the ' atom-bomb ' or ' nuclear-energy bomb ', the most terrible weapon yet conceived by the mind of man.

At this point We cannot refrain from giving expression to a thought which has always weighed heavily on Our mind—as it does, no doubt, on all who are truly human. To illustrate Our meaning, We turn to the words of St. Augustine in his work *"De Civitate Dei"* (Bk. 19, ch. 7), where, referring to the horrors of war, whether the war be righteous or not, he writes:

" If I wanted to relate in suitable words the manifold evils
and devastation of war, the harsh and cruel sufferings that
follow in its wake, it would be impossible for me to deal with
it adequately, and I know not how anyone could exhaust so
vast a subject. If one sadly reflects on such horrible and
sinister evils, one must admit the misery of war; but whoever
can bear the thought of such things without anguish of soul,
is the more wretched of men for thinking himself happy—
because he has lost all human feeling."

Now if the wars of those days could elicit so heavy a condemnation
from the illustrious Doctor, what judgment ought one not to pass
on the wars that have stricken our generation, and have brought to
their work of destruction and extermination an incomparably
greater technique? What horrors face human kind in any future
conflict, should it prove impossible to stop or restrain the misuse
of ever new and more astonishing scientific discoveries!

Turn aside for the moment from the idea of employing nuclear
energy in warfare, while confidently hoping that such force will be
used only to make safe the ways of peace. Regard it simply as a
happy instance of man's enquiry into the real laws of nature, laws
expressing the essence and intimate activity of matter.

THE PERIODIC SYSTEM OF THE ELEMENTS. Properly speaking,
there is involved in these enquiries and researches only one law of
nature, namely, that which manifests itself chiefly in what is called
the ' Periodic law of the elements '. Lothar Meyer, and Dmitri
Mendeleev, in 1869, with the scanty chemical data available to
them, had some ingenious inkling of the law, and they gave it its
first tentative form. Their classification of the chemical elements into a system had many gaps and inconsistencies. The system itself
was still obscure. None the less, it led to enquiry about how chemical affinity might be related to atomic structure, how chemical properties might depend on the way the parts were arranged inside the
atom. Thenceforward, the picture became clearer year by year,
flaws vanishing and richer meanings growing gradually more
obvious. We limit Ourselves to mentioning just a few of the
milestones on the long road to deeper knowledge of the periodic
system of the elements, such as: the discovery of radium by the
Curies; the atomic model of Rutherford and the formulation of its
laws by Bohr; the discovery of isotopes by Francis William Aston;
splitting the nucleus by bombarding atoms with alpha particles
(and soon afterwards the synthesis of new heavy atoms with the
aid of slow neutrons); discovery of the trans-uranium elements sug-

gested by Fermi; the production of 'transuranics' in measurable quantity (among them and taking pride of place, plutonium, obtained with sufficiently massive layers of uranium and constituting the active principle of the second uranium bomb); in short, significant facts that progressively developed the idea and importance of a natural system among the elements.

If we win through to an all-embracing view of this wonderful series of researches, we meet no finality but rise step after step to further knowledge and to the beginning of an era that has been called 'the atomic age'. Up to recent times, research was preoccupied with molecules and chemical compounds. Interest has now shifted to the atom and its core or nucleus, and one can be sure that investigators will not slacken their efforts until they have found a safe and economical way of releasing atomic energy, with the desire and hope of serving civilization.

These are noteworthy triumphs of the human mind, which searches and studies the laws of nature, and beckons men to travel new roads. What finer conception than this!

NATURAL LAWS PARTICIPATE IN THE ETERNAL LAW. Law is order, and universal law is order in all things great and small. Law is an order which you discover by mind and sense as deriving from the inmost tendency of things. It is an order that nothing can create for itself or give itself any more than it can give itself existence. Law is an order that tells of the ordering Mind in the one Spirit Who has created the universe, and on Whom " the heavens and the whole of nature depend " (*Paradiso* 28, 42), an order which matter received with its being. The tendencies and activities of matter, working together, make a well-ordered world. Such is the wonderful system of natural laws which the human mind has discovered, thanks to untiring research and deep pondering. It is in this way that you, gentlemen, make progress and win triumph after triumph over nature's stubborn secrets. Yet, what is this system of laws but a faint and imperfect image of the grand idea and the divine plan conceived by the creative spirit of God as a law of the universe from all eternity. Then it was that from the fathomless depths of His wisdom He fashioned the heavens and the earth; and then His creative power made light shine over the dark chaos in which the cosmos was cradled. He left the print of His creative finger on time and the centuries, giving wings to movement and space to flight; and He bestowed activity and life on all things in their separate kinds even down to the tiny atom.

How right it is, therefore, that minds such as yours contemplating the depths of the heavens and measuring both the stars and the earth, should turn to God and exclaim: "Thou hast ordered all things in measure, and number, and weight" (Wisdom xi, 21). Do you not feel within you that the firmament above and the earth below, thanks to your measuring instruments—your telescopes, microscopes and scales, and all your varied apparatus—speak to you of the glory of God; and that they reflect in your vision a gleam of that uncreated wisdom which "reacheth from end to end mightily and ordereth all things sweetly" (Wisdom viii, 1).

STELLAR ECONOMY. The scientist vibrates, so to speak, to the throb of this eternal wisdom when his research reveals to him that the universe is fashioned like a casting in the immeasurable foundry of space and time. He sees the starry heavens in all their splendour composed of identical elements throughout, and he sees them follow everywhere and always the same cosmic laws. Atoms of iron emit thousands of well-defined rays under the hot impulse of the arc or the electric spark. The rays are seen to be identical with those discovered by the astrophysicist in the socalled 'flash-spectrum' obtained just as a solar eclipse reaches totality. Throughout all space, the same laws of gravitation and radiation-pressure operate to determine star-size even amongst the most distant nebulæ. The domestic economy of the fixed stars— the come and go of their energy—is regulated by the same enigmatic laws of atomic nuclei which describe and explain to some extent the synthesis and disintegration of atoms.

Not less imposing is the rule of law, rule of the one kind of law, in the living world. Forgetting for the moment the purposefulness one encounters at all stages of life, consider for instance causality. Just glance at various organisms and consider their structure in the light of recent findings in comparative anatomy and physiology. What do you see? Look at the skeleton of the higher animals, see the organic likenesses, note the arrangement and function of the sensitive organs, the eye for example, and pass from simple forms to the more perfect visual apparatus in man. Or see again how the same basic laws of assimilation, growth and reproduction operate in living things. Does not all this strikingly reveal a single idea splendidly realized in variety. Do we not see here a plan, a system of natural law closed and absolutely fixed?

ETERNAL LAW AND SECONDARY CAUSES. Assuredly there is here a unity of design whose secret is universal order. Against this order, dependent as it is on the First Cause which is God, God the Creator Himself cannot act. Were He to do so, He would be work-

ing against His own foreknowledge, His own Will, His own Goodness. Now in Him "there is no change nor shadow of alteration"
(St. James i, 17). But in this order, in so far as it depends on
secondary causes, God holds the key to everything in such a way
that He can leave it closed or He can open it and allow it to operate
freely of itself.

But did God, in creating the universe, subject Himself to the
command of secondary or inferior causes? Is not this order subject
to Him in so far as it proceeds from Him, not by necessity of
nature, but by free choice of His Will? Indeed He can, when He
so wills, operate outside the established order, for instance by
producing effects of secondary causes without using them, or by
producing effects beyond their capacity. (Aquinas, *Summa
Theologica*, 1a Pars., q. 105, art. 6.) That is why the great doctor,
Augustine, wrote long ago:

> "We say with good reason that God acts against Nature
> when He acts in a way that runs counter to Nature as we
> know it; but God in no way acts against the highest law of
> Nature any more than He acts against Himself (*Contra
> Faustum*, 1, 26. c. 3. Mig. P.L. t. 42. col. 481, cp, *Summa
> Theol.*, loc. cit.).

What kinds of operation have We in mind? Precisely those of
which God alone holds the key in the secret of His design; those
operations which throughout the ages He has reserved to
Himself within the specialized order of lower causes. In this
way, as the inspired poet sang, things are accomplished "for which
Nature neither heated the iron nor hammered the anvil"
(*Paradiso* 24, 101). In the face of such happenings—unusual either
in themselves or because of the subject in which they happen; or
again because of the manner and the order of their production—
both unlettered and lettered folk pause in wonderment. Something astonishing happens. The effect is manifest. The cause is
hidden. The very ignorance of the hidden cause, while it bewilders
the unbeliever, sharpens the vision both of the faithful and of
the truly learned. For they know and calculate within sure limits
how far the laws of Nature can operate, and they discern above
and beyond them all a sovereign hand, hidden and almighty—
the hand that created the universal order. They understand that
in the working of particular systems of causes and effects, it is this
sovereign hand that marked the moment and the circumstance of
its own wondrous intervention (cp. St. Thomas, loc. cit., a, 7).

ENTHUSIASM OF THE STUDENT OF NATURE. The divine government of the world with its hierarchy of orders cannot fail to excite wonder and enthusiasm in the man of science. For in his research he discovers and recognizes the marks of the Creative Wisdom, and he becomes aware of the unseen hand belonging to the Supreme Lawgiver of the cosmos Who pilots the natures of things " across the mighty sea of being to those different harbours whither they are led by an instinct divinely bestowed " (*Paradiso*, 1, 112-114). What, indeed, are these mighty laws of Nature, if not shadows, and, in some sort, dim images which indicate the depth and immensity of the Divine plan operating in the vast cathedral of the universe?

" The highest privilege of the scientist," wrote Kepler, " is to recognize the Spirit and to trace the thought of God." Often—and here we must confess our human weakness—in the presence of things seen or of their sense-images, our mind is bewildered and hesitant. But if the investigator has always before him the thought of God, he does not fall into the error of identifying his own notions and percepts with the mind of God. Indeed, the habit and inclination to seek and recognize God, give him the right directive and spur in his task, and reward him generously for all the labour he expends. Far from making him vain or conceited, this inspiring thought makes him humble and unassuming.

HUMILITY. Certainly, the deeper scientists go in their study of Nature's wonders, the more readily do they recognize their own insufficiency either to exhaust the riches of God's structural plan or to penetrate the canons of its government. Listen again to the beautiful words of the illustrious Newton, who so shrewdly said: " I do not know how I appear to the world, but I see myself as a child playing by the seashore, who is glad because every now and then he finds a pebble smoother than the rest or a shell more fascinating, while the mighty ocean of truth rolls unexplored before him."

These words of Newton, written three centuries ago, come to us to-day with even deeper meaning amidst the bustle of modern science. Again it is said that Laplace, as he lay sick, was surrounded by friends who recalled a great discovery of his. He smiled sadly and said: " All that we know is so little; what we don't know is enormous." (*Ce que nous connaissons est peu de chose; ce que nous ignorons est immense.*)

The distinguished Werther Von Siemens, who investigated the principle of the self-induced dynamo, spoke with no less discernment when at the 59th Assembly of German savants he declared:

" The deeper we delve into the harmonious disposition of the natural forces governed by eternal and unchangeable laws that are nevertheless hidden from our complete understanding the more do we feel ourselves moved to humble self-effacement. The more clearly we understand the range of our knowledge, the more eager becomes our effort to wrest further secrets from this inexhaustible fount of knowledge and power, and the more does our wonderment grow in the presence of the infinite wisdom and order which permeates all creation."

OUR KNOWLEDGE OF NATURE. To tell the truth, our knowledge of Nature is neither wide nor deep. In a treatise on the electro-magnetic theory of light, one comes across the remark: " Is it a God who wrote these formulæ?" Maxwell's equations are certainly the work of a genius. Yet, as with every similar advance in physical theory, they both suppose a simplification and imply an idealization of reality without which mathematics cannot fruitfully develop. How often at the present time, instead of exact laws, can one only propose a restricted rather than a general explanation? Where phenomena occur involving countless hosts of elements similar in kind and action but which seem at first sight to have no guiding rule, one begins by noting the character and structure of the bodies under study. The investigator then does what he can to provide an explanation for their behaviour and his explanation is based on probabilities. Since, however, he does not know what is the dynamic principle behind the observed activity, he must content himself with formulating a mere statistical law.

The advance of science is unceasing. True, successive steps have not always followed a constant path from the first observations and discoveries to hypothesis, thence to theory, and finally to the sure and undoubted attainment of truth. Sometimes investigation has moved rather in a circle. Cases are known in which theories triumphed and reached the category of undisputed doctrines (earning for their advocates the esteem of the scientific world) only to fall back into the region of hypothesis, and be eventually discarded.

Yet, notwithstanding the uncertainties and aberrations that beset all forms of human endeavour, the progress of science knows neither pause nor sudden leap, as the research workers hand on to one another the discoveries destined to pour light on the pages making up Nature's book of mystery. In the order of things naturally occurring, as the Angelic Doctor St. Thomas remarks, there is a gradual progress from the imperfect to the perfect; so also, he adds, man arrives step by step at knowledge of truth. In the beginning, fragments are collected; and then, little by little, men acquire a more comprehensive knowledge. They do not attribute the origin of the world and its contents to chance. They contemplate established truths with increasing earnestness and attention. From visible signs and reasons they deduce that the natural order is ruled by Providence. For how else, could one find fixed unvarying system in the movements of celestial bodies, and in the other workings of Nature, if all were not governed by a sovereign intelligence? (St. Thomas in Lib. Job. Prolog.).

So it is that following newer and wider paths, men steadily march on towards deeper knowledge of the universe. Mankind thirsts for truth and presses forward in search of it. Yet, thousands of years hence, knowledge of the intimate laws and dynamic forces of matter, of the origin and evolution of the world, and still more, of the design and divine impulse that penetrates, moves and directs everything, will be an imperfect and faint image of the divine idea. With the marvels of that eternal Wisdom blinding and stunning them—that Wisdom which, in the ocean of being, governs and guides each thing without fail towards the hidden harbour of its destiny—the learned enquirers, dumb and dazzled, turn at length to humble adoration. They feel themselves to be in the presence of a created splendour where the hand of man has no part and can do naught to imitate, but wherein his mind catches a flash of omnipotence. Faced with the endless and unfathomable problems of cosmic law and cosmic order (embracing all things great and small) man can only echo the cry: "O, the depth of the riches and of the wisdom and of the knowledge of God! How incomprehensible are His judgments, and how unsearchable His ways!" (Rom. xi, 33).

MESSAGE OF THE GREAT BOOK OF NATURE. Happy indeed are the men of science, if, in making their way across the vast spaces of heaven and earth, they have learned to read in the great book of Nature, and to listen to its message. It is a message that traces the Divine footprints in creation and in history. The footprints of God and the letters written by His hand cannot be blotted out. No human hand can remove them. These footprints and letters are none other than the facts which reveal the work of God to every man. Hence it would seem that it is to the learned world that are directed the following words of the Doctor of the Gentiles:

"The knowledge of God is clear to their minds. God Himself has made it clear to them. From the foundations of the world men have caught sight of His invisible nature, His eternal power and His divineness, as they are known through His works. *Quod notum est Dei, manifestum est in illis! Deus enim illis manifestavit. Invisibilia enim ipsius a creatura mundi, per ea quae facta sunt, intellecta conspiciuntur, sempiterna quoque ejus virtus et divinitas."* (Rom. i, 19-20.)

An inscription adorning the tomb of the astronomer, Angelo Secchi, reads: *A coeli conspectu ad Deum via brevis.*— " From the contemplation of the heavens, short is the way to God."

As we look down from this vantage-point on the spread-out world lying at the feet of God, it is not hard to see how things follow the bent of their nature; how no natural tendency can run counter to the design of the Supreme Creator, Conservor and Governor, Who is above everything, above all the laws of creation which He has framed. Indeed, for His own wise purpose He remains free to hinder or divert natural effects and activities. Confronted with the wondrous reality of the cosmos which the learned diligently contemplate, we can regard as mere Utopian fiction the universal spirit imagined by Laplace. He expressed it in a formula, which (at least according to materialists) could embrace events dependent on human thought and free choice. By contrast, the divine Wisdom of which We have spoken is an infinite reality. This is the Wisdom that knows and measures each atom with its activity, and assigns to every subatom its place in the compact structure of the created world. This is the Soveregn Wisdom, Whose glory penetrates the whole universe and is seen in all its splendour in the firmament of heaven. (Cp. *Paradiso* I. 1. sqq.)

4. *Origin and Nature of Law*

Most people are aware of the classic definition of law as " a rule or direction of reason for the common good made by one who has charge of the community, and promulgated to the subjects of the law."

In the bewildering complexity of life, man needs intelligent direction in his activities. Law gives him such direction. Law is not a ball and chain fettering his eager footsteps; rather it is a torch illuminating his path through treacherous country.

All law has its origin in God the Creator, the First Cause Who is the Uncaused Cause. All law originates in the Divine Mind, in the Will of God.

ETERNAL LAW IN THE MIND OF GOD. The Divine Mind directs all the activities of all creatures to the end for which God made the world. This direction or government of things is eternal in the mind of God. In God, then, there is the eternal law directing the affairs of the whole world, the affairs of atoms and of stars, of plants and animals and men, everything that happens or moves and has a being.

Since it is the Divine Mind that has fixed the goals of all creatures, and the road to these goals, all other laws will be based on the Eternal Law in the Mind of God.

THE NATURAL LAW. The natural law, or law of right reason, with its fundamental precept that admits of no exception—do good, avoid evil—is man's participation in the Eternal Law of God.

The Ten Commandments are secondary or derived principles of the natural law. Ignorance or passion impedes knowledge of the secondary precepts of the natural law. For example, the principle: " give property to the owner " is all very well, but not to the point of giving back a man his own gun if he wants to kill you with it.

Human Positive Law is derived from the natural law. " Thou shalt not steal " is a general principle, or precept, but the converse conditions of having, holding, acquiring property need definition and regulation concerning contracts, debts, bankruptcy and so forth. The proper goal of human positive law is the common welfare of members of society. Human laws should be for the benefit of all, not for private individuals. Natural law forbids all vices, but human positive law only those disturbing the common good of society. Again human positive law inculcates and commands only those virtues which concern the common good of men in groups.

The eternal law and the basic precepts of the natural law are unchangeable because they are founded on the unchangeable natures of God and man. But positive law, both human and divine (as in the Old and New Testaments) can change with changed circumstances. (Divine positive law arose because it was necessary for God to reveal to man the laws which would direct human activity to the supernatural goal, the vision of God, beyond the power of purely natural activity. The Ten Commandments are really secondary precepts of the natural law, but they were also revealed to the subjects of the Old Testament. The New Law [New Divine Positive Law] was given to the world by Christ, and it is God's final law for all men. It is the road-map to the vision of God: the perfect law, it will bring men to their true goal, happiness. Its efficiency derives from the grace of the Holy Spirit.)

MORAL LAW. The natural law, or man's participation in the

eternal law, is manifested in conscience as the moral law or sentiment of duty. It has three outstanding qualities. It is *obligatory*. That is, it commands but does not constrain. It is necessary but not necessitating. It must be knowable and practical to be obligatory, of course. We retain the physical power to violate the duty without escaping the obligation. The law imposes on the reason but not on the will, which is, therefore, left free.

Next, the moral law is *absolute*. It is an end in itself. It is unconditional. This is sometimes expressed by the categorical imperative, an absolute " must ". This absolute character, for example, is not applicable to the rule of health—" if you want to be healthy, do so and so ". But you are not bound to be healthy. Health is not an end in itself.

Finally, the moral law is *universal*. That is, it is the same for all men, for all countries, for all centuries; since morality expresses a relation between the nature of man and his end; and all men have the same nature and end. This is the criterion for distinguishing good from evil. It is the criterion of the good act which is truly in conformity with human nature and end.

PHYSICAL LAW AND MORAL LAW. A law of nature, a natural law or physical law, is quite different from the natural law, from moral law. A law of nature is not a moral imperative: it effects nothing and imposes no moral obligation: it " merely describes regular behaviour ", as Whewell put it.

Let us look at the distinction between physical law and moral law more closely, on account of the great importance these days of both.

Everything in this world has necessarily an end, and consequently possesses a law in relation to its nature. Since all things have not the same nature, they have not the same end or law. Under this aspect, beings can be divided into two groups, persons and things. Persons, endowed with intelligence and liberty, make up the moral order; while things, without the higher faculties, constitute the physical world. Hence follows the difference between physical and moral law. (We neglect elements common to both and view only those characteristic of each class.)

One can define a law in general, whether moral or physical, as the constant and uniform rule according to which a being acts or ought to act.

PHYSICAL LAW. Physical law ruling beings, which are incapable of understanding and choosing, can only be conceived under the form of an impulsion that compels them to act in a certain way.

Moral law, addressed to a being that is intelligent and free, has the character of an obligation, i.e., of an ideal directive which binds the will without, however, necessitating it. Moral law is a law in the strict sense, since it emanates from authority, commands obedience and inspires respect, while physical law is a simple formula signifying what is, and not an imperative of what ought to be.

It follows that moral law can be obeyed and observed only if it is known and accepted; that the agent subjected to it always retains the physical power to infringe it. Physical law, necessitating a being to act, is obeyed blindly, irresistibly.

Yet, since moral law expresses the necessary relation of human nature to its end, it cannot be modified or abrogated. Reason cannot admit evil and reject good, any more than it can conceive a phenomenon without a cause, or a whole less than its part. On the other hand, since physical law only expresses a contingent relation between events, it could be different from what it is. Absolutely speaking, the earth could turn quicker or slower than it does, gravity could be conceived to have a different value. Briefly, moral law is necessary in itself, but it does not necessitate; while physical law, which is necessitating, is not necessary. As Kant put it, moral law is objectively necessary and subjectively contingent, while physical law is objectively contingent and subjectively necessary.

From the difference in their nature may be seen the difference in the methods to be adopted in order to detect the operation of these laws.

Physical law, being objectively contingent, can only be known through observation. The agent being necessitated to conform, the fact has to be in conformity with the law, and one need only observe the former to infer the latter. In other words, observation is necessary and sufficient to establish physical law.

(A certain minimal of sense knowledge is required by the scientist whereby he recognises the object he studies and reads the instrument by which he makes a measurement. It is necessary and sufficient that he knows an external reality in space and time which has different qualities. He may use any one quality to distinguish one reality from another. Hence physics presupposes a *datum* and sense knowledge. Physics is not an absolute beginning. Accordingly, the physicist cannot give an ultimate explanation of what he studies.)

On the other hand, moral law being subjectively contingent, the subject retains his physical power of violating it. Discord is therefore always possible between the act and the law, so the latter cannot be learned by simple observation of the events. Yet since it expresses a necessary relation between man's nature and end, then knowing that nature, we can deduce the end, and consequently the law. Accordingly, moral law is not like physical law a simple fact generalized, but a principle, an *ideal* law inferred from psychological data, i.e., facts of consciousness.

Let me add: Both types of law in their own way manifest the existence of the Divine Legislator. As Kant said: "The starry sky above our heads, the moral law written within our hearts, are two things which fill the soul with a respect and admiration ever growing."

In fact, the starry heavens, by the number, mass and regular movement of the celestial bodies, constitute the most splendid witness there is of the physical order, and consequently of the wisdom and power of the Creator; while the moral law reveals to us by the perfect goodness, and absolute and immutable character of His decrees, a Sovereign Authority, infinitely worthy of obedience and respect.

CIVIL AND MORAL LAW. Plato saw no difference between civil and moral law. Machiavelli went to the other extreme and proclaimed them to be utterly and entirely independent of each other. In reality, while they are essentially distinct and different in nature, they are necessarily united. You cannot have civil law without moral law, though you may have the latter without the former.

The moral law is innate, objectively necessary, promulgated by conscience, and, therefore, it is universal, immutable, the same for all people in all ages. Civil law is positive, of human origin; written, it varies with time and country.

Two essential points follow. First, the moral law constitutes *right*. In imposing a duty, it guarantees it by guaranteeing the power to effect it. Civil law is only declarative and expresses the right. Proclaiming a right, it regulates the conditions of its use or exercise.

The two kinds of law differ in aim and scope. Moral law safeguards cosmic order by relating and co-ordinating all human acts. Civil law preserves outer order by protecting rights: it can regulate only such acts as threaten to harm others and compromise social order.

The two kinds of law differ also in scope and sanction. Civil law is applied and interpreted by human tribunals. Moral law springs from the tribunes of God and conscience. Men's justice is fallible like those who apply it. Conscience is in practice infallible.

In general, moral and civil law complete each other. The former is principle and end, the latter is consequence and means. Moral law gives human legislation its force, its degree of obligation. In making it a duty for us to live in society, it thereby commands us to obey the social authority. Hence civil law cannot oppose moral law: it cannot forbid what the other prescribes without losing its quality of law, since law is not the caprice of *a* man or of *an* assembly.

While Blackstone's famous definition of law as " a rule, not a transient sudden order from a superior or regarding a particular person, but something permanent, uniform and universal " is good as far as it goes, it does not go far enough and does not touch the essence of law. The statement in a widely used legal textbook that " the rule of law is whatever Parliament as the supreme lawgiver makes it " cannot be accepted as anything more than a definition of civil law in a particular country. Such law is worse than worthless if it conflicts with moral law, with the natural law. For it is then the negation of true law. It is a masquerade and will sooner or later lead to disorder and unhappiness because it is based on some injustice and is bound to produce tensions, sooner than later.

5. *Scientific Method*

W E all know the man with an infallible system for picking the winner of a horse-race or a dog-race and " beating the bookies ". We smile at the claims he makes for his system, which he says is " sure to win " and is " never known to fail ". Not so many of us smile at the claims made for scientific method. In fact, most of us are solemn when the phrase is mentioned. We are solemn with good reason. The advance of science, pure and applied, has been prodigious, wonder succeeding wonder until we grow dizzy or even uneasy. Advances are attributed to the power of scientific method. So great has been the success of the scientific approach to many problems that there are not wanting those who would apply it to all problems, whether political, social, philosophic, economic or ethical. To not a few people scientific procedure smacks of the magical; it is almost the twentieth century version of the universal panacea, the *elixir vitæ,* or the philosopher's stone.

Before he died in 1936, Pavlov asserted that all problems could be solved by scientific method. " Scientific method ", he said, " is omni-competent ". Yet, when we ask what precisely is this marvel, we are met with vague or discordant replies. Not all agree in their definition.

TECHNIQUES. The cause of disagreement is clear enough;

scientific method is not one but many. Like all overworked words, it can mean much or little. There are as many scientific methods as there are separate sciences. In other words, the phrase is often employed to denote the *techniques,* i.e., the specific procedures or processes or means employed in a particular department of knowledge in order to reach its objective. In any particular subject, you learn or assimilate scientific method by becoming an apprentice, you condition your mind, eye and hand by " going through the mill " in the company of a master, having intimate contact with the details of the subject, checking your own experiences in the light that has been slowly developed by countless generations of your predecessors; finally, by interpreting fresh experiences in discussions with your fellows so as to arrive at better statements of problems and find new and better ways of doing old and new things. Thus, advance may be made by the discovery or invention of *shortening processes* (as in the case of Napier and his logarithms), by replacing evolution with involution. Economy or efficiency, (which involves the ratio of result or achievement to effort and expenditure), is one of the notes of scientific method. It is more often found with men of science and business-men than with civil servants; it is more often found with men not tied to security, but happy when new things are attempted and adventure relieves the monotony of routine.

POWER OF REASON. An individual, if he could live long enough, if he had an infinity of time at his disposal, could solve any problem, in any subject, which is rationally solvable. Any normal person has this power within him. Individuals have not infinite time at their disposal, though in a sense the human race has. The economy of scientific method refers not only to an efficient use of time, but also to economy of thought (by conceiving powerful concepts and employing sound logical processes), economy of effort, and economy of means. Yet scientific method is painstaking and is not afraid of hard work where it is necessary.

OTHER DESCRIPTIONS. Scientific method is not infrequently called the *experimental* method, yet those who employ this term would not deny that astronomers and geologists, whose subjects are observational or inexact rather than experimental or precise, are scientists in the modern sense. Some too, would admit that mathematicians make use of scientific method; though, frankly, mathematics has a minimal of observation or experience behind it, and a maximum of *deductive* reasoning. Its concepts are on a different plane of abstraction from those of the experimental sciences, and its proofs have a different kind of cogency. Again, scientific method is at times identified with the *inductive method*, about which so much heat and so little light have been generated by Bacon, J.S. Mill, J.M. Keynes and other writers.

As every honest error, by the nature of the human mind, has a grain of truth in it, all these inadequate and highly imperfect descriptions of scientific method have something in them. So, too, when scientific method is looked on as the most up-to-date way of tackling a problem, there is a positive element in the view, indicating the *progressive* character of scientific procedure, and emphasising that men of science stand on each others' shoulders, and that scientific knowledge is by accretion, and is dependent on social cohesion and co-operation.

OBJECTIVITY. Science and its methods have world values; they transcend personal, subjective and national frontiers; and they are the same in China as in Peru. Occasional historic exceptions, as in the Newton-Leibnitz controversies about the infinitesimal calculus, by retarding development, only prove the rule. Though the history of science has many instances of punditry—as in the case of Ohm (who was victimised for stating his famous law)—and oracular utterances—as in statements of theories of phlogiston and evolution— scientific method is not dependent on authoritarianism or die-hard tradition. It is not tied to a great name, whether the name be British, American—or even Russian. (At least this was the way until recently.) We cannot say off-hand that scientific method is necessarily the method employed by a great scientist; say, Newton in his remarkable work for the British Mint; in the many years he spent on alchemy (shocking news to the contemporary Englishman now hearing of it for the first time); in his incursions into Biblical exegesis; as well as in his optical researches, mathematical discoveries and cosmological inventions. Scientific method can free itself from binding traditions and obsolete equipment: it has direct and intimate contact with its subject-matter, and is opposed to the bureaucratic system which is remote and often disdainful of the material it feeds on.

GIST OF SCIENTIFIC METHOD. What, then, is the gist of scientific method? What are its essential features? Viewing the ever varying and ever multiplying patterns of the sciences, and including all three groups corresponding to Aristotle's ceilings of abstraction, the physical, the mathematical, and the philosophical, we see that scientific method is first of all rational. What distinguishes man is his power of reasoning. As the old definition puts it, he is no

" featherless biped " but a " rational animal " (*potentially,* if not always *actually* so). Common sense is mostly rational method. Scientific method is an elaboration of common sense. It goes, of course, much deeper than common sense, so-called, and is more complex and is more highly organised and specialised. But the essence of both is rationality, man's rationality, which may be either discursive or intuitional. Both presuppose a climate of opinion, a background of ideas and beliefs substantially accepted by all or nearly all, but at different levels and usually with a time-lag. Common sense is usually built on the science of yesterday, and science helps to generate the common sense of tomorrow.

But each man at his own level is in the main conditioned and limited by the concepts and theories he shares with his fellows. He must pose his problems in familiar terms, and this may render the problem impossible of solution. If nature is not interrogated in suitable terms, it may be hard to make sense of her reply. She acts like the electronic computor which returns a nonsensical solution to an improperly stated problem. " Perceptive attitudes are required for meaningful answers ".

Infrequently, revolutions occur in the history of ideas, when men like Aristotle, Ptolemy, Copernicus, Descartes, Newton or Einstein alter some of the basic or common, everyday, categories, and set up new frameworks for men to think in. But rational method works on the new ideas after the same fashion as it worked on the old. Man's nature and faculties do not change. Logic is always logic, the same for Schrödinger as for St. Thomas. We may talk about multi-valued logic, mathematical logic and other techniques, but no one seriously believes that the nature of ratiocination has changed from Aristotle to Boole.

In the broad view, scientific method is fundamentally rational method at work in a science, whatever the nature of the science, whether it be on the natural, mathematical or philosophic planes of abstraction. Every science is a blend of reason and experience. Strictly speaking, there is no such thing as *pure* mathematics, for even the most abstract branch of mathematics presupposes some sense knowledge for its definitions and axioms. A mathematician without senses could never make sense. No more a philosopher. Least of all the natural philosopher. The amounts of reasoning and experience vary from one science to another. Technology is more experience than reason, and mathematics is the other way round, more reason than experience. In philosophy, the emphasis is on *reflection,* which is the exercise of reason at its highest level. Reflection is critical, questioning, and always seeks the *ultimate reason of things.* "The philosopher does not seek an explanation of things, he seeks the things which explain themselves," it has been well said. Natural science is content with immediate reasons, with the "how" rather than the "why" of things.

RATIONAL METHOD. Rational method is based on the two great ontological principles which are the basis of science and of all knowledge, namely, the principles of:

1. Contradiction (or identity): a thing is itself and not another, and

2. Sufficient reason: what is, is of itself, or of another,

along with their derivatives, such as the principles of causality and finality.

The reflective method of the philosophical sciences often utilises the same *four steps* as the species of *rational method* characteristic of the natural sciences. These steps may be called *observation, hypothesis, implication* and *verification. Observation* (which springs from curiosity) is selective, and isolates from the infinitely rich world—the manifold or plurality, as the philosophers call it—those brute facts which are the proper subject-matter of the science. The born scientist has a *flair* for the significant facts and ignores what is irrelevant to his department: he concentrates his attention on essential aspects of nature, that is, essential for his particular study, whether he be chemist, biologist, sociologist, theologian or other. Sometimes his selection (like his tests) is made by trial and error.

Hypothesis or supposition calls for imagination to classify, to inter-relate, and interpret or explain the observed, selected facts. It attempts to give organic unity to the brute facts, and may produce a highly organised and complex system, as in the vast syntheses of modern physics and chemistry and other branches of knowledge. Hypothesis is a *supposition* to explain or interpret something, and it is generally based on principles independent of the facts to be explained.

Hypothesis is followed by *implication* or inference, which is a purely logical process, an exercise of pure reason. It is sometimes called *prediction* and in this form is a well-known and sometimes spectacular mark of scientific method. (Note that in science, *prediction* is an assertion about an event which in principle could already have occurred; as, for instance, in Hamilton's "prediction" of conical refraction, and in the "prediction" and recognition or "discovery" of Neptune by Adams and Leverrier.)

The fourth step is *verification,* either by experiment or by further and closer observation.

And so the steps are recapitulated, like the digits of a recurring decimal, until one arrives—if one can ever be said to arrive—by successive approximations, or asymptotically, at the goal, which is *truth.*

It is misleading to call the method *induction,* since the third step is strictly deductive. The four steps can be applied to any order of experience, religious as well as physical, philosophical as well as mathematical; but the styles of observation and verification will naturally differ with the type of experience. The scientist with imagination devises really *crucial experiments* to test his hypothesis or theory.

The climax of the procedure is *verification.* This consists in *trying out* the hypothesis to see if the effects, which ought to appear if the hypothesis is true, actually do appear. Therein lies the *heart of the experimental method,* which was much studied by Mill. But the principle of verification is based on a fallacy in logic, which goes by the name of "the affirmation of the consequent". The logical form is:

> A implies B;
> B is true;
> Therefore, A is true.

Let us compare this with the argument:

> If the professor was in the accident, he must be injured.
> The professor has a cut on his right hand.
> Therefore, he was in the car smash.

We see the fallacy arises from failure to recognize that various causes might have produced the observed effect. The effect need not have been due to a unique cause. The professor could have cut his hand with a knife.

Why, then, is the method so successful? Paradoxically, we overcome the fallacy by committing it often enough. The logical form can be written:

> A implies B, C, D, E, F, G . . .
> B is true, C is true, D is true . . .

When we find the implications all true, verification is now such that only an improbable set of coincidences constitutes the alternative to our induction that A is true.

The safe inference is that A is true—pending further information. In other words, the conclusion is probable, not certain.

As Boole puts it (*Laws of Thought* 403 and 4), experimental results approximate to an order (that is, converge to a regularity), a statement of which is presumed as a law. When he says that the laws of physical science are only probable, and repeated confirmation makes them approach indefinitely closer to certainty, he did not mean this in any loose sense. He states plainly that "the general laws of nature are in all cases, and in the strictest sense of the term, probable conclusions, approaching indeed ever and ever nearer to certainty, as they receive more and more of the confirmation of experience. But of the character of probability they are never wholly divested". Elsewhere (*Mathematical Logic* 244), he defines probability as "expectation founded upon partial knowledge", the word "expectation" being taken in a statistical sense and not psychologically.

Thus, conclusions in science are never absolute or final: they may be further coloured, or tinted by fresh lights. Again, the conclusions are approximations; yet as time goes on, they are increasingly accurate approximations to the truth. So, too, as we shall see later, scientific method is not fixed, rigid or static, but it can be continually modified and perfected. Herein lies much of its strength. Scientific method is always learning, that is, it is always alert to assimilate new discoveries and fresh information about how to combine induction, deduction, analogies and "hunches". True scientific method is humble, never arrogant.

HISTORIAN'S VIEW. In the view of the historian, Herbert Butterfield (in *The Origins of Modern Science*), modern science with its developing method, is seen as a symphony in three movements. The symphony opens with the Greeks, with their discovery of rational method, how the human mind can deduce fresh knowledge from truths already known (the deductive method). The second movement occurred in the Middle Ages, when the general conviction was formed that the universe is rational and is subject to regular law, and is not arbitrary or capricious, the product of sheer accident or chance, or a whim of the gods, Greek or Roman, Celtic or Nordic. The last movement began three centuries ago, when, for the first time, it was recognized that the final appeal in science must be to observation or experiment, not to authority or tradition.

The scientific spirit is first found in the Greeks. They had a disinterested curiosity. They did not seek knowledge to increase their earning power or social standing. They wished to know just for the fun of the thing, unlike the "practical man". With the rise of the Greeks, human consciousness took a real step forward. They were the first people with a grasp of mathematical and philosophical reasoning, with insight into the nature or essence of things. Prominent among them was Pythagoras who had an intense feeling about the importance of *number* in the structure of the universe. But Pythagoras, like Descartes nearer to us, overestimated the scope and power of mathematics, the science of quantity. He is not without disciples in our own generation.

The medievalist lived in a purposeful, orderly universe; and he was familiar with its scheme and working. His outlook discouraged scientific enquiry, but it engendered an essential and basic element in modern science; for it established the position that nature is a *rational whole* and not an affair of chance or chaos. Without this principle, the incredibly painstaking and heroic labours of men of science would be in vain.

Not until the 17th century do we find resort to experiment, or refined observation, as a test of the correctness of a viewpoint. At this stage, the essential phases in the growth of scientific method had taken place, though no one realized it at the time. For instance, Galileo Galilei did not see clearly, or appreciate fully, the necessity of confirming mathematical deductions by experiments; and many of his successors thought that natural happenings could be inferred and predicted purely from metaphysical or abstract principles. Sir Arthur Eddington appears to have held a like view in his *Fundamental Theory*. He appears to have believed that one can infer the values of the constants of nature (such as the ratio of the mass of the proton to the mass of the electron) from mathematical principles, without any need for fresh experiment or measurement.

DESCARTES. In the history of scientific method, Descartes played the rôle which British writers like to attribute to Francis Bacon. Bacon was no mathematician; he lacked the mind and eye of a geometer and was quite inadequate to his age. Descartes, on the other hand, was an accomplished disciple of Pythagoras: he worshipped at the shrine of quantity and he believed that every regularity of nature could be reduced to mathematical terms. Loving the type of certitude afforded by mathematics, he desired to bring the same kind of certainty to all branches of knowledge.

The shadow of Descartes lies heavy on modern scientific method. Since his time, there is the tendency to concentrate on the " quantity " aspects of reality at the expense of other properties, and there is a constant endeavour to force all the sciences into the Procrustean bed of mathematical science, belittling or tending to ignore what cannot be timed, weighed or metred.

Descartes it was, too, who first stated succinctly and clearly the analytic method so characteristic of modern science that Newman summed it up simply in the phrase " science analyses ", while critics and poets peevishly complain that " science murders and dissects ". The principle of dividing a problem into as many units as possible and dealing with each separately is given by Descartes in his *Discours de la Méthode*; and it is applied in the principle of division of labour, so much a feature of modern mass-production methods (an instance of scientific method overflowing into technology).

MODERN VIEW. We get to closer grips with scientific method when we follow most moderns and restrict the phrase to mean the *exercise of rational method in the domain of the natural sciences*.

The sciences of nature display a bustling activity in our day. By comparison with the philosophical sciences they are like living things, they grow and develop and are always on the move. They give rise to new, burning, and topical questions, capable of solution, while the problems of philosophy remain perennial. Scientific method in this narrower, modern, technical sense achieves a satisfying type of *certitude* which leads to *agreement* about the answers it gives to questions. For instance, one person may say " the day is hot ", another may say " it is cold ", but the man of science takes a thermometer, reads it and says " it is 36° Fahrenheit "; and there is no further dispute or argument. This is because scientific method *depersonalizes* measures and makes them *objective* and independent of our feelings. It eliminates or tends to eliminate the *subjective*. In order to do so, it is ever on the look-out for new ways of conceiving problems so as to introduce " quantity " ideas or deputy (surrogate) quantifiable concepts.

OPERATIONAL DEFINITIONS. Notions and definitions are *operational* and refer to physical rather than to *logical* classes. The man of science has no definition of the properties he studies but in the description or recipe he gives of how to measure them. Unlike the Victorian who was a metaphysician without knowing it, the modern physicist does not define ' force ' as ' the cause of motion '; but says ' force is *measured* by measuring the product of a mass by its acceleration '. It is not his business to say what ' force ' is. That is the philosopher's affair. He abandons the anthropomorphic idea of force as akin to muscular force, and accepts only the operational definition. Again, in the search for ' quantized ' conceptions he tends to replace logical classes by physical classes. The former are clear-cut and depend on the principle of contradiction. An object is in class A or it is not. There is no third possibility. Physical classes, depending on measurable or quantitative properties, have not this definiteness. An object may have more or less of the property. So physical classes are represented by the so-called 'normal' distribution curve (bell-shaped or hill-shaped) of probability and statistics. The answer to a question about a thing being in a physical class is not a clear-cut 'yes' or 'no', but is 'more or less' or may be 'maybe'. But not all the ideas required by men of science are reducible to physical classes and operational definitions. This is the error of logical positivists and some exponents of semantics, the science of meaning, who tend to ignore that even science must have its imponderables, its abstract ideas, its ideals and spirit.

Modern science insists that man is the 'measurer' rather than the 'measure' of things. The philosopher adopts the opposite view, saying, if man ceases to be the measure of things, he abdicates his reason, ceases to be a rational animal, becomes emotional, instinctive (wonderfully so), yet reduces to a mere marvellous mass of conditioned reflexes, like Pavlov's dog.

EXTENSION. Through concentrating on operational ideas and developing them the scientist has been able to extend the frontiers of his territory. By inventing new concepts and new ways of looking at things, he has been able to apply measuring techniques (based on clock, rule and scales) to fresh areas of knowledge, hitherto not amenable to quantitative study. Thus, after successes in astronomy, physics and chemistry and the like, the measuring processes have been applied with some success to domains formerly regarded as the preserve of the philosopher, such as psychology and sociology. These extensions have back-fired and have changed the conception of scientific method itself. Scientific method is not something fixed or static, but it is constantly evolving, and adapting itself to meet the requirements in new fields.

SELF-CORRECTING. In order the better to understand the success of modern science and its methods, one should add a word on its *self-correcting power*, a remarkable power which derives from the spirit of truth-seeking. The self-correcting faculty shows itself in this way: in the long run, what is really known is taken up or subsumed in the development of science, and the rest is dropped because it has not stood up to criticism. As long as there is *free* discussion, something is formed which transcends its bearers, and no man fully understands; no one conceives or guesses the pattern of the endless quest, but we constantly move towards it, hopefully.

6. *Chance*

THE NOTION OF CHANCE. The term ' chance ' is employed in four very different senses, namely:

    1. In its absolute sense of *chaos;*

    2. As *likelihood* or moral probability;

    3. As *randomness* or mathematical probability; and

    4. As *frequency* or physical probability.

Statistics is a blend of 3 and 4, deriving its data from the one, and its techniques from the other.

The essence of chance is irregularity, whim or caprice. Where there is chance, there cannot be design or purpose or end, nor can there be rule or regulation or predictability: law is not only absent but it is impossible. True chance is without rhyme or reason. Pure chance is a metaphysical concept. At this highest level, chance is chaos—in contrast with ' cosmos ', and the phrase " law of chance " is a contradiction in terms.

Chance in this strict, absolute sense, denotes an absence of aim, end or purpose, regularity or law of any kind, conceivable or even inconceivable. Not only does it deny law or order, but it denies even their possibility. It is a moot point whether chance, in such a complete sense could exist; and if it did exist, could we know of it.

LIKELIHOOD. Legal men, punters, tipsters and may others employ the word " chance " in the sense of *likelihood* or *moral probability,* the opposite of a " dead certainty ". For instance, a barrister speaks of the chance of an acquital, meaning the likelihood of getting a verdict in favour of his client. He is referring to a possibility, the odds in favour of a certain event taking place, the event depending on a group of factors which he cannot evaluate with precision, such as the impact of the evidence and speeches on the minds of judge and jury. The best he can do, is to form a moral estimate by mentally " weighing " elements which are impervious to mathematical calculations. Chance in the sense, meaning likelihood, is often simply called " probability ", as, for instance, in Butler's famous dictum that " probability is the guide of life ". It is a common use of the term " chance ". Here we are dealing with moral certainty, a probability that cannot be expressed in numbers but may be so great as to admit of little or no reasonable doubt.

RANDOMNESS: METHODOLOGICAL CHANCE. When we speak of the *laws of chance,* we are usually referring to the mathematical theory of probability. In this case, as in all pure mathematics, we are concerned with the ideal, not with the real or physical. The domain is that of formal logic. We are dealing with logical terms, with abstractions, with ideas, not with things in the physical universe. We postulate the equalities of mathematics, not the inequalities of nature. We suppose an equal likelihood of events happening; we suppose that none of the events is privileged or ordered.

A further point to note is that chance in this context is not *pure* or *total* chance. It is only chance in a limited fashion. A character of " equal power of happening " is attributed to the variations of one or two elements in the problem, but all the other elements follow their ordered nature as they undergo changes. In so far as the majority are concerned, there is no suspension of law and order, there is no insubordination of effect or cause. Formulæ are reached by natural logical processes, by proceeding from premise to conclusion in the ordinary way. There is not universal caprice or whim. Chance enters in because a character of *randomness* is assigned to one or two variables or parameters.

Thus, in the kinetic theory of gases, we postulate or lay down the proposition that no direction in space is favoured or privileged —we suppose that a particle (a " molecule ") is *equally free* to travel in all directions. On this supposition, we investigate by rigorous mathematical logic the distribution of molecular speeds and arrive at Maxwell's classical formula. The aspect of chance is strictly limited to a single phase of the problem, and all the ordinary laws of mechanics (including those relating to elastic collisions) are considered to hold good.

In such problems, we are far removed from chance in the absolute sense, the sense of complete chaos. We suppose only that the particles possess a small and defined degree of freedom from constraint, order or hierarchy. So, too, in the mathematical theory of probability in general, we make the supposition that there is no bias or private law (privilege) favouring one set or kind of events: we consider there is *equal* likelihood of the various possible events happening. Thus we introduce a specific and limited element of randomness or chance. Mathematical probability is then conventionally measured as a fraction, namely, the ratio of the favourable cases to the total of cases, favourable and unfavourable, that can be conceived to occur.

DISTRIBUTION-FREQUENCY. Lamentable confusion exists concerning mathematical chance in the sense just described and the physical *frequency* of happenings, the occurrence-rate of actual events, such as birth-rates, death-rates, accident-rates, marriage-rates and so forth. The mathematical *probability* (or *calculated* chance) of an event taking place is, of course, quite different from the *actual* frequency with which such kind of event happens. Nevertheless, men of science commonly confuse the two, to such an extent that mathematicians are found who think physicists have demonstrated the mathematical laws of probability by experiment, and there are physicists who believe that men of mathematics have deduced actual frequency-rates by pure reason. One of the probability laws is known as the " law of errors ", and H. Poincaré remarks that everybody accepts it firmly because mathematicians imagine it is a fact of observation, and observers that it is a theorem of mathematics. There is a tendency to confuse not only the mental and physical worlds but also the ideal and the real.

The danger of confusing the real with the ideal is always present in applied mathematics. Much of the confusion that reigns at the present time in modern science springs from developments in the hybrid subjects, mathematical physics and theoretical physics. It is often forgotten that mathematical laws and formulæ are hypothetical, being to the effect that if such a premise is granted, then so and so follows—logically. Mathematics is not entitled to assert that a given premise is a fact. Such an assertion requires observation or experiment. Agreement between observation and a mathematical equation affords evidence in favour of the premise from which the equation or formula was constructed. (This is not the whole story, of course, since we have made no reference to *induction*.)

The usual example put forward to illustrate physical chance or physical probability—what we have called *frequency*—is coin tossing. For instance, take a ton of pennies, all head up, toss them in the air, how many will come down heads? It is of some importance to find that intelligent scholars, logically-minded and highly-trained, but unfamiliar with the physicist's universe of discourse, are invariably puzzled by the answer conventionally stated for this problem. The customary elliptical way of stating the problem suggests to these logical minds that it is an instance of the law of uniformity (" under the same conditions the same cause produces the same results "). They expect the coins to come down either all heads or all tails. They are astonished to be told the " correct answer " is that half a ton of the pennies will come down heads and the other half ton, tails. Their astonishment has its source in the defective statement of the problem, and arises from lack of a preliminary explanation that this is a physical problem, not an ideal one; that it is really a case of physical chance, because it is in practice impossible to toss up each coin in exactly the same physical conditions as its predecessor and successor.

In any experiment or observation, we are dealing with physical elements, with the real; we are not dealing with the ideal of the logician or mathematician. From the point of view of the physicist, mathematical treatment tends to oversimplify a physical problem— the nature and limitations of mathematics oblige it to do so, of course.

Chance (in the sense of frequency or physical probability) reflects man's ignorance rather than nature's aberrations, says Francis Bacon. Such ignorance cannot be overcome, because its complete removal would require that we should know every possible fact. This would entail traversing an infinite series, which is impossible. Every stir of the universe is a new fact capable of altering the world and of being experienced by man: it may generate a whole sequence of further facts. Increase or growth of knowledge cannot overcome the resulting chance which is a disorder or irregularity arising out of the criss-cross of causal series. Again, the scientist knows universals; he can never know all there is to know about individuals, about facts. Only God has such knowledge, and for Him nothing happens by chance.

The uncertainty of Heisenberg refers, not to human limitations, but to a natural uncertainty, or uncertainty in nature, brought about by the interaction of the observed object and the observing mechanism. It renders detailed and precise knowledge of physical events impossible, not only in practice but in principle. It sets a limit to what man can know of the physical world, and makes idle the boast of Laplace to predict the course of Nature.

STATISTICAL SCIENCE. Some of the confusion that prevails relative to statistical science has its origin in the source we have been dealing with, namely, the identification of the ideal and the real, of mathematical chance with physical frequency. Mathematical chance is based on equalities, while the basis of physical frequencies is inequality, springing from the hierarchy of values in nature. Physical chance thus has its root in the linkage of natural causes and effects, or in the concatenation of " secondary causes scattered " as Bacon put it. Because statistical science is taken up with the study of actual frequencies that are functions of physical events, it is commonly described as being concerned with non-causal law. It is in this sense that what we may call methodological chance has been introduced into a good deal of recent physical theory. This simply means that statistical methods have been incorporated along with their character of randomness.

While the bookmaker usually deals in *likelihoods* (apart from those cases where he is rather an accountant concerned to balance his book) he likes to give his moral estimate a mathematical flavour and cry the odds as, say, five to four. The mathematician would, however, phrase it differently and say the probability was five-ninths.

Strictly, you have mathematical probability only if (1) all the possible events envisaged are of the same nature; (2) are determined in number; and (3) are known in advance, so that their degree of probability can be evaluated under the form of a fraction in which the denominator expresses the number of all the possible cases, and the numerator denotes the number of favourable cases. Suppose a bag contains 10 balls, of which 8 are white and 2 are black. The probability that I draw a black ball is precisely 2/10.

From the mathematician's viewpoint, *doubt* is expressed by the fraction " $\frac{1}{2}$ ", and certainly by unity " 1 ".

This calculus of probability, making use of statistics, is employed by insurance companies to fix the premiums for risks of losses. Thus, for example, if it is known from experience that out of every 200 ships, 10 are lost each year, the probability of a ship being lost is $\frac{1}{20}$, and the premium (apart from fees of the insurers) would be $\frac{1}{20}$th the value of a ship.

Moral probability cannot be pinned down to an exact evaluation, because the risks are not all known, nor are they all of the same nature. It occurs usually when there is question of free will. We meet it in history and in the administration of justice. If, for instance, in a criminal trial, 10 witnesses favour the accused and 15 are against him, you cannot say the probability of his guilt is $\frac{10}{25}$. In such matters, one *weighs* the probabilities rather than counts them, and one makes allowance for unknown elements. A mathematician *counts*, but a moralist *weighs*.

To conclude. By its very nature, mathematical chance is definitional, logical, an aid to reasoning and discussion. The mathematical ' laws of chance ', or theorems about probability, should not be confounded with the frequency of physical events, the actual rates at which events happen, even when the latter are studied in a non-causal fashion, statistically. The mathematical theory of probability in itself can afford no information about the physical universe. But a comparison of mathematical formulæ with frequencies of phenomena can be helpful in natural philosophy; and can furnish information as to the existence of random elements in a physical problem. The philosophical significance of such elements is not the business of physical science.

7. *Statistical Law*

To the plain man, statistics is a subject, statistics are figures and the statistician is one who counts things. To the physicist, the term ' statistical ' is opposed to ' individual ' and ' exact ', statistics being a subject that deals with groups and probabilities rather than with simple entities and certainties. The experimenter, accustomed to acquiring knowledge by carrying out researches under controlled conditions, thinks of statistical methods as those he employs when an accurate check is not feasible, as, for instance, in most branches of meteorology and biology, where a particular effect can arise from several different causes. Statistical techniques are fundamentally mathematical, and many think of statistics as a kind of mathematics. The statistician is, however, no abstract theorist, inventing a pile of figures out of his head, but a realist who collects his data from the world around him. Like other men of science, he studies what actually happens.

He studies the characteristics of groups in so far as they can be learned from examining the characters of the members constituting the group. He is concerned with mass-phenomena, with what characterizes a host of elements or individuals forming a collection of some sort, be it called an assembly, a crowd, a society, a population, whether of people or of things. The group, or ' population of individuals ' as statisticians commonly describe it, has characteristics of its own, derived from, and an aggregate of, those of the individual elements, but the qualities of the two sets can be as different as chalk and cheese. For example, the individual may have a birth, but it is only the group that has a birth-rate. The group is both less and more than the totality of individuals. The statistician attends to a few characters of the individuals, sorts the individuals into classes, and studies the distribution and nature of the class-characteristics.

ILLUSTRATION. Suppose a statistician attends to the ages of individuals in a group. He can first study the distribution of ages and obtain the *frequency* of distribution, that is, the number of individuals who fall into a particular age-class, say, not older than fifty and not younger than forty-five, and so on. He could next calculate the *average* age and study the *variations* from it, noting again the frequency-distribution. Usually we would find that frequency-distributions could be pictured by a curve shaped like a hill, a 'hill-curve', the height of the 'hill' representing the percentage of individuals with more or less average characteristics in general, the average age in our example. Hill-curves may be sudden (high and narrow) or slow (broad and flat). The latter would represent considerable scatter in the ages of the individuals, and indicate that the average age was of little significance. A sharp hill-curve would, on the other hand, indicate that the average age was a feature deserving of attention, and might even serve to 'typify' or characterize the group.

HILL-CURVE. This hill-curve, and what it may represent, is assuming increasing importance as statistical science develops and impinges more and more on everyday life. It serves as a picture, and explanation of 'statistical definition', a concept which conflicts with, and in many minds has come to usurp the place of, logical definition. The latter is abstract and ideal, rigorous and clear-cut, while the former is concrete, physical and blurred. Statistical notions result, as it were, from the superposition of many individuals each possessing the class-character but in various, that is, different degrees. The meaning of words in everyday language is statistical.

Statistical definition has become important in our democratic day for another reason. We tend to become the victims of 'visual aids' and to lose the power of abstraction, through the prevalence of illustrated papers, television, the cinema, advertisements and other such instruments of mass-education and propaganda. The *idea* tends to be displaced in the human mind by a composite resulting from a misty blur of sense images. The resultant sense-image of the imagination, the phantasm, is analogous to a statistical definition. More and more it is taking the place of the purely intelligible concept, which cannot be pictured or imagined.

CORRELATION. The statistician is interested, then, in such things as averages, departures from average or normal or type, frequency-distributions, trends and correlations. Diagrams and tables which relate pairs of characters give rise to notions of association and correlation. Correlation expresses the general notion of two characters being related or not related. A high correlation indicates that characters are inter-dependent, a low correlation that they are unlikely to be so. Like all statistical results, correlation merely describes relations within a given set of data, referring to a particular set of conditions and taken at a particular time. It may or may not be possible to generalize from such results and conclude, for instance, from a set of high correlations that red hair is accompanied by blue eyes in a certain nation.

As it is generally impracticable to examine one by one a whole population or race or other large group of individuals, we perforce operate on a sample. The statistician must consider the precautions to be taken in sampling, and the probable value of his results, employing probability theory as a guide but not as a check. This is often forgotten. Probability theory being mathematical and abstract, and statistics being concrete and physical, the function of the mathematical theory is purely methodological.

Statistical method is rational method specially adapted in order to elucidate data affected by a multiplicity of causes. It tries to draw order out of, or recognise some kind of order in, a 'tangled skein of causes and effects', as Yule remarks. The data are not simple but usually very complex, since they result from a variety of causes all operating together in an unknown fashion. This it is that introduces what is called chance into statistical law. Chance, in the statistical sense, arises purely from ignorance. (Cp. our earlier discussion of Chance.)

CHANCE EVENTS. The degree of chance reflects our ignorance. The ignorance may be fundamental, because the relevant exact causes or laws are unknowable. According to present ideas, we do not and cannot know the precise motion of an electron (Principle of Indeterminacy). The ignorance may be non-essential and perhaps transient, because the exact laws do not happen to have been discovered. Thus the departure from a 'bull's-eye' of a shot on a target depends in an unknown, but not unknowable, way on a host of factors: there is steady progress in ballistics. Or the ignorance may be deliberately assumed because the exact laws and causes do not lend themselves to statistical treatment—the data may have to be 'randomized' before they can be used. It does not help an insurance company to know the exact details of its clients' motor accidents when it is calculating future premiums for car insurance. It treats accidents as 'chance' events, that is, events which happen for unknown complex reasons.

The outstanding feature of statistical method is that it enables us to discern and predict mass regularities where the individuals are unpredictable. The individual in a population may vary, but the population has stable characteristics. Statistical stability is a striking phenomenon. We do not know when an individual member of a community will die, but an insurance society can estimate the incidence of death among its policy-holders with great accuracy. As Eddington has well said: "Human life is proverbially uncertain: few things are more certain than the solvency of a life-insurance company."

Galton has called the law of error-frequency the supreme law of unreason. "Whenever many chaotic elements are taken in hand and marshalled in the order of their magnitude", he remarks of the hill-curve, "an unsuspected and most beautiful form of regularity proves to have been latent all along". Perhaps we would say to-day, that we recognise a hidden order and bring it to light by treating the statistical data in a systematic or scientific way.

STATISTICAL METHOD. There is no doubt that statistical method has power, and one is not surprised to find it being extended to domains formerly believed impervious to it. The various departments of economics, biology (especially genetics), medicine (especially public health and vital statistics) and agriculture are its natural terrain. But psychology has come under its sway in such diverse items as intelligence-tests, accident-proneness, and psychic phenomena. Engineering is not immune, and there is a sluggish effort to replace its ' safety-factor ' (which is a factor of ignorance) by statistical coefficients. Several sections of physics and chemistry now employ statistical methods. Statistical-experimental investigations have been initiated by R.A. Fisher at the agricultural station of Rothamstead. Industry increasingly employs statistical techniques to control costing and the products of mass-production. Sport is not immune, and in the Irish Sweep we find recourse being made to statistical procedures to ensure a thorough mixing of tickets.

Physical science has generally been thought of as concerned with properties of nature that are determinate and precisely measureable (apart from the restrictions we have mentioned elsewhere). When atoms were regarded as all alike, there was no room for statistical treatment. Allow them to have different speeds and directions, say, and they afford fit data for statistical processing, as, for instance, in the kinetic theory of gases. Here the aggregate becomes statistical, and its laws—the laws of statistical mechanics —are called " non-causal " laws. More and more, " non-causal " laws of this kind are being met with in modern physics. The statistical approach is of little or no use to the physicist as long as he is interested only in the properties of matter in bulk, but it enters in when he tries to relate such properties to observations on elementary components such as molecules, atoms and electrons.

Physicists have developed their own statistical processes and techniques which are independent of the work of statisticians in other fields. There is little in common between the statistics of Bose and Fermi in modern physics and the work of actuarians or State statisticians.

RANDOM INDIVIDUAL. We have seen that statistical laws and methods refer solely, strictly speaking, to mass-phenomena, to characteristics of groups and not to individuals or unique events. By reflex action and by virtue of formal similarity in the mathematical expressions (one characteristic in a mass can be treated in the same way as a mass of characteristics or variables affecting one individual) statistical laws may be transformed into probabilities and applied to individual persons, things or events. Statistical probability thus obtained is a trick or dodge for attaching to the random individual in a population the characteristics of the whole group. Probability is applied to events that do not occur as frequencies, e.g., to a particular bet on a horse, to predicting an accident, or your luck in a sweep, and so on. We attempt to describe an individual's chances from what we know of the population of which he is a random member. Probability is here a measure of our degree of confidence that a thing will happen: it measures the strength of our belief in an event.

NON-CAUSAL LAW. The main point of this short study is to indicate how and to what extent statistical law is of its nature indeterminate for the individual, and in what sense it is to be understood as a species of " non-causal " law. Physical law, we have seen, is a generalization which includes and describes the regular behaviour of an individual and his class, while statistical law refers to group phenomena and in no direct way describes individual events, persons or things. Unlike physical law, statistical law does not necessitate or " determine ". It is in this sense that physical law is ' causal ' while statistical law is not.

8. *Epistemological Physics*

Is the physical world real, and to what extent can I know it?

The *idealist*, struck by the immediacy of his conscious states, holds that the object of external perceptions consists in ideas. His view is in contrast with that of the realist who believes that matter can be directly perceived. The attitude we adopt is realist but not in an extreme or crude form. The solution we propose is moderate and critical realism, an attitude which is in agreement with everyday experience. It is the system implicitly or explicitly followed by most men of science. According to this solution:

1. The familiar world I live in (called external or physical world) is real, that is, it is distinct from and independent of the activity by which I know it.

2. The objects that make it up are also real.

3. The primary or common quality of objects, called *extension* (resistance or inertia—and movement—may be represented as aspects of it; or extension may be reduced to inertia), is also real; that is, extension is in an object as I experience it, though the *amount experienced* may be increased or decreased by my activity.

4. The secondary qualities of objects, such as colour, taste, smell, and so forth are not in an object as I perceive them, but only causally or " virtually ". In other words, the object has the power (virtus) to produce the experience of secondary qualities in me but my experience is influenced not only by the exciting object but also by my receptive faculties and the physical medium in between. For instance, a red rag produces the experience of *red*. Not all objects can produce this particular sensation, and therefore there must be some power or virtue in the rag which causes this sensation. But the kind of the medium and the state of my visual faculty also affect my perception, as can be inferred from the existence of colour blindness, and the laws governing colour-contrast and refraction of light. I distinguish red from blue, and shades of each, and I find I can confirm my distinctions and impressions with the aid of various kinds of instruments (tintometer, spectro-photometer and other colour comparators). There is a *correspondence* of some sort connecting in turn the subjective experience, the physical object and the measure of the physical quantity. These correspondences are in themselves realities.

POINTER READINGS. In contrast with what has been written by some ' popular ' expositors of science in recent times, the moderate realist finds that the familiar world of everyday experience is not eliminated from the domain of science, and is not replaced by a series of pointer readings. If the familiar world were removed, he wonders how science would have any domain left to work on and in. Even though a scientist's head is in the clouds or in the stratosphere, his legs should be long enough to reach back to the ground. He should not be like the man who climbed a ladder and from the topmost rung cried out: " Take away the ground, I don't need it any more ".

Taken by and large, physical measures are objective, precise, impersonal, independent of the physicist, and communicable, while many of our everyday impressions are by contrast subjective, relative, personal, imprecise and incommunicable. For instance, we know of no way of communicating to others our knowledge of qualities so as to compare our impressions of colour, sweetness, sounds, odours, and so on, to see if they are similar. With regard to my knowledge of intensities, such as ' more or less sweet ', I ' feel warm ' or ' taste sweet ' but I don't know what warmth or sweetness is in the object, apart from analysis of causes.

The pointer-reader physicist asserts: " To find if a body has such a property we *apply* the *appropriate* instrument and read the index ".

CRITICISM. The moderate realist replies that pointer-readings by themselves mean nothing; and he amplifies and explains with statements like the following: —

(1) You do not apply just any instrument. The whole theory of qualitative study with its basic ideas, laws and causes is involved at this stage.

(2) It is important to know how and where the instrument is applied.

(3) No instrument reading can ever assure us that the object is devoid of the property. The mark "0" on the instrument does not mean " none " of the property, but rather an amount too small for us to detect with this instrument.

(4) The numbers furnished by the instrument are not abstract or pure numbers. The physical study of the material world is carried out with instruments that are quite different in nature (i.e., qualitatively different). We do not say 7° F. = 7 amperes.

(5) Instruments extend the scope and sensitivity of the senses and help to depersonalize the measures, and make them less liable to bias or error; but there is no measure without the physicist. Recording and automatic equipment have to be set, calibrated and ultimately ' read ' and corrected or ' reduced ' by the physicist, who has to employ much theory and interpretation before he is finished with a reading. His data do not come to him without a good deal of processing. The telescope, clock and barometer extend the sensitivity of our senses but they do not thereby replace them. They extend the threshold of observation, but only as servants not as masters of the human senses. The index

or pointer must be read by the senses ultimately, and *interpreted* by the physicist.

Hence a certain minimum of sense knowledge is necessary for the scientist, namely, that minimum whereby he recognises the object he studies and reads the instruments by which he measures them. It is necessary and sufficient that he knows an external reality, in space and time, which has differing qualities. He may employ any one quality to distinguish one reality from another. Hence physical science pre-supposes a *datum* and sense knowledge. Thus, for instance, a blind man may ' read ' by ' hearing ' the print and some of our readers are doubtlessly aware that this miracle of modern technology or applied science has been achieved.

It is well known that there used to be apprehension in the Cavendish Laboratory whenever Sir J. J. Thomson went near a delicate piece of apparatus. Lord Kelvin was another who could be as dangerous to scientific instruments as a bull in a china shop. Both were great physicists. But, usually, the physicist is " good " with his hands and eyes and is not all thumbs. One has only to see a spectroscopist or a cosmic physicist read and interpret a few smudges on a photographic film to appreciate how little sense impression is required for advanced science.

Since the Renaissance, the power, penetration and precision of our senses have prodigiously increased because of equipment that daily becomes more perfect, and because of experimental methods that daily become more refined and detailed. At the same time, researches, in ever growing numbers, with each more specialised, and more profound, and more minute in the field studied and covered, introduce new ideas or modify old ones. The physicist now has a subject-matter of astonishing wealth, a wealth that is constantly growing.

THEORETICAL PHYSICS. " Theoretical physics constructs a symbolic representation of what our senses, helped by instruments, tell us ", say Duhem and Poincaré. " Each logical notion in [theoretical] physics corresponds not to a metaphysical reality but to the geometric or algebraic character of the symbol substituted for the notion. For instance, the notion of a [chemical] compound is replaced by a chemical formula in which the analogy between two compounds is expressed by equality of indices affecting certain symbols [letters]. In optics, geometric dissymmetry is used to represent rotatory power. But this symbolic representation of the data of experience is unconnected with the reality [metaphysical] of sense data ".

This may be theoretical physics, but it is not physical science, according to the moderate realist, who holds that physics gives true and genuine knowledge about the physical world. He points out that he has direct contact with, and direct knowledge of, the physical world in various operations as when he observes and makes measures of extension, resistance and movement of matter. These are the ultimates in all his measures and they constitute the real bases of his subsequent refinements and elaborations, ideas and laws and theories. No matter how many removes there are between the observation and the conclusion, if the observations are just and the reasoning valid, the conclusion contains true and certain knowledge about the external world.

9. *The Uncertainty Principle*

Like a great book, a great principle may be a great evil, temporarily. When Heisenberg in 1927 first published his principle of " unbestimmtheit " [in the *Zeitschrift für Phyzik,* 43 (1927) 172], he scarcely thought of the fuss he was about to create, the gallons of ink that would flow, the batteries of typewriters that would rattle into action, the loose wild statements that would be flung around proclaiming free will for atoms or asserting the end of causality and the beginning of a reign of universal chance. More sober thoughts now prevail, and many people see that Heisenberg's principle is after all just a principle of physics, and that it has nothing to do with free will, psychological determinism or causality, but that it is an affair of atoms and sub-atoms.

The principle has its basis in *wave properties* of matter, which are conceived to be such that the physicist cannot hope ever to achieve precision in atomic measures. Suppose we try to locate an electron and measure its speed. We must take two snapshots at successive moments and this entails employing beams of radiation. The reaction between a ray and an electron is such that we can measure either the position or the velocity of the electron precisely, but not both simultaneously. Fine-grained radiation, say X-rays or gamma rays, will allow us to locate an electron accurately, but they disturb the speed vastly in an unpredictable way. They give a violent and incalculable kick to the electron. Coarse radiation, on the other hand—say, visible light—could be used to measure the speed precisely, but not to locate the electron—it would be like trying to take a speck of dust out of a wristlet watch with a crowbar. (The experiment we have described to locate an

electron and measure its speed is purely imaginary and impracticable, but it illustrates the principle of Heisenberg.)

This uncertainty principle, also called the principle of indeterminacy or indeterminism, is really a principle of indefiniteness.
It is a physical principle. The mathematician can still think of a
small particle having a definite position and a definite speed, but
his ideas will be without physical significance. The physicist's concepts are operational. Only those magnitudes which in principle
can be observed and measured are accepted as part of the physical
description of nature. Until someone can think of a way to get
round the indeterminateness inherent in measuring small bodies,
arising from the *incalculable* interaction of observer and object,
the uncertainty principle will remain a sort of Boyle's law in
epistemological physics—the more precisely one aspect of a particle is measured, the less determinable is another or complementary property. The interaction is incalculable because the wave
properties of matter introduce indefiniteness when we deal with
small bodies, and we mislead ourselves if we conceive atomic
objects as having sharp outlines or definite edges. There is no
question of instrumental defect or inadequate theory. It is the
nature of things. Small entities in the physical world are neither
particles nor waves, but *wavicles*. No physicist can at present conceive how it is possible (or ever will be possible) to get round the
uncertainty principle.

DETERMINISM. The principle is physical and has nothing to do
with philosophy or psychology. As a physical principle, it is not
really in conflict with physical determinism, though some seem to
think so. Physical determinism simply means the existence of fixed
universal laws, that a cause having been placed, its effect follows,
invariably. This is the basis of induction. No one seriously main-
tains that the same ray of radiation meeting an electron in the
same circumstances will to-day do one thing and to-morrow
another. Acceptance of the uncertainty does not mean that physical
determinism has ceased to rule the atomic world. If determinism
or causality did not apply to the world of atoms as to the large-
scale world, atomic science would be impossible.

Some confusion arises from the way in which the word " determines " is employed in two different senses, sometimes to mean
' cause ' and at other times to mean ' measure '. The uncertainty
principle states there is a natural limit to precise *measurement*
of atomic properties. It does not deal with *causal* relations. The
principle implies that by the nature of things there is a limit set

to the precision attainable in the operational definitions character-istic of physical science. There is a natural limit to preciseness both in measures, and, reflexively, in operational definitions. This, however, only emphasizes that physics is not an abstract or ideal science like logic or mathematics, but deals with things. Heisen-berg's indefiniteness or uncertainty has no reference to causation.

FREE WILL. Some of the older physicists went to the other extreme, and, going outside their domain, interpreted physical determinism to mean a denial of free will. In other words, they held that natural determinateness implied physiological or psychological determinism. The basis of this identification of differ-ent orders was a crude materialism that is no longer in favour with scientists.

Materialistic determinism represented man as a dead object driven hither and thither by his environment, antecedents, circum-stances and so forth all adding up together like a polygon of forces to produce a mechanical result. Psychological determinists thought of the will as a balance which inclines as weights go into the scale-pans, and they affirmed that the decisions of the will are deter-mined by the strongest motive acting like a weight in a scale-pan. To them the will was not master, but passive and swayed by motives it did not assess. The physiologist attributed our volun-tary acts to temperament, to the state of our nerves, to the rhythms and condition of our brain. The will was not a cause, but the resultant of forces acting on us. In all this, there was much mis-understanding of what is meant by free will and there was mis-reading of the data of consciousness available to everyone.

Now, free will is the power of the rational will to determine itself. Freedom is not doing what you like but what you will to do, as Ronald Knox has remarked. The term ' free will ' is a misnomer. The free act comes only formally from the will, but fundamentally it comes from the mind which presents the rea-soned choice or end to the will. Freedom is a psychological fact, a fact of consciousness more immediately known to us than any physical data. There is an apparent contradiction between freedom and strict causality. The problem, so-called, of free will is to formulate properly and explain the relations between ontological causality and human freedom. A few solve the problem to their own satisfaction by denying the fact of free will, saying it is an illusion. In practice no one consistently or really denies the existence of freedom and responsibility. The whole purpose of education is to free the will from constraints of passion and pre-judice, and to strengthen the individual will against mob values and human respect and the sheep mentality. In enforcing sound education, we do not deny freedom of the will, rather the contrary. Good training, we all believe, helps to set the will free for those voluntary acts which consist in the deliberate pursuit of an end or the choice of means.

CAUSALITY. Though the electron could not be thought of as a rational being, Bohr's theory of how it behaved in the atom (1913) suggested to some people that it was a wilful creature. This view appeared to receive confirmation from the uncertainty principle. Eddington in the *Nature of the Physical World* wrote: " The future course of very small particles is not merely mathematically in-determinate but ontologically undetermined." That is to say, the future path of an electron is not subject to the law of causality. Eddington thought he was helping the case for free will by dis-carding the principle of causation from mathematical physics. As if freedom measured in Angstrom units had a bearing on freedom determined by the conceptual presentation of alternatives to the mind.

To try to establish free will by dropping causality and by intro-ducing wilful electrons and chance, is to begin at the wrong end. Whether a particular act is free or not, whether we are responsible creatures, has significance for each one of us. In deciding the point, we consider the psychological data and pay no attention to theoretical physics. We assert the freedom of some human acts without waiting for physics to tell us that electrons are undetermined.

Again, the will is called free, not because its acts are undeter-mined, that is, uncaused; but because it is the cause of its own acts. The will is an agent. It causes the acts by embracing an end (or the means to an end) which the mind has set before it. Ultim-ately, of course, it is God Who causes it to operate, God Who gave it its nature to act freely, as He gave to a tree to grow. If strict causality were abolished, we could not logically believe in human freedom any longer. There is no real contradiction between freedom and causality. This is a case where we can both have our cake and eat it.

The attempt to discard causality in atomic physics arises, I would suggest, from a misunderstanding about what Eddington calls 'strict causal behaviour'. Causality is here confused with prediction, that is to say, the power of prediction is taken as the test of causality. If you can predict the future path of an electron, there is causality; but if you cannot do so, then causality is absent. So the argument would run.

There appears to be a double confusion here. First, physical or phenomenal causality is taken as being the same thing as ontological causality, that is, secondary and proximate causes are identified with ultimate causes. Causes in which there is no more than an *invariable* connection between cause and effect are regarded as being the same as causes which are *necessarily* followed by their effects. Secondly, the subjective and the objective orders are confused. An attempt is made to identify (subjective) ignorance with (objective) chance, and then the absence of causal law is alleged. (Cp. §§ 6-7 on chance and statistical law.) According to present views, we cannot predict the course of events in the atomic world because we are the victims of an ignorance which is fundamental. But, can we be sure it will always be thus? The whole history of science would indicate the contrary. But even grant that our ignorance will always remain fundamental; that no exact law is known or knowable. The physicist is then without an exact cause and effect relation, and he can only predict by statistics and by probability. This absence of exact physical law and physical causality does not, however, mean that ontological causality is missing.

Planck has summed up the position in his book, *Where is Science Going?* (London, 1933) in this way: "Indeterminism in physics is only subjective. The physicist cannot forecast the future course of a particle, which is none the less determined." The famous father of quantum theory goes on to express his belief that "eventually, equations will be found for it [the particle of atomic physics] consistent with the law of causality".

Let us take first things first.

No activity of electron or ray of radiation can be undetermined, that is, uncaused. Every action or change must have a cause, an agent. That is fundamental, prior to all knowledge of electrons, prior to electrons.

The principle of causality is a principle of common sense justified by the wisdom of the ages and proved by reflection and criticism. It is an aspect or derivative of the principle of sufficient reason, the foundation stone of all knowledge and of all reality. Physical science, above all the sciences, is rooted in the soil of good sense and sound principle. What madness then seizes some of its exponents to dethrone the deity and try to set up in his place a goddess of unreason?

II *THE GROUNDS OF SCIENCE*

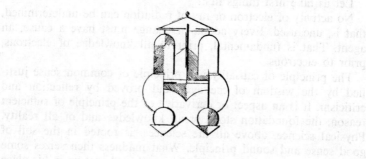

1. *Abstraction and Generalization*

SENSATIONS and mental images are only the stuff of knowledge, and they do not of themselves constitute knowledge of a high order. Memory retains, and imagination combines in a thousand and one ways, the data of sense experience; but the images remain material, concrete and individual, like the objects from which they were drawn. Human knowledge worthy of the name transcends matter and distils something out of the individual items that have been contacted through the senses. In this way science becomes possible, for there is no science of the individual concrete thing. As a preliminary to science, we must therefore obtain an immaterial, abstract and general representation of the sensible data; namely, the *idea* (also called the concept or notion). Ideas constitute the prime elements and the true raw material of scientific knowledge.

(Common knowledge knows only facts, and can make assertions but cannot prove them. According to the traditional view, we require only sensation, imagination and memory for common knowledge; while for scientific knowledge we need in addition reflection and judgment.)

The idea is a simple *intellectual* representation of an object, and should be clearly distinguished from the mental image, which is material, concrete and individual. My *idea* of a chair as ' something for sitting on ' is quite different from any *picture* I may have in the mind or any *feeling* I may experience of resistance or support. The mental image is not necessarily visual only, it may derive something from the senses of sound, taste, touch or smell. People blind from birth do not have our visual images, yet they have mental images, as I understand.

The distinction between image and idea is fundamental for science, as for all true human knowledge. Ideas are the beginning of science.

Once in the possession of ideas, the mind can compare them by an act of *judgment* and see if there is a relation or not between them. A *truth* or *proposition* is the affirmation of a relation between two ideas, but the idea itself is no more than the simple representation in the mind of a thing, and does not involve any affirmation. We have ideas of ' cause ' and ' purpose ' or ' end ', but we state or assert the principles of ' causality ' and ' finality '.

Reasoning is the operation which compares judgments or propositions. By making explicit and evident to the roaming and imaginative mind the relations which exist between propositions, it may lead to new knowledge. The two outstanding forms of reasoning are *deduction* which proceeds from the more general truth to the less general, and *induction* which operates in the other direction.

Such are the three great processes, ideation or conception, judgment and reasoning which give the qualities of clarity, precision and generality as well as reasoned certitude and methodical linkage to our knowledge, and so produce true scientific knowledge.

Let us consider a little further the operation of abstraction and generalization, in view of its importance for all knowledge. In particular, the process furnishes us with the special concepts of a science and makes for powerful economy of thought if the concepts are well chosen. Such concepts do for thought what coins did for trade and commerce when they took the place of barter. Specialized concepts are indispensable tools for the intellectual craftsman and for the scientific thinker, as long as they do not degenerate into mere technical terms and jargon, which tend to embalm thought instead of energizing it.

Intellectual abstraction enables us to consider separately properties of an object which are really inseparable. It is the process that furnishes us with our so-called abstract ideas, such as our moral ideas of truth, honour, duty, justice, or our metaphysical ideas of being and substance. We do not call it abstraction to consider separately the pages of a book or the limbs of a tree or of an animal: these can be actually separated from the object they belong to. Nor is the intellectual abstraction the same as sense abstraction, which is rather a subtraction. Indeed, our senses are abstracting machines, since they succeed in separating qualities which are in reality inseparably combined in an object. Thus, our sense of touch only detects relief and resistance in objects, our sight can only see coloured extension, our ears can only hear sounds. We have not in such instances true abstraction, for the colour and shape seen by our eyes as separate from the resistance and temperature of the object, are still concrete and individual; these qualities are still taken in by us under the conditions that fix matter in its strait-jackets of space and time.

Intellectual activity furnishes a new kind of being, quite different from that which objects possess in reality. In the object, a property is concrete and individual, and is bathed in the ether of material existence. The concept of a property is completely free from everything that makes it exist as a concrete, material, individual reality:

it no longer has a definite habitation in a material world, and it loses all its 'here and now' or 'then and there' associations.

In a word, abstraction is an operation by which the mind withdraws an object or a property from its concrete existence and from everything that lets it fall under the senses and makes it capable of being represented by the imagination. From material objects it produces a representation which is quite immaterial.

There are persons who possess this power of abstraction in an unusual degree, such as talented people and geniuses. We say of them that they 'take in things at a glance' or that they have 'insight'. But we all have the power. We can all abstract from material objects that which makes them what they are, i.e., their nature or essence; and, for instance, we can all see a tree as a 'real, substantial, living being', without anything material in the concept. (One must not confuse 'abstract' with 'immaterial', or 'concrete' with 'material'. God and the soul are *concrete* realities, spiritual as they are; that is, they are real and existing; while the length of the desk, considered as distinct from its breadth, colour and other qualities, is an *abstract* notion.)

DEGREES OF ABSTRACTION: CEILINGS OF THOUGHT. Aircraft cannot all climb to the same height. Each type, fighter or bomber, helicopter, jet or turbo-jet or other, like guided missile, V-2, rocket and man-made satellite, has its ceiling, its limit of ascent, its maximum altitude of climb. It is much the same with the concepts or ideas characteristic of the various sciences. Each science has its ceiling of abstraction.

An idea is the more abstract, the more removed it is from the existing reality. From this point of view, one can distinguish four degrees of abstraction as having importance for modern studies. It has been traditional to distinguish only three, but such differentiation was based on inadequate notions of mathematical and physical science, we would suggest.

The first degree is reached if we neglect the concrete, material and individual existence of an object. Let us abstract from what is individual in our experience and let us concentrate on the specific qualities of the world as presented to us by the senses. We then arrive at properties which cannot exist without matter nor be conceived apart from it, e.g., colour, sound, temperature, taste, smell and so forth. These are what Galileo would call the secondary qualities of matter. Here we have the ceiling that is reached in the concepts proper to the descriptive sciences and descriptive laws of nature. Here we have the limit of qualitative law. Here we have the tropopause of secondary causes.

In the second degree of abstraction, we leave behind the secondary qualities of matter and concern ourselves only with its primary properties, extension, resistance and motion. Considering these under the aspect of *concrete quantity*, apart from which matter does not exist, we arrive at the basic concepts of the physical sciences, namely, quantity of extension (whence shape, and space or *distance*), quantity of motion (the measure is *time*), quantity of resistance or inertia (the measure is *mass*). All measures and operational definitions in the physical sciences are derivatives of these aspects of concrete quantity.

We can think of quantity, however, apart from extension, resistance or movement of corporeal bodies—in fact, we can conceive it apart from matter and its inevitable properties. We can think of *abstract quantity* and we can conceive it as attributable even to immaterial beings. We in fact speak of the number of persons in the Trinity, the number of souls, the number of angels, of virtues and vices, and so on. We have reached the third degree of abstraction. At this stage we are concerned with a property in which all the secondary and primary qualities of matter are rooted, and without which matter cannot exist, though the property can be conceived and can exist apart from matter. This is the mode of conception proper to the concepts of the mathematical sciences.

Quantity, the quality in virtue of which things are measurable, may be continuous or discrete. Discontinuous quantity is the basis of number which forms the subject-matter of arithmetic and algebra. Continuous or extended quantity affords a basis and raw material to the geometrical sciences.

How important is the difference between abstract and concrete quantity, the one proper to mathematics, the other to the physical sciences, may be illustrated by an example. In abstract science two and two necessarily make four, but not so in physics where two and two may have any value from four to zero. For instance, a two-pound force added to another two-pound force may annul it, much as light added to light may produce darkness as in phenomena of interference. In such instances we are dealing with concrete quantities, and their laws of combination may be quite different from the laws governing analogous operations in pure mathematics.

Finally, we can consider concepts which apply to everything, whether material or immaterial. Properties or qualities can be thought of as existing in a spiritual as well as in a material object. Such are the concepts of being, substance, potency, relation and so on. Here we have reached the fourth degree of abstraction which constitutes the metaphysical ceiling. Metaphysics deals with concepts that have been abstracted and purged from all material traces, and considers only Being with its transcendental characteristics, properties which can be conceived not only apart from matter but can exist without it. Metaphysical concepts are the true ultimates for the philosophical thinker. At the same time, each mode of abstraction furnishes its own valid and legitimate approach to the study of reality.

The degree or order of abstraction, the ceiling of thought, is not necessarily altered by mere removes from observation or experiment. Mathematical physicists may play around with physical concepts and bring them further away from concrete reality, but without turning them into mathematical concepts. Thus, the notion of ' entropy ' is further removed from physical reality than, say, the notion of ' specific heat '; but the principle of entropy remains a physical principle and does not become a mathematical one, since it represents (albeit at many removes from the laboratory and nature) a fact of observation expressed in terms of concrete quantity.

THE UNIVERSAL IDEA. In abstraction, the mind concentrates on the essentials of an object and penetrates below mere surface qualities and appearance. Abstraction is the act by which the mind draws forth from an object the determinate part of the object which constitutes and reveals its nature, while neglecting all else. It is called abstraction because the nature of the object is abstracted or drawn out of the object whose nature it is: the nature of the object cannot be grasped or apprehended until the intellect has drawn it forth from the object. Abstraction is therefore prior in thought to simple apprehension. The mind by an act of abstraction grasps an objective reality in the object, not just something mind-made. Simple apprehension grasps and concentrates into one concept certain qualities of the object selected by the mind, but really existing in the object, not invented by the mind but mind-grasped. The concept no longer represents one single object and no more. It is now applicable to each and every member of a class. It is a *universal* class. The imagination perceives individuals, but intellect has the special function and power of seeing the universal under the particular.

Abstraction is a perfection since through it our knowledge rises above matter. It is the condition of all science, because it is the necessary means for every clear and distinct thought, and of every general or universal idea. It is the condition of every art, since combinations by the imagination suppose there has been a previous dissociation of properties from the objects they inhere in. It is the condition of language. Apart some names, all words express abstract ideas of substances, qualities, actions or relations.

By the nature of the human mind itself, what we can call spontaneous abstraction automatically drops off the concrete conditions attached to the individual object. But in order to get at the *nature* of an object and form the essential notion of a thing, it may be necessary to elaborate the first concept. This we do by reflex abstraction, in which the constituent elements are special attention, abstraction, discursive comparisons and all-embracing generalizations.

GENERALIZATION: GENERAL IDEAS. Generalization is an operation by which the mind reunites in a simple notion the common elements that have been perceived in a variety of objects; and the mind goes on to conceive the notion as identically applicable to an indeterminate number of objects. Thus, for instance, the general idea of man represents the constitutive elements of every man, and can be affirmed of all the members of the human race.

It is usual to distinguish two kinds of general idea.

The first is imperfect and relative. It is the *composite image* formed by the imaginative memory. Characteristic of the young child, it is proper to animals. A child is struck by external resemblances which may be the source in him of picturesque comparisons and unexpected associations. Thus to a French child, a dog, his wooden horse, the chair, his little brother crawling on all fours are one and all a *toutou*. To an English child a *puff-puff* may represent a train, his asthmatic aunt, wheezing grandmother or pipe-smoking papa. A dog will bark at a beggar he never saw before and will wag his tail at the approach of strange children.

True generalization is complete and absolute. It requires the cooperation of the intellect. The result is the *general idea* or the *universal,* so-called because it represents that by which several are *one.* This kind of idea is the necessary result of intellectual abstraction. By the fact that an object is isolated by the mind from the elements which gave it concrete individual existence, the idea becomes capable of realization in an indefinite number of actual or possible things. Being *one* in the mind which thinks it, it is *multiple* in its legitimate applications. It is a universal idea.

In science we can distinguish various levels of generalization corresponding to ideas, laws and theories. In various sciences we can generalize by classification. We note similarities and differences; and our classification, based on knowledge of cause or principle, expresses what is constant and common in facts and truths of the same type or order.

THE BASIC IDEAS OF REASON. Our ideas are not *intuitions* or *perceptions*, but they are the result of the mind working on the data of experience.

Human experience is of two kinds, *external*, which puts us in touch with the external world; and *internal*, which concerns the events in our own psychic life, the prime data or facts of psychology. External experience leads to our *sensible* ideas and the concepts characteristic of the physical sciences. External perception cannot generate our *psychic* ideas. Only consciousness furnishes us with ideas of pleasure, pain, memory, remorse, certitude, doubt, volition, free will—in short, the ideas corresponding to the facts of our psychological life. These intimate data are necessarily impervious to external observation.

We go on to distinguish a special type of psychic ideas, the ideas which have their origin in the immediate apprehension of the self, the Ego, by our consciousness. These are the ideas of *being, substance, unity, identity, duration, cause* and *end* or finality. Logically, they are the first ideas of reason, the bases of all the rest. We may call them the basic concepts of reason, the fundamental rational notions. They are produced by the highest mode of abstraction and are therefore sometimes called metaphysical ideas. They are abstracted from the data of the self-conscious, which are evident in introspection, that is, in the study of our own thoughts and feelings. Let us say a few words about each of them.

1. *Being* cannot be defined beyond saying, it is or can be. We do not get the idea from sense experience, but from the intellectual experience of our own being in the fact of consciousness.

2. *Substance,* the being which exists in itself, the substrate of change, can only be conceived, not imagined or contacted in any way by sense experience. Our senses do not penetrate beyond qualities, and never get as far as the substance of a thing, which is quite immaterial, a principle. It is the great prerogative of consciousness, of intelligence, to grasp not only modifications or qualities (properties of being) but the substance of them; in the first instance, we form the idea of our own soul or spirit by grasping the permanent self, or Ego, along with its various modes of existence, its moods, its calm or angry states and so forth.

3. *Unity and identity.* These are the two essential attributes of myself or my Ego that are directly attested by consciousness. There is no need to elaborate. It is one and the same 'I' that thinks, suffers, remembers, desires.

4. *Duration.* We perceive duration as the succession of our mental states, and by comparison we go on to measure time and

the duration of external things. In this sense we can say with Leibnitz: "*Si non esset anima, non esset tempus*—No mind, no measure of time."

5. *Cause*. Cause is used here in its strict metaphysical sense as that which concurs directly to produce a being or an event. Only consciousness can perceive cause in this sense. The senses cannot perceive strict causality, though they can detect the sequence and regularity of phenomena. It is the exclusive privilege of the intelligence to seize in one and the same apperception, (that is, in the mind's perception of itself) not only the intimate event but also its real and concrete cause, the 'I' that produces it.

6. *End*. The end of an act is the goal pursued by an intelligent cause, or, that in view of which a cause acts. The end may mean the *result obtained* or the *intention*. In the first case, it is the real effect following the act; in the second, it is an idea which moves the agent to act, and directs his operations. It is therefore the purpose, and precedes the act as the cause of its cause, one might say. The senses may perceive the act, but the purpose and abstract goal are beyond their horizon and capacity. We can perceive only our own intentions, we have to infer those of others.

It is pretty clear even from a cursory survey that we owe these fundamental ideas to consciousness, to an examination of our own thoughts.

NOTE ON NOMENCLATURE. Modern philosophers tend to give the name 'general' to 'sensible' ideas, the ideas got in the two lower orders of abstraction; and the name of 'abstract' or 'metaphysical' to ideas got in the highest order of abstraction. For the scholastic, both classes are 'universal' ideas, though some moderns restrict the term to 'metaphysical' ideas. The unfortunate lack of agreement about nomenclature arises in part from confusing *ideas* with *images* and *statistical definitions*.

THE PRIME CONCEPT OF REASON: THE ABSOLUTE. The prime notions of reason are different aspects of the absolute. Considered in itself the absolute is necessary, infinite and perfect. Considered in its relations to the relative, it is the first cause, the last end, absolute substance, the true, the beautiful, the absolute good.

These notions are prime logically, not chronologically, because they are the ground and reason of all others. They are also of prime importance because the idea of the perfect, the infinite and the absolute good as the supreme ideal constantly inspiring us furnishes us with the reason and spring of all our efforts and progress in science, art and virtue. Our notions are, of course, inadequate and analogical, but none the less positive and sound as far as they go. If the attributes of perfect and absolute are necessarily incomprehensible to our finite mind, they are not inconceivable. With Descartes, we can touch a mountain though we cannot hold it in our arms. The absolute is 1, *necessary*, because it is its own sufficient reason. The opposite notion is found in the *contingent* which has not in itself its *raison d'être*. The necessary being, absolutely independent, cannot be limited in any form of reality, and is therefore

2. *Infinite*. The negative form of the word may give a wrong idea of its meaning. Finite being is limited being, and limit is the denial of further reality. Infinite being lacks nothing, it has everything. This is the richest idea there is. Since it is unlimited in every positive quality, the absolute is

3. *Perfect* or complete being to which nothing can be added. That is, it possesses being or reality in all fullness, completely, without any restriction or limitation whatsoever.

Opposed to the absolute is the *relative*, which is conditional being, dependent, and, therefore, contingent, limited or finite in its reality or possession of being, and imperfect.

It is in considering its relations with the relative that we see the absolute under its aspects of the first cause, last end, absolute substance, the true, the beautiful and the absolute good.

2. First Truths

SCIENCE is possible because the universe is intelligible. The big wide world makes sense and does not violate reason. Every new advance in science is itself fresh evidence that the scheme of things is rational.

The reason of things is studied in metaphysics which seeks the last answer to the last question about everything. Its principles are rooted in the intelligibility of things, and express the necessary conditions for thought and reality to be free from contradiction. If things are intelligible, then certain principles such as the Big Two, namely, 1, the principle of identity or non-contradiction; and 2, the principle of sufficient reason, and their derivatives, must be true. They are metaphysical reasons that cannot be denied without denying reason itself.

The principles are called first truths for several reasons. First, by their importance. Without them it is impossible to reason or even to think. How, for instance, affirm a thing is or is not unless one is convinced that affirmation and negation are not the same;

that there is a true and a false, and everything is not indifferent to the mind. Second: these being the most general truths, they are necessarily implied in all other truths which are instances and examples of them. Third, chronologically: everyone proves he has them by the use he makes of them, from childhood's days when he puts his first " why?", persuaded that all has a reason, and that the answer to a simple question cannot be both ' yes' and ' no ' at the same time.

These truths are evident by themselves, they are necessary truths, they are absolutely first, they are universal in application, they are the foundation of all science. They are prior to all experience; indeed, without them we could not have experience. If a man attacks them, his very reasoning supposes the validity of the principles he assails. He cuts the ground from under his own feet. Or, he is like a man sitting on the branch of a tree engaged in sawing off his support.

The basic concept in metaphysics is ' thing ' or ' being ', whence the name ontology, the science of being. It is the most general notion there is. It underlies everything and it is all-embracing. It is the true ultimate. It cannot be defined because there is nothing simpler. You take it or leave it. When you have said: being is that which exists or can exist, you have gone as far as you can to describe it, and you have indicated the two kinds of being, actual and possible, which together make up reality. What is true of being is true of everything, for everything is being. The principles of being underlie every science. They are in fact the foundation of all knowledge, of all reality, of existence and activity and even mere possibility, in every domain, material and immaterial.

Metaphysics has its own degree or ceiling of abstraction. Its ideas are not limited to matter but transcend it. Thus, being and its various attributes, which include causality, are transcendental notions, understandable only in the philosophical mode of abstraction. These notions cannot be pictured or imagined: they resemble Wells's invisible man who could only be inferred from his clothing.

The principles of being are also the principles of logic, of thought. A philosophical principle is that by which a thing is or is known. That by which a thing is, constitutes its metaphysical principle, its *raison d'être*. That by which a thing is known, is a principle of logic, which reveals to the mind how and why a thing is so. A logical principle organizes our knowledge and directs our science. Logic studies necessary truths of the conceptual order and follows the same highways as metaphysics in studying truths of the real order. The basic principles, the Big Two, have their logical and ontological aspects and formulations.

THE PRINCIPLE OF NON-CONTRADICTION. The first of the Big Two, in a positive form known as the principle of identity, and in a negative form as the principle of contradiction, is probably best described, as Hamilton suggested, as the principle of non-contradiction since it forbids the mind to contradict, or be untrue to, itself. In its ontological form the principle states: a thing cannot exist and not exist at the same time. Contradiction cannot exist, since it is the negation of being and amounts to saying that non-being exists. A thing is what it is, and none other, not something else. The positive form of the principle is sometimes expressed as *A is A,* but this, of course is tautology. More correctly one would say: everything is its own nature. We could proceed to the derivative principle of finality and say: a being operates towards its own end, always. These would be aspects of the principle of identity or non-contradiction. Let us illustrate by an example. If you want to know what a thing is, watch it in action. Even when its actions are apparently " unnatural ", cross-grained, wrong-headed, cussed, as sometimes in the case of a human being, they reveal the nature of the creature. For instance, only a rational being can act irrationally.

The logical form of the principle of identity or non-contradiction has also received many formulations, not all of them being acceptable. Properly understood, the principle expresses the basic quality of the human mind which cannot really think a contradiction once the contradiction is recognized. Anything that contradicts itself is inconceivable, that is, it cannot be grasped or accepted by the mind as an actual or possible reality. For a thing to be comprehensible, the ideas representing it must not hold any contradiction. Of two contradictions, if one is true, the other must be false. There is no alternative, no third possibility (principle of excluded middle). This is the law of the mind, this is reason, this is the touchstone of truth, this is the basis of mathematical demonstration.

While it is self-evident that a thing is itself and not its contradictory, that A is A and is not not—A, the whole tribe of those who would persuade you that black is white, propagandists, quacks, bucket-shop promoters, misleading publicists and sophists in general, constantly deny the principle in practice, while, of course, persuasively paying lip-service to it.

The negative form of the principle leads to the three derivatives: 1, excluded middle; 2, third equivalent; and 3, contenance.

The principle of the third equivalent may be expressed symbolically as: if A=B, and B=C, then A=C, or things equal to the same are equal to one another. The principle of contenance may be expressed as: if A contains B, and B contains C, then A contains C; or, if Timbuctoo is in Cork, and Cork is in Africa, Timbuctoo is in Africa.

Examples of the positive form of the principle, the principle of identity, are: ' every triangle has three angles '; ' every square has four sides '; ' 2+2=4 '; ' man is a rational animal '.

All these principles are analytic, that is, the attribute is in part or entirely identical with the subject, and, therefore, they are implied in every *deduction*. Mathematics knows no other principles of reasoning. Its favourite argument of *reductio ad absurdum* is a clear example of using the principle of contradiction to demonstrate the truth of a theorem.

THE PRINCIPLE OF SUFFICIENT REASON. The second member of the Big Two is the principle of sufficient reason. "Nothing occurs by chance," said Leucippus, "but there is a reason and a necessity for everything." Leibnitz put the principle this way: "Nothing happens but there is a reason why it is so and not otherwise." The term " reason " is used in two senses: (a) ontological: the reason of a thing is the source from which the thing draws what it is or has; (b) logical; the reason is that which lets us understand why and how a thing is. Hence the principle is also called the principle of universal intelligibility. In the one case the reason is a cause, a metaphysical cause; in the other, it is an explanation. In other words, the principle means that for a thing to be comprehensible, there must be something which accounts for its existence or reality either in the order of existence, in the order of possibility (for instance, a square circle is not possible but a trip to the moon may be), or in the order of essential truth (e.g., the whole is greater than the part).

Applied to concrete reality, the principle yields immediately the *principle of causality*.

The principle of causality is an application of the principle of sufficient reason to the existence of a contingent being. A contingent being is one that can be or not be. If he exists, he must have a reason for his existence. But not in himself, for he is contingent. Therefore, he has it in another outside himself, who produced him: this other is his cause.

It is important to note that the word cause is unfortunately employed in two different senses which we must distinguish clearly. We may call one the *true cause,* and the other the *pseudo cause.*

There are two elements in a cause of unequal importance. The essential element involves *necessary dependence* of the effect on an agent. A cause is a substantial active principle which *produces* an effect. There must be efficacious influence of a real being on the existence and nature of the effect. This is the essence of cause in its strict sense.

Of less importance is the second element, *anteriority* to the effect. Unfortunately, this superficial characteristic of causality has alone been retained by the positivists and popularized in theoretical physics. The positivists have made a scientific axiom out of the sophism *post hoc, ergo propter hoc.* Cause for the phenomenalist is nothing more than the regular antecedents of an event, but without any necessary connexion or dependence as far as he knows. This pseudo cause is nothing more than invariable concomitance. The constant and exclusive presence of an antecedent can make *manifest* the cause without constituting it.

In metaphysics, a true cause is an agent that transfers from non-existence to existence what was incapable of self-existence. It is that on which the being of another depends. It is a principle which of itself produces something else or determines the existence of something else. It is more than a condition. It exerts an active influence, and there is *otherness* in the form of some perfection or some positive quality produced. Metaphysical causality is a principle of change in another.

The metaphysical idea of a cause is the same as that of common sense, and the same as that of the experimenter who works with actual physical agents and uses them to *produce* actual physical effects. Metaphysics demonstrates that the common sense concept of causality is good sense. An absolute beginning, that is, passage from nothing to something is inconceivable: it is contrary to the principle of sufficient reason. Hence the need for true causes.

There have been various formulations of the principle of causality, not all of them satisfactory. The form " every effect has a cause " is equivalent to saying " whatever has a cause has a cause " and is clearly tautological. If we amend it to " every fact has a cause " it is now too narrow, since it omits being. Again " everything has a cause " is false, since God is uncaused. A consequence has its principle, but not a cause. Kant's formulation " every phenomenon has for cause another phenomenon " makes cause only phenomenal in character and never reaches the concept of a true or ultimate cause.

Better formulations are: " Everything that begins to exist has a cause ": or, " everything that is, and has not received from itself what it needs to exist, has received it from another, which is its cause (whether this cause be itself produced or not produced)." Everything of such a nature that it can begin to exist must have a source whence it proceeds. Everything coming into existence must result from an active agent whose agency has produced it. A cause is not identical with the invariable, unconditional antecedent, for this ignores the necessity of an *active* influence in producing the effect. The effect is *dependent* necessarily on the cause.

The principle of causality is narrower than the principle of sufficient reason, for while every cause is a reason, not every reason is a cause. Only real being can have a cause, while a reason suffices to explain a simple possibility. The principle of sufficient reason applies to abstract notions, to possible beings, to necessary truths, to God.

UNIFORMITY OF NATURE: THE PRINCIPLE OF NATURAL LAWS. The term ' nature ' is used in many senses which are reducible to two. There may be reference to a particular nature or to nature in general. The nature of a particular being is the group of constitutive characters and essential attributes of the being. In its general sense, nature means either (a) the force or cause of all the changes we perceive in corporeal bodies; or (b) the total of laws that preside over the existence of beings and the succession of facts. Nature appears to operate in a framework of space and time. The principle of the uniformity of nature refers to nature in its general sense.

The principle may be stated: in the same circumstances, the same cause always produces the same effect. There is an equivalent form sometimes described as the principle of natural laws, according to which: "Every fact has its law," or " nature obeys fixed and constant laws ". The principles are derivatives of the principle of sufficient reason. If two identical causes in identical circumstances produced different effects, the difference in the effects would not have a sufficient reason, and, therefore, could not be.

The uniformity of nature or the principle of laws makes prediction intelligible and induction possible. Every natural cause having been placed is necessarily followed by its effect if the principle of uniformity holds. On this assumption, knowledge of the former gives the power to predict the effect, the event. The ground of the prediction is the principle of the uniformity of nature. The same principle is the justification and necessary condition for inductive reasoning about nature.

Physical law is the regular linkage of the same antecedents to the same consequents and is an aspect of the principle of uniformity. It constitutes the basis of what has been called the *determinism of nature* or physical determinism. Historically, Democritus in the 5th century B.C. derived a theory of *universal* mechanical law from naturalistic speculation. The theory developed from the observation that certain natural processes were seen to be the outcome of mechanical forces operating in a regular way. It was found possible to frame general laws which accounted accurately for what happened. If true in some cases, why not in all? If in all, this would simplify thought. It would eliminate chance. But it would also eliminate choice and purpose! So the free-will controversy had its origin. Early on, it was kept in mind that freedom of the will is a datum of experience, a fact, while physical determinism was a theory, an extension but not a necessity of scientific thought. Determinism had no real scientific backing until after the publication of Newton's *Principia*.

The principle of philosophical substance is another derivative of the principle of sufficient reason. In philosophy, substance is more extensive and more profound in meaning than the idea of chemical substance. It is the permanent reality underlying qualities. It remains the same despite accidents and changes. It is the principle of activity, of action and reaction, of resistance. Every quality supposes a substance, every change supposes something that endures. There is no action without an agent, no movement without a body moved, no thought without a thinker.

If we accept the view of the phenomenalists, that there is no substance in nature, we must suppose—to explain change—that everything is annihilated and recreated instant by instant.

Another derivative from the principle of sufficient reason is the *principle of first cause,* which states that every secondary cause supposes a first cause. Every cause that has itself been caused supposes eventually an uncaused cause. We keep traversing a chain of insufficient causes until a sufficient reason is reached. This is why we do not admit the possibility of an infinite regress.

The principle of finality can be seen as a derivation of either member of the Big Two. According to it, everything has its end, destination, goal or purpose and acts always in view of it or to achieve it. There is nothing aimless or useless in nature. As everything emanates from a cause, ultimately the First Cause, so everything tends towards a goal or ultimate end. Here we have a progressive series. The principle of finality interprets the present by the future, and explains antecedents by consequents. The principle of causality, contrariwise, gives rise to a regressive series, and explains the present by the past, consequents by antecedents. The one is a history, the other is a future in the womb of the present, an oak tree in an acorn. (Formerly, both principles were regarded as having equal validity, but most present-day scientists appear to be ignorant of the principle of finality.) We note there can be two meanings of "why?", namely, by what cause? or, for what end?

According to the principle of finality, beings act so as to attain their end. Look at the complexity of man's actions and of the many motives that urge him on and ask yourself: what inner drive moves man to his labours? Is it the desire for a crust of bread, a roof over his family, a reserve of wealth, or just mere pleasure, or a sense and reality of power? If men are one, if all men have a similar nature, what is the key to their actions?

Beneath the manifold and even conflicting desires of men we can see the one feeling that gives unity and meaning, as well as force and direction, to every human desire. All seek what they seek for one reason only, to be happy. Happiness is the goal of human activity in so far as it is free and deliberate. Happiness is the final end of man, the determinant of his acts, of all the acts that characterize him as a man.

So, too, all beings have a final end towards which, willy nilly, they always act to realize themselves and their destiny.

It is of interest to recall that another derivative of the principle of sufficient reason, namely, the principle of economy, has inspired men of science from Fermat to Newton, from Leibnitz to William Rowan Hamilton, and occasioned history's most farcical slanging match between science and criticism, involving Maupertius, Frederick the Great of Prussia and Voltaire and causing gales of laughter to sweep Europe. There are several formulations from Fermat's principle of least time in optics to the principle of least action in dynamics and to statements such as: "Nature always takes the simplest and most direct paths," "nature always acts to achieve her ends with the greatest economy of means", and "nothing goes to waste in nature".

It is argued that if there were a simpler way of attaining a specified end, there would be an expenditure of energy without sufficient reason. "It would be making useless things," says Newton, "to employ many forces to achieve what could be done with few."

The principle of least action has its counterpart in the logical principle of economy which concerns explanation and is summed up in Occam's Razor: *"Entia non sunt multiplicanda præter necessitatem,"* that is, in accounting for facts, one should not multiply needlessly the causes, laws and principles. Since we do not know the plan of nature, it is now generally recognized that we can only use the principle of economy of nature sparingly in science.

3. *Analysis and Synthesis*

M ETHOD signifies the road you have to travel to get to your goal or destination, your journey's end. For the logician, method is the group of procedures the mind should adopt in order to find and establish or demonstrate truth. Descartes in his *Discours de la Méthode* (Part II) examined the general conditions required for scientific research and formulated four rules dealing with 1, the evidence; 2, analysis; 3, synthesis; 4, verification. Since his time, method in general is regarded as an interplay of analysis and synthesis. The special methods proper to individual sciences are various forms of analytic and synthetic procedures adapted to the purpose and subject-matter of a particular discipline.

Analysis breaks down a problem into simpler elements, while synthesis integrates the various elements in order to form a comprehensive and satisfying view of the whole question. Without analysis, knowledge is superficial; and without synthesis, it is incomplete. Science is not limited to knowledge of details (this is the disease of over-specialization); it sees their place in the pattern and appreciates how they contribute to the whole scheme. Analysis and synthesis are complementary processes. Each supposes the other and both are needed for complete knowledge. Synthesis without a previous analysis can yield only illusionary knowledge. Analysis which loses sight of synthesis as its ultimate goal is apt to wander down every side-road and boreen and get lost.

Analysis decomposes a whole into parts, it goes from the complex to the simple, from the composite to its elements, or should try to do so. Analysis does not divide a thing into homogeneous and integrant parts like a butcher cutting meat; rather, like an anatomist dissecting a subject, it divides its material into heterogeneous and composing parts. A child does not analyse a watch when he smashes it any more than he analyses Homer when he tears a copy of the *Iliad* to tatters.

The first aim of science is to understand and explain things: i.e., grasp the necessary relation linking things to their cause or principle. The great obstacle the mind encounters in this endeavour is complexity. Our intellects are unable to cope with the complex, and especially, to sort out of a tangled skein of entities, facts and ideas, the delicate relations of cause and effect, of principle and consequent. Hence the need to analyse, to water down the difficulties the better to separate them and take them one by one, and not be overwhelmed by them in mass.

Every science practises analysis in its own way. The chemist decomposes his substances. The anatomist dissects organs. The botanist examines separately the different parts of a plant. The psychologist distinguishes the various faculties of the mind and soul. The dramatic critic gets at the dominant ideas in a play. The geometer reduces solid figures to the surfaces which bound them. And so on. All these analyse.

While, in general, analysis decomposes and synthesis recomposes, the precise meaning of these procedures in the various sciences may differ very considerably. Mathematical science gives a character of its own to analytic and synthetic processes, quite different from that produced in experimental science. This is because the former deals with ideas and general abstract truths while the latter deals with facts and concrete entities. The chemist decomposes water into hydrogen and oxygen, and recombines the same elements in the eudiometer to form water again. With his prism or diffraction grating the physicist splits white light into its constituents and he can restore white light by mixing colours in just proportions. The psychologist is restricted to mental analysis and synthesis. All such processes differ hugely from the procedures of analytic and synthetic geometry, where analysis no longer decomposes but *resolves* or reduces a problem to a simpler one already solved; and synthesis starts with a general principle that is simple and evident, and proceeds to *deduce* the answer to the problem. Thus, for instance, the analyst would measure the area of a triangle by first showing it is half that of a parallelogram with appropriate base and height, while the synthetic geometer would start with the area of the parallelogram and go on to deduce that of the triangle. Euclid is synthetic geometry, but Cartesian geometry is analytic. While, in general, synthesis goes from the more simple to the less simple, it is not exact to say it always goes from the simple to the composite, or that it reconstitutes the whole from the parts that have been decomposed in analysis.

It is only in mathematical reasoning that exact reversal of the analytic and synthetic propositions is possible. This is because here alone the propositions always express equalities.

4. *Induction and Deduction*

THE mind reasons more or less rigorously either by way of induction or by way of deduction. Reasoning enables us to get new knowledge from old, to proceed from the known to the unknown. Reasoning permits us to use what we know already in order to find out something we did not know. It is an operation of the mind by which from one or more known relations we can conclude logically to some fresh proposition. This can be done in either of two ways. We can start from a general truth that we know and arrive at a less general truth or a particular case up to then unknown. If we thus proceed from a known principle to an unknown consequent, we call the process *deduction*. Deduction, then, goes from the more to the less general.

Or, again, we can start from a known fact, a particular case, and conclude to a principle or general case hitherto unknown. This is called *induction*: it moves from the particular to the general, from the less to the more general, from an instance to the principle or general rule or law.

There are three forms of induction. In Socratic induction one generalizes from the individual to the species or genus. In Aristotelian induction (of which mathematical induction is a form), one proceeds from the members of a group to the whole collection by complete enumeration of the members. Properly speaking, this is not generalization but simply addition. In scientific induction, also called Baconian induction, which alone concerns us here, we generalize to a relation of causality between series of phenomena, although we have observed the relationship in only a limited number of cases. We conclude from a *causal* relation to a *law*.

The idea of beginning with a few notions and then deducing a host of conclusions from them by strict reasoning, is a Greek invention. It is a marvellous process that reveals the prodigious capacity of human reason. We are forever the debtors of the Grecian philosophers who developed deduction as a powerful mental tool for gaining fresh knowledge. The Greeks were not very given to experiment though they were acute observers. Perhaps, like some modern theoretical physicists, they hoped to find a short cut to knowledge by way of logic that would save them the expense and trouble of manipulation. They looked down on manual labour. Geometry was an occupation for free men, but working with hands and tools was for slaves. So they passed from social to intellectual snobbery. Knowledge obtained by deduction became fashionable, was called science and was associated with the name of the greatest of all thinkers, Aristotle. Though Aristotle himself was a shrewd observer, medicine was to him just the art of healing: it was not a science any more than carpentry or agriculture, all of which were regarded as empiric and elaborations of brute experience or rules of thumb. The Greeks would have smiled derisively at the expressions " medical science " and " scientific agriculture " as phrases without sense, the words of babblers.

The perfect type of deductive science is Euclid's *Elements,* which still remains the model of modern algebras and geometries, and perhaps a good deal of theoretical physics. The fashion set by the Greeks in intellectual disciplines persisted down the centuries with such force that when Newton wrote his *Principia* and did his calculations by a better method than Euclid's, he dared not print the new system in his book but had to show his computations in Euclid's laborious way. Theology and philosophy made much use of the deductive method and, like all the other sciences, kept Euclid before them as an ideal or model. It was overlooked that Euclid did not show his rough work. Nor was there advertence to the laborious nights of shepherds by the Euphrates and the strenuous days of builders in Egypt, whose discoveries laid the foundations of *The Elements* and of Greek science.

The fashion changed. The slave method came to be honoured. Bacon took up the cudgels for it and belaboured Aristotle. In the reaction, extravagant claims were made for the inductive method, which is a mixture of much experience and a little reason that has defied reason to explain. The method works and no one can say exactly why. The failure of John Stuart Mill to reduce scientific induction to logical deduction is well known. The old method had abuse heaped upon it, and Aristotle was blamed for many evils. Bacon was loud in his condemnation, and chauvinists, who had never read his works called the inductive method after him. But, to quote de Morgan's weighty verdict in *A Budget of Paradoxes,* if Newton had taken Bacon for his master, then not he but someone else would have been Newton.

The pendulum of appreciation is now swinging back, and the deductive method again finds favour with scientists, especially with theoretical physicists. That odd fish and bizarre personality, the eminent theoretical astronomer, Arthur Stanley Eddington, has gone so far as to propose a deductive epistemology (really a cosmology) in his *Fundamental Theory.* Thales said: " All is water." Sir Arthur, with the Pythagoreans, holds that " all is number ". Given a few constants of nature such as the velocity of light, the mass of an electron and a proton and so forth, he would say that all the properties of the universe can be deduced, much as the circumference of a circle can be inferred once its diameter is known.

5. *Analogy*

We can consider analogy as a relation between things or as a mental process.

A first glance suggests that analogy consists in an imperfect likeness between objects of different orders. There is analogy between the physiology of a plant and that of an animal. In literature, analogy is the basis of allegory and metaphor; metaphor applies the name of an object to another it resembles, as, for instance, in the phrase ' the springtime of life and the winter of old age '.

As an activity of the mind, analogy is a process of reasoning that infers from observed resemblances the existence of other resemblances not yet observed. It is in this sense that analogy is of importance in the development of science. Clearly, the argument from analogy can never produce certain but only probable conclusions. It would be an analogical argument to say Mars is inhabited like the earth because it resembles the earth in so many ways: it is like the earth in shape, it is like the earth in having an atmosphere, it is like the earth in being a planet in the solar system, and so forth.

Historically, analogy has often been fruitful in the physical and other sciences. The idea of the kinetic theory of gases was suggested by the behaviour of a flock of birds. Priestley, remarking the analogy between rust and the products of combustion, concluded that all oxidation is but slow combustion. Franklin, struck by the resemblance of lightning to the electric spark, inferred the existence of atmospheric electricity. Similar effects having been observed in the case of light, heat and sound which were deemed to consist in vibrations of air or æther, scientists supposed they were all ruled by the same laws. In fact, reflections, refraction, absorption, interference, and polarisation are common to thermal, optical and acoustical phenomena.

Analogy differs notably from induction. Induction reaches a general law from a few observations, and argues that the many have the *same* characteristics as the few that have been observed. Analogy argues from like to like characters, not from same to same. Inductive reasoning generally supposes essential and specific resemblances, while analogy is content to discuss accidentals and superficial likenesses. True induction can beget certitude, at least in theory, and inspires a robust faith. Analogy can give birth to nothing better than hypothetical conclusions. In both forms of reasoning, the conclusion outruns the premises, and the transition from the data to the generalization needs to be validated by some general principle such as the uniformity of nature or the plan of nature.

Perhaps the greatest triumph of analogy in science is that it may lead to the discovery of a physical cause by its suggestiveness. Franklin's inference from lightning to atmospheric electricity is a case in point.

6. *Space and Time*

THEORIES of space and time are legion but they can be reduced to four types. The *objective* type would make space and time independent of us and of things. Then there is the purely *subjective* theory of Kant. Leibnitz advanced a *relativist* theory, according to which time and space are orders of relations between events. Finally, there is the *intermediary* theory of the moderate realist which is both subjective and objective. According to this view, space and time are notions conceived by the mind but suggested by things themselves.

As we see them, space and time are general ideas with a foundation in experience, but they owe their existence to the abstracting intellect. We do not follow Newton who believed in absolute space and time, we do not with Newton conceive time as the eternity of God. We do not go to the other extreme and follow Kant, for whom space and time were mind-made, not merely mind-processed; for whom they were mental moulds " *a priori* forms of internal sensibility ". Nor do we follow the empiricists who give themselves over body and soul to concrete images and do not see the need for subtler enquiries or for *quasi-abstract* entities. Thus, we do not accept Brown's plain handling in his *Philosophy of the Human Mind* when he paints a vivid and charming picture of a baby brandishing its little arms and kicking its little legs in space and time, and concludes that *feelings* of relations of co-existence originate the notion of space, while feelings of relations of succession give rise to our idea of time.

In our view, space and time are correlatives of matter and events. No matter, no space. No change, no time. Space is, so to speak, the container or background of matter; while time is the container or background of events, the texture of change. Absolutely, the phrases ' empty space ' and ' uneventful time ' are contradictions.

The absolute space of Newton is the same as empty space. We have to speak of space and time analogically. Rightly or wrongly, we conceive them as (1) *homogeneous :* each bit is like any other bit apart from the presence of matter or the occurrence of an event; (2) *continuous :* there is no solution of continuity in space or time, no hiatus or lacuna is possible; (3) *unlimited :* no matter how far back our imagination thrusts the bounds of the universe and of the past, we can conceive a space and time beyond, a space and a time that is capable of receiving other bodies and other facts; (4) *necessary :* we cannot conceive space and time as not existing. (Here enters the distinction between real and imaginary space, but we will not go into it.)

ATOMS OF SPACE AND TIME. Space and time being continuous quantities, are not made up of units which could serve to measure them. No one suggests there are quanta of space or quanta of time: there are no atoms of space or time. Yet, metaphysically, and *in itself,* a unit or atom of time exists *ideally* as a limit: it is the time (duration) shorter than any assignable time, and we call it a *mathematical instant.* Psychologically, and *for us,* the unit of time is the shortest interval of which we can be conscious, say, the blink of an eye. Similarly for space. To the philosopher, the unit of space is the limit called the *mathematical point,* while to the psychologist the atom of space is the smallest extension perceptible to the senses.

To try to construct space from points and time from indivisible instants is like trying to build concrete reality out of abstractions, or real things out of conceptional limits. Reality, in the language of Pythagoras, consists in intervals, not in limits (*pace* Sir James Jeans and Sir Arthur Eddington); in continuity, not in numbers or quanta. Space and time constitute the indispensable framework for nature, the stage on which she plays out her drama. Space-time is more than a mathematical theory but less than a physical or metaphysical reality.

MEASURES OF SPACE AND TIME. We measure space by a definite amount of extension taken conventionally (that is, by implicit or explicit agreement) as a standard. As for time, since it cannot be measured in terms of itself (because it changes as we proceed to measure it), we get round the difficulty by measuring space, on the supposition that we can find a uniform motion. That being so, the space described measures, as a surrogate or deputy, the time during which the motion has lasted. In physical science, the day, the hour, the solar second, the season, the solstice, and such standards or dating-terms correspond to various amounts or positions of the earth's diurnal rotation or orbital motion, and are therefore measures or markers of motion.

THE IDEAS OF SPACE AND TIME. Our idea of space has its origin in the data got from our senses of sight and touch. When we abstract from colours, shapes and resistance, and consider only relations of position (relations of contiguity and distance), we arrive at the idea of abstract extension, that is, the possibility of indefinite extension in three dimensions, equally capable of receiving all shapes, all colours, all possible bodies. Such is the notion of space as we understand it. Space, by analogy with extended matter, is conceived as being made up of co-existing parts.

Our idea of time comes from the data of conscious experience.

By abstracting from the data of consciousness we see time first of all as something that *endures*. We see this when we consider the *contiguity* and the *permanence* that between them unite the separate instants during which our conscious states are in existence.

Absolutely speaking, to endure or to last, is to persevere or continue in being, to have one's existence go on; for persons, it is to go on living. Under this aspect, time is the *duration* of things that change or pass through different successive states.

In considering the same facts of our conscious life under their aspect of *succession*, as *before or after*, as a series of events preceding or succeeding each other, we conceive the possibility of indefinite and unlimited succession in two opposite directions, the past and the future. Here we meet a second element and we recognize that time *passes*. For an individual, time is the succession or series of passing instants in his life, and he thinks of time as a steady flowing stream.

Finally, we note that two or more events of our conscious life happen together; for instance, we see a flower and at the same time inhale its perfume. We then form the abstract idea of *simultaneity*, which is the third ingredient in our idea of time. Time is such that different events may coincide on a time scale.

The foregoing analysis shows that our idea of time involves the ideas of duration, succession and simultaneity.

The senses of themselves cannot furnish us with the idea of time. Time is essentially the measure of movement or change, as Aristotle said. Now, motion or change cannot be detected without a fixed reference point. You could not see that a river flowed if the banks on which you stood moved with the water. The senses respond only to changes and have no fixed point from which to measure the lapse of time. Consciousness, aided by memory, with one and the same look embraces the permanent and ever identical substance of the Ego, the "I", together with the modifications which occur in it one after the other. So, consciousness is able to give us the idea of time as duration plus succession, as enduring change, because it is conscious of a fixed point, namely, its own identity.

The *idea* of time is not to be confused with the *feeling* of time. The idea is fixed and invariable, the feeling or sentiment depends on our internal states. Time is long in idleness, pain or worry, and when we are turned in upon ourselves, or introverted. Time goes quickly when we are in agreeable company, or taken out of ourselves.

Recognition of these three ingredients in the concept of time—duration, succession, and simultaneity—permits us to understand the distinction between time as duration and time as date. The science of chronology depends on time as date. According to this science, events can be placed in a series of 'before' and 'after' terms, each term being a 'before' to its successor and an 'after' to its predecessor. Several events can be properly put at one and the same place in the serial list. Here we make use of the two aspects, succession and simultaneity, but the aspect of duration is not required for dating and so does not enter in.

Our ideas of space and time are analogous but they are far from being identical. There is nothing in the idea of space corresponding to the flow of time, there is nothing in the idea of time corresponding to the extension of space. The parts of space coexist, but the parts of time succeed. Time being a continuous succession has no actual parts in extension, its parts are in duration, instants or moments we call them when they are small enough, atomic-like. Two particles of matter cannot occupy the same point in space together, but two events can occur at the same instant—at the same point in time. We conceive space as an immobile receptacle, but time we conceive as essentially on the move always, mobile and never stationary, like a river ever flowing in one direction, steady and never changing its speed, unhurried and inevitable. Its parts being successive exclude one another, but since the parts of space co-exist they subsist alongside each other and reciprocally suppose one another. An event can be situated in time by means of two points, its 'before' and 'after' neighbours, but we need at least three points to locate an object in space. We derive our notion of space from external perception, through sight and touch; but the concept of time is derived from data of consciousness (helped by memory) through internal perception of our own intimate states and the changes occurring in them.

We shall not enter into the distinction that is sometimes made between 'real' (physical) and imaginary space except to remark that in our outline we have been concerned with the physical space that corresponds to the kind of matter known to the physicist. The four or more 'dimensions' of mathematical space are mathematical constructs, and have nothing to do with the physical world beyond analogy of mathematical form or similarity of symbolic representation. (Just as the geometrical terms 'square' and 'cube' passed into the more general language of algebra and signified the second and third powers of a quantity, so the expressions '4th, 5th, 6th dimensions' may in algebra, without any prejudice to their meaning in geometry, designate powers higher than the third).

SPACE OF "N" DIMENSIONS. If we speak of physical space as the space corresponding to the kind of matter we know and have experience of, then such space has only three dimensions, neither more nor less. Space is the receptacle of matter. We cannot contain matter with only two dimensions. Nor can the real quantity of matter in a body extend or spread itself in more than the three irreducible directions which correspond to the length, breadth and depth of a body. (Starting from a point, one can draw three mutual perpendiculars, no more; one can draw less, but they cannot contain the kind of matter we are acquainted with.)

III *SCIENCE AND PHILOSOPHY*

1. Science and the sciences.

2. Papal discourse on the challenge of modern science and the need for philosophy.

3. Note on scientism.

1. *Science and the sciences*

To-day's need. Though science has been advancing triumphantly, there is an uneasy feeling among scientists that all is not well. It is felt by some that science, having dismissed philosophy, has fallen a victim to mathematics. It is agreed that there is much loose thinking in scientific circles. Relativity treats time as if it were identical with space. Light has assumed some of the qualities of parking regulations for one-way streets: it is particles on odd days of the week and waves on other days; or *vice versa*. Scientists have become vague—worse, they have become their own throat-cutters—on the subject of causality. The text books are full of contradictions—not to use any harsher term—in their discussions of what are called " physical dimensions ".

Mathematicians quibble about petty points of logic that have no relevance to realities or to the public interest, as an English critic complains. In great tomes they worry themselves sick over questions like the Cretan problem, the antinomy of the liar. (A Cretan tells me all Cretans are liars. How can I make anything of his statement, since no matter how I take it, it involves a contradiction.) It is being felt more and more that there would be improvement if the acute, trained minds of philosophy were made use of. In the time of Descartes, Leibnitz and Kant, the influence of science led to a great revival in philosophy. It is desirable to have a repeat that would in all likelihood prove a benefit both to philosophy and science.

This part of our book contains a plea for unification, or at least reciprocal understanding, of the various sections of man's knowledge, from mathematics to metaphysics, so as to include the physical, biological, moral and social sciences. It compares and contrasts the methods characteristic of the great divisions of human enquiry, and indicates that they are not of themselves antagonistic or mutually exclusive. It concludes with the Papal address to the Pontifical Academy of Science on the abiding necessity of metaphysics and the need for friendly relations between science and philosophy.

Science. The youngster who tears his toy inside out is not necessarily a vandal. He may be a budding scientist eager to see how a thing works. If he is full of intelligent curiosity, he reflects the beginning of science. The scientist is curious and wants to know about things, why they are so, how they operate. He goes around with a note of interrogation in his mind. Looking at the wide world he sees something happen, asks himself why, and he goes on to suppose a reason. Then he reflects; if my supposition is correct, something else should happen if I do so and so. Let me see does it really happen that way. And he tries it out. And he generalizes. The true scientist is not passive, and his curiosity is not idle. He is active and on his toes to test bright ideas. He is not slow to check up on them and he is not slow to discard them if they are proved wrong or unsatisfactory. He will readily switch to new ideas when he has to. He has no vanity or bias about his first notions of things. He is objective and a realist. His outlook is different from that of the artist who defends his viewpoint as if it were divinely inspired, and to whom a personal way of looking at things—his vision—may be more important than anything else in the world. Each has his own type of integrity.

The scientist of old was called a natural philosopher, or a philosopher simply. Usually a man of leisure or of means he was often a doctor or a clergyman but rarely a university don. In the early days the universities looked down on experimental science as a form of carpentry or plumbing, and to-day they are still suspicious of technicians. In contrast to the natural philosopher who was just curious about nature and her ways, there was the military engineer, generally consultant to a power-conscious prince. He knew that to make use of nature for political or mechanical ends, you had to know and follow her laws. He has been succeeded by the technologist and technician, just as the amateur scientist has been succeeded by the professional. Interplay between pure and applied science has been to the profit of both, a fresh discovery or advance in the one invariably reacting favourably on the other.

As the purpose of the scientist in history has been twofold, so likewise his style of reasoning about problems, his logic or method. Among the ancients and until modern times, the deductive method of Euclid was in favour, then the inductive method, while nowadays we see that scientific reasoning makes use of both systems.

Each science gets its basic concepts hammered out in the forge of experience where there is constant interplay between the idea and the fact. The dominant element as well as the final test is experience. But experience without the operation of the reflecting mind is of no avail. Here again we have two aspects that are complementary and not contradictory or exclusive of each other. Science is a product of reason and experience.

While the term science is commonly used in a restricted sense to denote natural science or even physical science, we see that on the canvas of history science has been the sustained endeavour of a body of like-minded men down the ages to understand the world around them, partly out of sheer curiosity and partly with the hope of applying the fruits of increasing knowledge to improve the lot of mankind.

In the wide sense, science denotes a systematic body of truths relating to a subject as viewed from a special standpoint. So there can be as many sciences as there are subjects and viewpoints, in other words, an infinity of sciences. As we look back from our vantage point at the middle of this century, we see that in every field of science there have been fundamental changes in point of view. This is the great trait of science, that it is alive, active, growing all the time, constantly adapting itself to new knowledge. As one man has put it, science is " sciencing ".

Science, of course, is more than knowledge, just as a house is more than a heap of stones. It is knowledge by causes and principles—proximate causes or ultimate causes. It is an organic group of *certain, general, methodic* truths. Facts are not simply juxtaposed as in common knowledge. Familiar with laws, the scientist knows how to produce and stop, or modify an effect, or even make a prediction.

THE SCIENCES: CLASSIFICATION. The maxim has it: divide to conquer and sub-divide to know. Knowledge is one and infinite. To grasp it and use it, you must break it down into sections corresponding to the various aspects of reality. At the same time, you must keep in mind that the universe is not a mosaic of facts, a statistical conglomeration, or strips of crazy pavement, but a cosmos, a harmonious system with its parts dovetailing into each other, a symphony of causes, laws and principles. So, there is order and relation, colour and music, among the sciences. If we wish to obtain a view of the whole, we accept some system of classification.

The sciences are variously classified. Let us refer first to some very broad divisions. If we go by the matter studied and consider the three great themes, God, man and nature, we get theology, anthropology in its wide sense, and natural science. If we look to the aim or purpose, we divide science into pure or applied (theoretical or practical), according as knowledge is sought for its own sake or for use. If we advert to the type of reasoning employed, we speak of inductive and deductive science—sometimes referred to as *a posteriori*, or, from effect-to-cause reasoning; and, *a priori*, or reasoning from abstract principles to (concrete) consequents.

We cannot hope for finality in classifying the sciences, since new departments of knowledge spring up not by logic but fortuitously through the unpredictable activities of individuals and groups, and the varying needs of the community. Many systems of detailed classification have been proposed from Aristotle to Ampère, from Bacon to Kant. The most useful at this stage of development is probably a modified version of Comte's, which proceeds from the simple to the complex, from the particular to the general, apart from its start and end.

According to this scheme, we can classify the sciences under the following heads:

1. The mathematical sciences.
2. The physical sciences.
3. The biological sciences.
4. The moral and social sciences.
5. The metaphysical sciences.

The first and last groups are not strictly according to plan. There is ambiguity in the term ' simplicity ', since it can refer to logical simplicity, as opposed to what is familiar. What is simple in structure may be strange and hard to understand. Our scheme is therefore a compromise.

THE MATHEMATICAL SCIENCES. The mathematical sciences have a place apart because their subject-matter is abstract quantity, a property common to all the sciences of matter, but conceivable apart from matter, and therefore applicable to the immaterial. Since they deal with quantity, and quantity entails measure, the name of exact science is given to these disciplines.

Mathematical laws are based on ideal notions and do not relate to the real but to the possible. Hence the character of necessity and universality enjoyed by the exact sciences. Their language is precise for the same reason. Their characteristic method of reasoning is deduction.

It is thanks to abstraction that mathematics became distinct from the arts of calculation and mensuration. Arithmetic began with the herdsman's numbers and mathematicians went on to conceive a great variety of numbers and assigned them all sorts of properties. The history of the science is strewn with the corpses of still-born children, monstrosities of number. Viable and fertile mathematics was spun out of controlled imaginations that some-how kept contact with the physical world. In arithmetic, the generalization of number was related step by step to the practical activities of the farmer and the business man. Algebra began as generalized arithmetic. With its concise symbolism and funda-mental operations of arithmetic, it became a powerful tool for dealing with the constant happenings in the restless universe. Geometry grew out of mensuration, and its surfaces, lines and points were abstractions from the real properties of things. The famous postulate as to parallel lines fixed the nature of Euclid's geometry. Other definitions have given us other geometries equally valid as logical systems. Various algebras have also been in-vented. The application of any system of geometry, algebra or calculus to the physical world is legitimate so long as mathe-matics is recognized as a tool and not as a blue-print. It is capable of representing a set of physical data, and it may provide an analogy that can serve to predict fresh phenomena as likely to happen. But mathematics has to be constantly checked by refer-ence to the physical world. It is the handmaid of the sciences and not their queen. The contrary is a modern heresy that is finding itself out.

Kant, like other modern idealists, considered that what marks out a true science is the mathematization of basic concepts and the deduction of facts from laws expressed in terms of mathe-matical formulæ. We are reminded of Ampère's dictum about language, that it " begins as music and ends up as algebra ". These views we can accept in so far as they call attention to the *pre-cision* that develops in a science as it progresses. It is probably in this sense we should understand the remark often made that one science can be more scientific than another, that physics, for instance, is more scientific than psychology or sociology. As a science advances, its concepts, laws and theories become more precise and less ambiguous. This is true scientific progress.

If we followed logic, metaphysics would come first in any classification of the sciences, since it is the science of being, of first principles and ultimate causes, without which there cannot be either reality or knowledge. But since it is the function of philo-sophy to appraise and systematize all knowledge, it is also natural for philosophy to come after the other sciences.

As in the case of mathematics, its true place must be apart, since metaphysics, the crown of philosophy, is an architect and a critic, a support and a probe, the foundation, acid and cement of all the sciences.

THE PHYSICAL SCIENCES. Besides the two fundamental sciences of physics and chemistry, the physical sciences embrace special departments concerned with separate parts of inanimate nature such as the heavens, the earth, rocks, minerals, metals, the ocean, the atmosphere. While all these latter make great use of the basic disciplines, they draw their conclusions in the first instance from direct observation of nature. Physics and chemistry arrive at their conclusions today not only through observation but more especially through laboratory experiments. Hence the name of experimental science often given to them and others.

While physics and chemistry have the same subject-matter, their viewpoints and basic concepts differ, the one being interested in the general properties of matter, the other in the properties peculiar to each chemical substance. We cannot define logically physical or chemical properties and changes, we can only point to instances or write books about them.

In physics the basic concepts are inertia and acceleration, and the most fruitful analogies have been drawn from our intuitions of particles and waves. The wave analogy has played no appreciable part in the development of chemistry, but the basic notions of chemical substance, affinity, molecule and atom are particle notions. The physicist uses atoms and molecules also, but his point of view (and, therefore, the meaning of the entities) has been different from those of the chemist. However, as research proceeds, and the two sciences develop, their viewpoints approach closer to each other, and the sciences now overlap in regions such as physical chemistry and nuclear physics, where the distinction between them has almost disappeared.

It is no extravagance to say that along with analysis, a natural synthesis is going on gradually if slowly so that we are already afforded a glimpse of the whole physical sciences fusing into one vast panorama of physical cosmology.

The position of theoretical or mathematical physics among the physical sciences is ambiguous. (There is a subtle and purely accidental difference between theoretical and mathematical physics, which we shall ignore: the subject-matter of the one is classical, of the other modern, physics.)

Theoretical physics seeks to rationalize the whole of physical experience and express the whole of physical science in a single law by means of a few powerful concepts. Its ambitious aim is to invent a single equation which will subsume the whole material universe and every phenomenon in it from atoms to stars, from neutrinos to nebulæ.

This branch of physics is experimental only in the sense that Kepler's researches were experimental. It works by trial and error, and it is at the present time seeking basic concepts by experimenting on *ideas*. Thus, nearly every year sees a new form of the quantum theory appearing, new because there has been incorporated a new ' rule ' or a modification of previous notions.

The logic is essentially deductive. From this aspect, theoretical physics is mathematics and should be called physical or applied mathematics. But the new material on which it works is concrete quantity, the quantitative conclusions of experiment. From this aspect it is a physical science. The spectacular success of relativity theory and of some other speculations by theoretical physicists has notably affected the climate of scientific opinion and has led to big claims being made for the powers of mathematics in physical problems.

The shift in outlook during the course of the last hundred years can be illustrated by reference to Boole's conception of scientific method in his *Laws of Thought* (1854). Boole was himself a pure mathematician, but he marked four stages in the construction of a physical science, namely: 1, Observation of many facts; 2, presumption of a law or cause; 3, test by experiment; 4, investigation of the supposed causes or law by a mixture of hypothesis and deduction. His description or analysis is nowadays widely familiar. The modern theoretical physicist would alter item 2 into " assertion of a functional connection " or some such phrase, and replace item 4 by " construction of a theory ", a theory being " a functional unification of the laws ". Also, stage 3 would be phrased something like " comparison of calculations from theory with the experimental figures ".

MODERN MATHEMATICS. Up to the middle of the 19th century, mathematicians made much use of *sense intuitions*, both as the starting point of their subject, and later on in the course of developing it. Thus the demonstrations of Euclid and his successors were often based on *sense experience*.

At the end of the last century, as a result of inconsistencies and contradictions, scholars began to distrust sense intuition, and some tried to eliminate it as far as possible from mathematical science which they hoped to make purely logical and based only on reason. In this way a greater rigour might be achieved.

There may be discerned two parts in the movement, one bearing on the body of mathematical science, and the other on its principles.

1. Consider for instance arithmetic. Taking for granted its basic axioms and definitions, the modern mathematician tries to construct the whole science from the prime notions without having any recourse to intuition. The definitions become purely formal, without dependence on the physical world, but chosen to hold of the objects that were defined more or less intuitively in classical arithmetic. But *theorems* are established by pure logic alone, and without any appeal to intuition.

2. The edifice so erected still depends on experience, since the source of the postulates and definitions is intuition. So the attempt is made to eliminate intuition altogether by treating the basic concepts as *pure symbols,* and the fundamental propositions as pure logical relations between the prime symbols, independently of any meaning that might or could be assigned to these primitive concepts. But here we come up against a big difficulty: the postulates which form the basis of a deductive science must be consistent, that is, they must imply no contradiction between themselves. Now, logic alone cannot prove the absence of contradiction, because the consequences that can be drawn from a set of postulates are infinite in number, and we can never verify or test them all. The famed Gödel theorem of 1931 shows that no " absolute " proof of consistency may be given.

The tendency of modern mathematics towards pure or formal logic has been designated *Logistics* (this term is unfortunate as it is also employed in quite a different sense by the military and by organizers of industry) or *Mathematical Logic,* in connection with which one may mention Whitehead and Russell's *Principia Mathematica* (1910-1926); the Cork professor, George Boole, who with his Boolean algebra (1854) originated the whole movement; and Hilbert, leader of the Formalist School of Mathematicians, who obtained remarkable results by applying the above ideas to geometry and other branches of mathematics.

NON-EUCLIDEAN GEOMETRIES. We can connect with the preceding section the geometries which do not admit Euclid's postulate about parallel lines, or, consequently, his idea of a straight line.

Euclid's definition of a straight line is insufficient to give anyone an exact notion of it unless he has already had the sense intuition of it. If we add to Euclid's definition this intuition, then the postulate about parallelism becomes evident. If on the contrary, one neglects this intuition, one can complete the Euclidean definition of a straight line, *without introducing any contradiction,* either by following Riemann and say: " Through a point outside a line, *no* parallel line can be drawn "; or with Lobatchewsky say : " Through a point outside a line, *an infinity* of parallel lines can be drawn." In this way, we arrive at two other lines, different from Euclid's, but equally capable of leading to systems of geometry which in logical rigour are in no way inferior to Euclid. Mathematically, the three geometries are equivalent, and we use whichever suits our purpose, usually Euclid's. In this sense, Euclid's postulate about parallelism is a ' disguised definition ' of a straight line. On the other hand, Euclid's straight line is an idealization of sense experience, and so has a contact with the physical world or reality, which the others have not. It is in this sense that world-geometry may be said to be Euclidean.

THE BIOLOGICAL SCIENCES. As the name implies, the biological sciences study living things, along with their laws and the various forms under which life is found. The two kinds of life, plant and animal, divide the whole subject between them. Each of these primaries splits into numerous secondary sciences concerned with definite problems relating to, for instance: (a) the structure or shape of limbs and organs; (b) the working or functioning of organs; (c) the development of the living thing from its initial cell; (d) the types of life that have died out and become extinct; (e) description and classification of the different species of life.

The last of these divisions has in turn as many subdivisions as there are notable groups or categories in the animal and plant kingdoms. By way of illustration, we may refer to those which deal with birds, fishes, insects, shells. Two relatively recent additions to the biological sciences are anthropology (in the modern, narrow, sense) and ethnology; these branches study the origin and distribution of the separate races of mankind over the earth.

Leaving to physical science the subject of inorganic matter, biology studies living matter, its structure and chemical composition, the reactions within it, the laws of its development, the nature and functions of different organs, as well as the various kinds of life. It is not the affair of biological science to examine the inner nature of life or the vital principle; that is the business of philosophy. The field of positive science is limited by its proper and basic concepts—its conceptual ceiling—to describing living things and finding out the facts and laws of vital processes.

As in physics, the biological sciences employ the rational method consisting of observation, hypothesis, experiment and induction with the difference that the greater complexity of their subject-matter demands greater finesse in the first and fourth of these procedures. We note that it is in the domain of biological science that the experimental method has yielded its finest results. Witness the fruitful and masterly experiments of Pasteur on the control of microbes—his experiments were at once clear and decisive.

Let us come to the points which characterize scientific method in biology and distinguish it from its use in the physical sciences. The chief difference is imposed by the difference of subject matter and basic notions. Biology being the science of creatures and forms (systematic botany and zoology), and entailing examination of organs in normal and abnormal functioning (that is, in health and disease through the departments of physiology and pathology), there can be no question of proceeding from fact to law. Rather, we have to rise from the variable and ephemeral individual to the general and permanent type, the species. This is conceived as a set of characters which imply and suppose one another reciprocally; and, consequently, co-exist always. The individual comes and goes, but the species remains. Physical law refers to the invariable concomitance of events. The natural species refers to the necessary co-existence of different forms and the exclusion of others. Thus, cows and other ruminants, or cud-chewers, are even-toed, have a cloven-hoof, a multiple stomach, and are without front teeth in the upper jaw: unlike flesh-eating mammals, such as dogs, cats and bears, they exclude claws, the single stomach and canine teeth.

The special aim of biological science as the study of living creatures is to investigate the co-existence of characters. For this we require a special form of induction, called generalization, with characteristic processes of observation and comparison. Here, experiment is useless for determining the co-existence of characters and organs. The generalization consists in affirming of a group what was found true for some individuals in the group. The result is a law of organic correlation.

This procedure can be defended only by invoking a principle of reason, which in this case is not the uniformity of nature but the principle of finality. A law of organic correlation may indeed find an immediate reason in certain laws of physics and chemistry, or even in certain biological laws. But to get an explanation of the observed fixity of species, of the constant and necessary co-existence of certain forms and the exclusion of others, one must have recourse to a higher principle, which is none other than the destiny of creatures to live in a certain way: this entails adaptation of all their organs to suit that end.

General species having been determined, they have to be grouped methodically, according to their resemblances and differences. Hence biological classification. One may then give a scientific definition of a species according to proximate genus and specific difference. This is the last word in the natural sciences in so far as they are sciences of living creatures.

(We note in passing that the biologists have an atomic concept in the *cell*. We note, too, that experiment can modify in limited fashion some characteristics of a living being, as has been made clear by modern work in breeding, genetics, grafting and artificial mating. Nevertheless, we must say that in comparison with the physical sciences, biological science is still in an early stage of development and that there is little justification for dogmatic conclusions.)

THE MORAL AND SOCIAL SCIENCES. Next in complexity come the moral and social sciences. They deal with moral beings, that is, beings that have intelligence and are free to make a choice— beings that have a mind and can make it up—and are, therefore, objects of praise or blame, responsible for their acts. Amongst all the vast variety of creatures here below, there is only one being that falls into such a class, namely, you and me and our like— in other words, man. Yes, we are unique animals—no doubt about it—there is nothing like us, if not under the sun then most certainly below the moon.

Man, as we have seen, is studied in the biological sciences only in so far as he is a living organism, a complex structure that can live as a unit. The moral and social sciences approach him from a narrower and higher angle, and examine him as a creature that can think, feel and will as well as live. They seek to find out what it is that marks him off as an intelligent, free, social being, first in himself and his acts, and secondly in those external facts and institutions which stand out as manifestations of his moral and social life. These studies can be split along planes of cleavage into the following three groups:

Group 1, the *psychological sciences*. They consider how human nature expresses itself generally in thoughts, feelings, volitions, habits and so forth; and they go on to enquire what are the laws that govern the expressions of such psychic activities.

This group comprises (a) *psychology*, in so far as it is a theoretical science, that is, a science interested in the facts and laws relating to the conscious, subconscious and unconscious states of the human spirit. (This study—part of which is experimental— should be distinguished from *rational* psychology, which approaches the same facts at the metaphysical level, and enquires into their source or agent, the soul, asking questions about its inmost nature, its spirituality, and whether it is everlasting.) Then there are the three sciences called *normative*, or regulative and practical, because they investigate the rules and directives the mind or spirit of man should follow in order to achieve its end most perfectly in the great domains open to it, namely: (b) *logic*, which directs the mind in its search after *truth;* (c) *esthetics*, which guides the higher imagination in its appreciation and realization of the *beautiful;* and finally (d) *ethics*, which can direct a man in the conduct of life, that is, in the pursuit and practice of *good*. (We note that in the theoretical science we study *actual* man, while in the practical, or normative disciplines we direct our attention to *ideal* man. In the one we seek a law to fit the facts, in the other our aim is to assist man to realize his ideal through ascertaining and formulating the best principles to follow.)

Group 2, the *historical sciences*. They are concerned with the succession of events in the life of humanity, and they investigate the causes and laws governing such happenings. This group includes not only *history* in the ordinary sense, that is, as the science of past events and of the causes which determine them, but also *geography, chronology, archæology* and such like.

In its wide sense, history studies each and every manifestation of human activity, considers them in their succession, development and relations of mutual dependence. Thus, there is a history of each art and science, and, indeed, of all the departments of knowledge. Such studies narrate the chronological order of the discoveries and development of ideas which are expressed in logical order by the sciences themselves. Geography and chronology are indispensable handmaidens for the historian, enabling him to locate events and facts in space and time.

The feature of history as a science is that its subject-matter consists in *unique* events. In this it differs from all the other sciences except Revelation. The problem arises at once: how can we know facts that have ceased to exist? They cannot be repeated, and direct observation of them is impossible. The reply leads us to the method characteristic of the historical sciences. While facts of history can never be repeated, they can be known indirectly, sometimes (a) through their *traces;* or, more generally, (b) by the *testimony* of those who saw or heard them. The historian applies rational method to the study of testimony, and he has developed special techniques for testing sources and witnesses, for interpreting documents and other records, for checking on their authenticity, reliability and cogency. These processes constitute the historic method which most often reduces to making out the meaning of a document, determining the author, and assessing his trustworthiness as a witness and reporter of an historic event. The same method is applied to Revelation. In applications of the method, we note that the truth of a document or the authentication of an event is not established directly by the historian's labours, but by witnesses. In principle—though not in fact—none of the other sciences gets its data from testimony. (Any trained person can, in principle, find for himself the significant facts pertaining to a natural science.) Herein lies the basic distinction between history and other departments of scientific knowledge.

Group 3, the *social and political sciences*. They deal with the general structure of human institutions, the conditions of their development and stability, and the laws regulating their normal operation. Examples are *law, jurisprudence, political economy* and several other very complex sciences, such as *sociology*, which was founded by Comte. This last may embrace such diverse themes as the study of pure society, religion, work, family, property, while leaving to political science such items as civil legislation, taxes, the constitution of a state. As with the psychological sciences, a dual approach is possible in the case of social studies, so that they can give rise to theoretical or normative disciplines, according as we consider *actual* men and institutions, or *ideal aims*.

We may sum up by saying that the psychological sciences consider man in himself, the historical sciences study him in relation to time and space, while the social sciences regard him in his relations with his fellows.

A word should be said about the method characteristic of psychology which may be employed in most of these sciences involving human nature in action. This is the method of *introspection* or *reflective analysis*. It is one of the wonders of the mind, of the stream of consciousness, that it can examine itself. It can be both the subject and the object of study. This marvel we too often take for granted like the air we breathe. In reflective analysis, the human mind, as subject, examines itself or its states, as object. *But no use is made of empirical generalization.* A single instance examined is enough, if thoroughly analysed, to lead to a law or principle. We gain insight not by correlation, as in induction; not through generalization as practised by the natural sciences; but in deeper fashion. Also, with greater certainty, be it noted. In introspection, there is, so to speak, direct contact between the knower and the known, there are no intermediary layers of psychological, neurological or physical media separating the subject and the object. Our knowledge about our own existence and nature is the most accurate and certain part of our natural beliefs, because it is based on interpretation of the most intimate experience we have, our own human operations.

The difficulty of reaching general agreement in moral and social questions arises from the complexity of the data. The data are moral facts, the intricate and delicate facts of human consciousness, involving the elemental and profound basic concepts of duties and rights. They are not easy to know, and it is naturally difficult to express what we do know of them to others. It is easy to occasion confusion and error when we discuss or try to describe the subtleties of the mind and of conscience at work. Therefore, there is bound to be diversity of opinion and of formulation on ethical and political questions. This is generally true of questions in moral and social science, which are rendered extremely complicated by the freedom of the will.

THE PHILOSOPHICAL SCIENCES. The philosophical sciences at the metaphysical level can be grouped under the five heads of ontology, logic, cosmology, psychology and natural theology, corresponding to the principles of reality and thought, and the three great themes, nature, man and God.

1. The principles underlying not only the natural sciences but all knowledge and reality are discussed in metaphysics, the science of sciences, the generalization of the most general truths. The basic study is *ontology,* the organic body of propositions relating to the most general notion there is, namely, being.

2. The laws of thought, or the principles and processes which show how the mind can arrive at sure and certain knowledge, constitute the subject-matter of *logic,* which may be (a) formal, (b) material, or (c) critical. Certain aspects of logic concerning the generation of ideas are discussed at the lower phenomenal level in experimental psychology.

(a) *Formal* logic deals with the conditions and requirements for forming correct *ideas,* sound *judgments,* and valid *reasoning.* The attempts made in the last half century to reduce mathematics to formal or pure logic under titles such as *mathematical* or *symbolic logic* must be said to have failed. Following the historic example of Descartes, Russell tried to reduce knowledge to the least number of elements of which one could be reasonably certain. He sought to express these axioms or 'atoms of thought' clearly and unambiguously 'beyond vagueness and dispute'. In the *Principia*

Mathematica, he tried to develop all mathematics from a small number of postulates and indefinables. The introduction to the first edition gave as one of its aims "the complete enumeration of all the ideas and steps in reasoning employed in mathematics".

Kurt Gödel and others have shown, however, that no system of logic with a finite set of axioms and rules of inference can settle all the questions that can be put and answered in mathematical science. Given any such system, a theorem can be found which cannot be either proved or disproved by the rules of the system. It is by availing himself of a latent ambiguity or shift of meaning in his symbols that the human mathematician overcomes the limitations of the formal system. Russell's search for a 'single comprehensive logical language beyond vagueness and dispute' has not been successful, simply because from the start it was hopeless. (For further details, see M. H. A. Newman in the *Listener,* May 6, 1948.)

The attempt to banish our intuitions of quantity from mathematics and reduce the science to mere logical symbolism (that is, to symbols emptied of all assigned meaning), having failed, it is likely there will be a return to more traditional views about the nature of mathematics and its relation to formal logic.

(b) *Material logic* is concerned to find out the best logical processes to follow in order to attain the objective of a particular science. It might be called a study of comparative method. It is in fact called by the far from happy or attractive title of methodology. There is now a tendency to discount the extravagant claims that had been made for the experimental method and it is being more and more recognized that blind brute experiment is no substitute for thought and reflection. It is seen that it was a mistaken idea to think that want of thought could be compensated for by multiplying rule-of-thumb processes. It is being appreciated that the trained mind of a philosopher can be very helpful to scientists. This is because the mode of conceiving a problem, the way of putting a question to nature, involves the concepts used in stating the question, as well as interpretation. Unambiguous concepts and sound reasoning about them fall within the province of the trained mind, the philosopher's mind.

Consequently, we see institutes of methodology beginning to function in advanced countries. In such an institution, philosophers and scientists work together, the philosopher having specialized in at least one department of natural science before taking up problems of method. He co-ordinates research in various ways such as:
1, he applies general tests to see if the experimental investigation

initially proposed is adequate; 2, he criticizes the techniques; 3, he defines the degree and quality of the experimental control; 4, he defines how the problem has meaning; 5, he estimates how much of a problem should be worked out in the mind ("conceptualized") and how much of it should be investigated by experiment. Somewhat after this fashion unusual problems have been tackled, amongst which we may mention: how to devise ways of measuring public opinion, consumer-interest, audience-reactions; how to apply statistical methods to marketing and sampling, to costing and "regression-analysis" (that is, cutting costs in a factory by finding how the factors of production affect the output); and how to inspect mass-produced articles so as to guarantee their quality to the purchaser. (Cp. Schanck: *The Permanent Revolution in Science.*)

(c) *Critical logic,* also called criteriology or epistemology, examines the conditions and studies the kinds of certitude attainable in human knowledge. It seeks to answer the question: how certain can we be of things, of our various grades of knowledge?

3. The nature of the material universe can be studied, and is being studied, at three different levels in three different sciences, so that we have physical, mathematical and metaphysical *cosmology.* Just as the same countryside presents different appearances to the farmer, the geologist, the rate-collector and the artist, so the same subject-matter can give rise to very different sciences. Each is a valid approach and is not inferior to the other because it is different in aim and basic concepts, or even in method and technique. In what is called rational or philosophical cosmology, the basic concepts pertain to the metaphysical ceiling, and the enquiry concerns the ultimate principles of living and inert matter.

4. Likewise in *rational psychology,* which studies the principle at the back of human activities, namely the soul along with the question of its immortality, the characteristic concepts are metaphysical, and the method is deductive.

5. *Natural theology* enquires by the sole light of reason and without any assistance from Revelation what we can know of God, His nature, attributes and relations to the world. The great questions of creation, the problems of pain and evil, and the nature of natural religion are considered in this science.

This department of knowledge differs considerably from the science of revealed religion. The theologian, depending on Revelation to furnish him with the data of his study, has to employ the same basic techniques as the historian since he draws the raw material of his subject from *testimony*. This is the essential feature which serves to mark off theology from natural science. All branches of knowledge are subject to rational method, and all branches of knowledge have a certain amount of procedure in common. Each starts with data or significant facts, interprets them by presuming there is a cause or law to account for them, guesses what the cause or law is, draws a conclusion from this supposition and checks the conclusion against the original data; and then may have to start all over again at a slightly higher level. Science draws its data from nature, and new or fresh data are always possible or available; and the method or logic of proof is inductive or by analogy. On the other hand, theology is concerned with God, not nature animate or inanimate, and the data of revelation are complete and final. Conclusions are reached by deduction. Here there is resemblance with historical science, since both theology and history get their data in the same fashion, through *testimony,* and then proceed by strict deduction (utilising maybe a philosophical premise) to their conclusion.

Formerly, theology was queen of the sciences, regulating their precedence and setting their value. What is the position at present? Some seek a science of values, axiology. The breakdown of the attempt to achieve perfect mathematical rigour may induce science, which had fallen a victim to mathematics and had dismissed philosophy, to look for another queen. In an address to the British Association for the Advancement of Science in 1952, on the subject of science, morality and the community, Professor Hill referred to the conflict a man feels between himself as a scientist, "following the evidence of fact wherever it may lead" and as a citizen with "ethical obligations to his fellows". He asked how to-day's need can be met, how we can restore the concept of moral responsibility to the individual? Commenting on the address, *The Times* said: "If science as the servant of humanity is to be sure of its direction, the queen needs to be either reinstated or replaced." Douglas Jerrold (*The Tablet,* Sep. 13, 1952) goes further and argues that if the world is to survive, there is no alternative to reinstatement. It is the only way to end the insane doctrine that scientific research, understood as "going anywhere, as long as no one has been there before", is progress.

2. *Papal discourse on the challenge of science and the need for philosophy*

[The address was delivered to about 100 persons gathered in the Vatican Consistory. They included cardinals, members of the diplomatic corps accredited to the Holy See, new academicians, and a group of biologists and botanists who were participating in a scientific symposium in the Vatican.

Declaring that "alas, for some time past, science and philosophy have become separated," the Supreme Pontiff said he would not accept the dissolvent "pessimism" that tolerated or even tried to justify this divorce. The separation had its origin not in the "nature of the two ways leading to truth" but in "historical contingencies and persons without the necessary good-will and competence".

"We think that the natural sciences in close and enduring contact with the philosophy of critical realism can arrive at an all-embracing view which would satisfy the quest and desire for truth." Experimental science alone cannot relieve man's confusion and anguish. "The breath of living knowledge" is needed to "enliven acquired knowledge. It is in this way that science becomes fruitful culture and begets an organic teaching."

But the nature of science does not allow it to accomplish a universal synthesis of thought. In any synthesis of knowledge it is "philosophy with its broad concepts that states precisely the distinctive traits of vital factors, the principles of unification, the unity of the living being".

Referring to the limitations of philosophy as well as those of science, the Holy Father said:

> "If science has the duty of striving for coherence and seeking inspiration from sound philosophy, the latter should never attempt to define truths which are drawn solely from observation or experiment."

Pope Pius then called upon scientists to fulfil their rôle of teachers. He urged them to lead men to God, saying:

> "Interpreters of nature, be you also teachers who explain to their brothers the wonders that are unfolded in the universe and which better than others you see assembled as in a single book. Teach others to behold and understand and love the created world so that the admiration of splendours so sublime may cause the knee to bend and incite the minds of men to adoration."

Warning the scientists never to betray these aspirations, he cautioned:

> "Woe to them who make use of falsely taught science to make men leave the right path. They are likened to stones placed out of malice on the road of the human race: they are obstacles whereon men stumble in their search for truth."

Throughout his speech the Pope spoke in high praise of scientists and their mission, saying:

> "Yours is a noble mission, for in a sense you discover the mind of God. Yours it is to interpret the book of nature, to study and describe its contents, and apply what you learn for the good of mankind. You have in your hands a powerful instrument with which to do good."]

1

Welcome

WE bid you welcome, eminent sirs, members of Our Academy, and We rejoice in your being here. As you know, the doors of this house are always open to those who cultivate science or the arts.

2

Natural law is the basic alphabet

Your life is dedicated to the study of nature. Day by day you attain to ever deeper understanding of the wonders written in the heart of matter by the Most High. The physical world is truly a manifestation of God's wisdom and goodness, since everything has received its being from Him and all creation reflects His greatness. Every single item in the universe is one of His words, and bears the mark of what may be called the fundamental alphabet, namely, those laws of nature which the mind of man constantly seeks to discover in all their fulness and perfection.

3

The book of nature

Created things are words of truth. In themselves they are neither confused nor contradictory, but they always run together in perfect consistency. They may not be easy to understand because they are so profound. Yet, as you become familiar with them, you see how they are in harmony with reason. Nature is a book that opens up before you, full of mystery and wonder. You make progress and you advance as you read one page after another, fixing your gaze on each line and omitting no detail. Taken in due order, each fresh chapter confirms those that went before and leads to a deeper insight into the scheme of things, into the plan of nature.

4
Scientists have a noble mission

Yours, then, is a noble mission, for in a sense you discover the mind of God. Yours it is to interpret the book of nature, to study and describe its contents, and apply what you learn for the good of mankind.

5
Crisis for science

We are aware that science is passing through a critical phase, and We know that not everybody appreciates its gravity. Indeed, there are three quite distinct attitudes toward scientific knowledge.

6
First attitude

Some (and they are the majority) are content to admire the remarkable results obtained in the technical sphere, and they tend to regard these tremendous achievements as the sole, or at least the chief, object of science.

7.
Second attitude

Others better informed, can appreciate what is needed by way of equipment and effort for the prosecution of scientific research. Accordingly, they can understand its extraordinary progress, its sorrow and joys, its triumphs and checks. They can see how new instruments and new mathematical methods help to improve techniques and advance experimental procedures. They follow with ardour the proving of hypotheses and the demonstration of conclusions, while appreciating the intellectual labour involved in rationalizing the facts. They see with interest how old views are recast and fresh theories are formulated, to be in their turn subjected to test. These various aspects of science are well understood by the persons in the second group.

8
Third attitude

Those making up the third class are few in number. They envisage science both in its depth and in its breadth. They seek to see it in itself, in its most high purpose. We rejoice that you, gentlemen, are among them. And so, We put the question: has science now reached the point that having analysed the details and got as far as ultimate entities it should turn to synthesis and seek a vision of the whole?

HISTORICAL SURVEY: STRUCTURE OF MATTER

9
Corpuscular theory of matter

A little over a century ago, the first sound physical theory was put forward about the nature of matter. It was to the effect that matter is discrete or discontinuous in structure, and consists in last analysis of particles or corpuscles, that is, very small bodies, molecules. Since then, molecules have been counted, weighed, and resolved into their components, atoms. Then the atom, at first regarded as an ultimate and indivisible entity, was split into parts which in turn received minute examination.

10
Ultimate particles

Various parts of the atom were studied. The charge on the electron (or ' atom ' of electricity) was measured; also the mass of the proton [core or nucleus of the hydrogen atom]. The neutron, the various mesons, the positron and several other ' ultimate ' particles were isolated and their properties determined. Means were found to control these particles, to accelerate them and shoot them in to the heart or nucleus of atoms. Eventually, with the aid of neutrons, men of science succeeded in producing artificial radio-activity, nuclear fission, transmutation of the chemist's elements, and—last but not least—enormous quantities of energy from small amounts of matter.

11
Recent ideas

On the scientific horizon ingenious theories and models of the universe have made their appearance. New algebras and new geometries have been invented. We shall mention only the special and general theories of relativity, quanta, wave mechanics, quantum mechanics, recent notions about nuclear forces, speculations on the origin of cosmic rays, and theories about the source of stellar energy.

12
Problems

All this permits us to glimpse the depths to which science has penetrated, and to get an inkling of the problems raised. There are problems of *extension* as well as of *depth*. For while bold sappers ever make fresh breaches in the citadel of nature, the bulk of the research army is spread over countless other domains of knowledge. Like the hardy climber winning to the mountain top, we long to take in the whole panorama with a single swift glance.

13
Present state of the sciences

If it were possible, We should like to mention one after another the most advanced positions that have been won in the various sectors, so that a general view of the present state of science might rise before your eyes.

14
Astronomy and geology

See how astronomy with new instruments unveils fresh mysteries in the heavens; and, aided by physical science, has suggested an answer to the problem of stellar energy. See how geology, by means of radio-activity and isotopes, determines how old are the rocks; and even goes so far as to indicate the age of the earth.

15
Mineralogy to genetics

In mineralogy, crystalline bodies are yielding up their secrets under the sharp eye of short-wave radiation. Chemistry, organic and inorganic, is solving the stiff problem of giant molecules and their structure: it has succeeded in its aim of building up great chains of molecules, and so has revolutionized vast fields of industry. Radio waves are now produced with frequencies bordering on those of the visible spectrum. The earth itself is probed so that its latent treasures are brought to light. The highest layers of the air are being explored. Genetics reveals new aspects of the power of life in certain assemblies of cells.

16
Biology and the virus

Physiology and biology, starting from the rich achievements of the basic sciences, daily uncover new marvels, forecast new facts and bring them to realization: the domain of the virus is yielding to the attack of electron microscopes and the technique of electron diffraction. The mass-spectrograph, Geiger counters, radio-active isotopes, all such means aid science to advance as it comes closer to the greatest enigma of all—the problem of life.

17
Philosophy unifies

In the synthesis of great sweeps of knowledge, it is philosophy with its broad concepts that defines what are the vital factors, and states in precise terms what is the character of the underlying principle of unification; what is the spring of action, of growth and reproduction; in what consists the true unity of the living creature. It shows, too, what matter must be in itself in order that there may be realized in the living being the properties which characterize it.

18
The future

These are, without doubt, the fields that will give most work to the science of tomorrow.

BASIC NEEDS OF SCIENCE

19
Limitation of natural science

The feeling of elation engendered by the foregoing results is damped by an impression of bewilderment and anguish in those who, with a sense of responsibility, watch the unfolding of the facts. Their pain and confusion are to be understood in a sense that does them honour, as a sign of aspiration towards a consistent view and clear perspectives. Now, natural science of itself does not, cannot, give insight into the nature of things; nor is it its province to produce a perfect systematization of thought.

20

Experiment is not enough:

(a) To achieve synthesis, the first task is to penetrate to the intimate structure of material things and to face the problems of their inmost nature or substance and mode of action or activity.

Can experimental science solve such problems by itself? Do they belong to its sphere, do they fall into the class of things that can be studied by its methods? One must return a negative reply. For the natural sciences take sensations as their starting-point, and sensations are by their very nature external to the mind. Through them, and with the aid of reasoning processes, science penetrates ever closer to the heart of things, but it cannot get past the point where questions arise that cannot be settled by means of sense observation.

21

A light is needed

When the man of science seeks to interpret the facts yielded up by experiment, he needs a light that proceeds from the absolute to the relative, from the necessary to the contingent; a light which can reveal a kind of truth that is unattainable by the experimental sciences, since it transcends the senses and therefore transcends the proper methods and processes of the natural sciences. This light is philosophy, the science of general laws. It applies to all being, and must accordingly hold too for the sphere of natural science, above and beyond the laws empirically determined.

Unifying ideas are needed. Philosophy unifies.

22

A mosaic of the sciences

(b) The second requirement springs from the very nature of the human mind which is not satisfied unless it has a logical and united view of truth. If one accepts a mere juxta-position of the various branches of knowledge, a mosaic of subject-matters, one obtains an anatomical dissection of knowledge from which life has departed. Men need to have their knowledge shot through with the breath of a living unity. It is in this way that science becomes fruitful and culture generates an organic body of doctrine. Hence a second question: Can science by itself achieve this universal synthesis of thought? If so, since science consists of sciences, which of them is fitted to bring about such a synthesis? Here again, We think that the nature of science prevents it from effecting a universal synthesis.

23

The unifying principle

Synthesis has to be built on a solid and deep foundation from which it may acquire its unity, and in which it will find the basis required for the most general truths. The parts of the building must find in the foundation their supporting elements. This requires a power of a high order which will unify by its *universality,* clarify by its *depth,* stabilize by its *absoluteness,* and make effective by its *necessity.* Once again such a principle is philosophy.

SCIENCE DIVORCED FROM PHILOSOPHY

24

Sad plight

Alas, for some time past, science and philosophy have been separated. It would be difficult to fix the cause and the responsibility for so harmful a fact. It is certain that the rift did not come from the nature of the two ways leading to truth, but rather it came from historical accident, and from individuals who did not in all cases have the needed good will and competence.

25

Consequences

At one time scientists thought that metaphysics was a useless burden, and they refused to be guided by its principles. On their side, philosophers neglected to follow the progress of science and stuck to formal positions they could have abandoned. Then, when it became necessary, as We have shown, to attempt a comprehensive work of interpretation and unification, men of science fell under the influence of those philosophical systems which the circumstances of the time threw in their way. Some were not even aware that their scientific investigations had been affected by the prevailing philosophical currents.

26

Mechanism

Thus, for instance, the interpretation of scientific data was for a long period coloured or dominated by mechanistic ideas. Those who followed the trend believed that every natural happening, even life itself, could be resolved into forces and particles, so that any activity or action could be attributed to a simple regrouping of forces and particles in space. Hence, in principle, one could predict with certainty every future event if one knew in advance the configuration at a given moment. According to this view, the world was no more than a vast machine made up of countless small machines joined together.

27
Its failure

Progress in experimental science, however, has shown that such a theory is untenable even in the physical domain. Mechanical laws, inferred from observations on the large-scale world, are inadequate for explaining all the phenomena of the small-scale or atomic world: here facts are encountered which defy explanation on a mechanistic basis.

28
The old atom

Take for example the history of ideas regarding the structure of atoms. In the early stages, the notions were based on a mechanistic approach which represented the atom as a tiny planetary system, made up of electrons circling around the core, as if in accord with the laws of astronomy.

29
The new atom

Quantum theory modified this picture and introduced an ingenious if strange compromise. It imagined a type of atom which combined a prominent quantum character with a mechanical aspect.

30
Quantum theory

The parts inside the atom were then supposed to behave in this new way: the electrons were still regarded as revolving round the nucleus, but now without radiating any energy—in defiance of the classical laws of electro-dynamics. Further, it was laid down that the electronic orbits could not change continuously, but only

in jumps. Also, energy was supposed to be emitted by the atom
only when an electron passed from one quantum state to another.

31

Wave mechanics

These ideas received precise formulation after the birth of wave
mechanics. The new branch of physics subsumed them in a more
satisfying mathematical framework from which traditional
mechanistic notions disappeared.

32

Statistical law

The question then arises: How is it that the large-scale world,
though composed of the same elements as the atomic domain,
obeys different laws? Science makes first of all the following
remark: When the number of elements in question is very great
(billions upon billions of particles), the statistical laws regarding
their global behaviour are considered to hold strictly in the world
of direct observation. (As a corollary to the statistical method being
valid in science, we see how ill-founded is a philosophical system
that recognizes no evidence unless drawn from sensory experience,
which it then arbitrarily extrapolates to serve as an explanation
of the whole cosmos.)

33

Nuclear force

That there is a difference between the laws obtaining in the
macroscopic and microscopic worlds is confirmed by what is known
of nuclear physics: it is believed that the forces holding the nucleus
together are different in kind from any met with in studying large-
scale phenomena. To understand nuclear forces, we have to alter
our traditional notions about particles and waves; about the possibility of specifying the precise value of a particle's position and
energy; and about the foreseeable character of a future event.

34

Scientific Idealism

The failure of the mechanistic hypothesis has led some thinkers
to the other extreme, to a kind of scientific idealism with the

observer playing the chief part. Thus, quantum mechanics and its basic law of indeterminacy (which is represented as a challenge to the principle of causality) appear as scientific hypotheses deriving support from metaphysical systems.

35

Scepticism

Since such views do not satisfy the desire of the mind for clarity, many eminent thinkers have fallen into scepticism when brought face to face with the problems presented by the philosophy of science. They assert that all one can do is to be content with verifying facts and including them in a formula which can be used to foretell how a physical system will develop from a given initial state.

36

Unjustified pessimism

The sceptic abandons the tool of critical reflection, and his state of mind makes him despair of ever reaching universal syntheses on the grand scale. We do not believe his pessimism is justified. Rather, We think that the natural sciences, by keeping in constant touch with a philosophy of moderate realism (like the *philosophia perennis* at its best), can reach a comprehensive view of the visible world which would to some extent satisfy our thirst and ardent desire for truth.

37

Duty of philosophers

It is necessary to underline another point. If science should aim at coherence and seek inspiration from a sound philosophy, the latter in turn should never attempt to define truths which arise solely by scientific means from observation or experiment. There is no end to the ' ultimate ' entities and laws of matter that are possible. Which of them, in fact, the Creator desired to realize, can be determined only by observation or experiment, understood in the very broadest sense.

38

Scientists are teachers

As authorized interpreters of nature, be you also teachers who explain to your brothers the marvels found in the universe. Better than others, you see the wonders assembled as in a single book. The majority of men are unable to devote themselves to the contemplation of nature, and the facts they perceive leave little impression. You who interpret creation should be teachers eager to reveal its beauty, its power and perfection so that others too may enjoy it.

39
Sublime splendours

Teach others to behold, understand and love the created world, so that in admiring splendours so sublime, men may bend the knee and give their minds to adoration.

40
Falsely taught science

Never betray this trust or these aspirations. Woe to those who make use of falsely taught science to lead men astray. They are likened to stones placed out of malice on the path of the human race: they are obstacles on which men stumble in their search for truth.

41
A powerful instrument

You have in your hands a powerful instrument with which to do good. Be conscious of the ineffable happiness you procure for others when you disclose to them the mysteries of nature and bring them to appreciate its harmonious secrets. The hearts and the gaze of those who listen to you are as it were, hanging on your every word, ready to chant a hymn of praise and thanksgiving.

3. *Scientism: bibliographical note*

THE name 'positive science' is given to the systematic study of natural phenomena. The marked progress of the positive sciences in the first half of the 19th century led some people to exaggerate their value and scope, and produced a species of philosophy variously dubbed scientism or naturalism. Its votaries included Comte, Renan, Taine, H. Spencer and T. Huxley. It is the basis of the remarkable philosophical theories expounded in the writings of William James, John Dewey, and Professor Samuel Alexander.

According to scientism:

1. The only valid knowledge is that obtained in positive science.

2. Positive science alone reveals things as they are: it furnishes absolute knowledge.

3. The spirit and method of the positive sciences should be extended to embrace all intellectual life, moral, religious and philosophical.

4. There is no supernatural.

Scientism is still common among English mathematicians; for instance in:

> SIR JAMES JEAN'S pseudo-philosophical writings: *The New Background of Science*, 1933; *The Mysterious Universe*, 1934; *Physics and Philosophy*, 1942 (all Cambridge).

> BERTRAND RUSSELL: *Philosophical Essays*, 1910; *The Problems of Philosophy* 1911; *Scientific Method in Philosophy* 1914; *Our Knowledge of the External World*, 1914; *Introduction to Mathematical Philosophy*, 1919; *Outline of Philosophy*, 1927, etc. His philosophical writings have been described as " the *reductio ad absurdum* of everything " (H. Wickham: *The Unrealists*).

> A. W. WHITEHEAD tends to scientism in *The Concept of Nature*, 1920; *Principles of Natural Knowledge*, 1925; *Science and the Modern World*, 1926; *Symbolism, its Meaning and Effect*, 1928; *Progress and Reality*, 1929; *Adventure of Ideas*, 1933.

There is scientism in:

> SIR ARTHUR EDDINGTON: *The Nature of the Physical World*, 1928; *The Philosophy of Physical Science*, 1939.

For criticism of Jeans's and Eddington's philosophical opinions see:

> L. S. Stebbing: *Philosophy and the Physicists* (London, 1937).

That confusions and contradictions abound in the popular writings of Russell, Joad, Eddington, Jeans and others, is shown by Dr. Stebbing. Usually mystification arises from an erroneous system of epistemology in which there is confusion of the physical world and the world of theoretical physics (which is not the world of experimental physics, be it noted); and from an imperfect description of nature and the goal of positive science.

Among the first to criticize and call attention to the shortcomings and excessive claims of scientism may be mentioned:

E. Boutroux, *De La Contingence des lois de la nature* (Paris, 1874);

M. Brunetière, *La faillite de la Science* (Paris, 1889);

J. B. Stallo, *Concepts and Theories of Modern Physics* (London, 4th edn., 1900).

M. J. Wilbois (*Revue de la Metaphysique*, 1899-1901), criticized J. S. Mill for confusing scientific facts with mathematical constructs.

IV *SCIENCE AND THE EXISTENCE OF GOD*

1. Papal discourse "Un'ora".

2. Commentary and notes.

1. *Papal discourse " Un'ora "*

[The address, " Un'ora ", delivered by His Holiness Pope Pius XII to the Pontifical Academy of Science, November 2, 1951, deals with the first of all questions, the cardinal fact that gives meaning to the universe and to everything in it—including you and me—namely, the existence of God. In what has been described as a feat of exposition, the Holy Father shows how the great discoveries of modern science have admirably reinforced the classical arguments of the philosopher, and thus serve to confirm the faith of the people.

The allocution breathes the spirit that is needed by Western culture if it is to survive. In showing how science and philosophy complete each other in a matter so vital to men, it sign-posts the road to health for our wonderful but sick age. If the spirit of the document could be widely disseminated it could constitute the tonic required by Western civilization to recover its lost nerve. The spirit is one of orderly co-operation between experts so that each has understanding of the other and is not blinded by the hubris or arrogance that results from isolated specialization. It is a spirit which recognizes that all must contribute their part to achieve the harmony of the whole, and have a vision of the whole to appreciate the importance of each part. The address cries an end to wrangling between the different departments of knowledge and human activity. It is not a time for contentions and rivalries. The preservation of Western civilization demands that all kinds —labourers, artists, priests, men of science, writers, technicians— should pool their gifts and match their skills. They should supplement one another and not be antagonists.

The address would persuade men to return to a sure knowledge of the principle, the only principle, by which we can decide how to employ the techniques we have so marvellously acquired. Mastery over material things will do us little good if we lose mastery over ourselves; and we lose mastery over ourselves if we forget the basic fact of life, the existence of God.

It is not good plumbing or marvellous engineering that will sustain the spirit of man in his coming trials. In the Papal allocution we find what we need if we are to stop being inert and discouraged. Here we have the spirit which is not content to let our Christian culture go with the wind and wait passively for whatever will follow, a fresh brand of materialism, Oriental despotism, a brave new world run on holiday-camp lines, mass destruction of humanity with nuclear weapons, or a psychiatrist's consulting-room and couch.

The address resolves itself into three components, the introduction, the body, and the conclusion. The introduction will be found in paragraphs 1-9. The body of the discourse is in two parts which show how the first and fifth ways of St. Thomas for demonstrating God's existence are strengthened by the findings of modern science. Part I (paragraphs 10-17) deals with the first way, while Part II (paragraphs 18-36) is concerned with the fifth way. The conclusion is contained in paragraphs 37-43.]

THE PROOFS FOR THE EXISTENCE OF GOD IN THE LIGHT OF MODERN DISCOVERIES

1

The Holy Father salutes the Members of the Pontifical Academy

This meeting of the Pontifical Academy of Science brings Us an hour of serene happiness for which we are grateful to Almighty God. Also, it affords Us a welcome opportunity of spending some time in the company of a select group of eminent Cardinals, illustrious diplomats, outstanding personages, and of yourselves, the members of the Pontifical Academy, who are truly worthy of the solemnity of the gathering. For, by your researches which unlock nature's secrets, and through your teaching which leads man to direct the forces of nature towards his own welfare, you employ the language of number, formula and discovery to show forth the ineffable harmony of the works of an all-wise God.

2

Science increasingly discovers God

Indeed, according as it advances, and in flat contradiction to assertions made in the past, true science discovers God in an ever-increasing degree—as though God were waiting behind every new door opened by science. We would even say that through the progressive discovery of God, which accompanies the growth of knowledge, benefits accrue both to the scientist when he reflects as a philosopher—and how can he escape such reflection?—as well as to those who share in his discoveries or make them the subject of their consideration. The professional philosopher profits from the discoveries in a very special way, because, when he bases his speculations on the conquests of science, he attains enhanced certainty in his own conclusions, while at the same time he is supplied with clearer illustrations in the midst of possible shadows, and he is provided with more satisfactory answers against difficulties and objections.

3

Natural science contributes to the Five Ways

Thus stimulated and guided by science, the mind approaches the philosophical arguments by which Christian wisdom is wont to demonstrate the existence of God, arguments which have been sifted down the centuries by giants in the world of knowledge, arguments well known to you in the 'five ways' of the Angelic Doctor, St. Thomas, who showed they conducted the mind to God by a swift and sure road. We have called the arguments 'philosophical'. This does not mean they are *a priori*, as narrow and confused positivists have said. They are based on concrete realities established by the senses and by science, even though their demonstrative force derives from human reason.

4

Philosophy and natural science are not opposed

In this way, both philosophy and natural science, by analogous methods and by distinct but compatible activities, carry on their work. They both make use of experience and reason, though in different measures; and side by side they labour harmoniously for the discovery of truth.

5

How scientific discoveries affect traditional arguments for God's existence

Now, if the restricted experience of the ancients could furnish weighty enough arguments to demonstrate the existence of God, then surely with the multiplication of experiment and the growth of knowledge since their time, the mark of the Eternal One is discernible in the visible creation in ever clearer and more striking light. It would seem useful, then, to re-examine on the basis of the new discoveries the classical proofs of the Angelic Doctor (St. Thomas, p. 1, q. 2, art. 3), especially those based on change and order in Nature: that is to say, to inquire whether, and in what degree our more profound knowledge of the great world and the small strengthens the philosophical arguments. We should consider also if, and to what extent, the proofs have been weakened, as is sometimes alleged, by the fact that modern physics has introduced new basic principles and abandoned or modified older conceptions, concepts such as space, time, motion, causality and substance—of prime importance in the question now before us—concepts which in the past were perhaps judged to have fixed and unalterable meanings. The aim then, is not to revise philosophical proofs, but rather to examine the physical foundations from which they flow—though exigencies of time will limit Our consideration to a few of them. There is no need to be fearful of surprises. Not even science itself aims to go outside that world which to-day, as yesterday, presents itself through the ' five modes of being,' whence the philosophical demonstration of the existence of God proceeds and draws its force.

6

Modern Science confirms philosophical arguments

Of the ' modes of being ' noticeable in the world around us— perceived equally well by philosopher and layman though at different levels of comprehension—there are two which modern science has probed and proved in wonderful and unexpected fashion, namely (1) the mutability of things, including their origin and their end, and (2) the orderliness, or sense of direction, which characterises every corner of the universe. The contribution thus made by science to the philosophical arguments based on mutability and finality—constituting the first and fifth ways of St. Thomas—is indeed remarkable. Physics, especially, has brought to the support of the first way a prodigious wealth of experiment, showing the existence of change in the very heart of nature, where previously no man could suspect its presence or envisage its extent and ramifications. The physicist has thus supplied the philosopher with an impressive body of helpful facts. We say ' helpful ' because the sense of direction revealed in these facts, together with the kind of certainty characterising them, appears to Us to do more than just confirm the philosophical reasoning: it almost takes on the dignity and dimensions of a new argument, of its nature physical, and apt to be welcomed by many minds as most powerful and persuasive.

7

Modern Science makes manifest the unity of the universe

No less richly do other sciences, especially those dealing with the heavens and with living things, contribute to the argument from their vast stores of knowledge. Stunned, so to speak, by the stupendous vision of unity which they see underlying the universe, and struck by the orderliness of its movements, they begin to anticipate for modern man the joy imagined by the poet in the highest heaven when he beheld in God,

> ' . . . into one volume, girts by love,
> The same the universe holds scattered through its maze.'
> (*Paradiso,* xxxiii, 85-87.)

8

The idea of God is confirmed by new discoveries

Nevertheless, Providence has disposed that, just as the notion of God, which is so essential to the life of each individual, can be gathered easily from a simple look at the world—in such a way that not to understand the voice of creation is foolishness (Cp. Sap. xiii, 1-2)—so, also, this same idea of God finds confirmation in every new discovery and every fresh advance of science.

9

Modern Science serves religion

Aiming to give here no more than a rapid summary of the priceless services rendered by modern science to the demonstration of the existence of God, We shall limit Ourselves, first of all, to the fact of change, calling attention to its amplitude and extent, and, so to speak, its universality in the universe studied by modern physics. We shall then refer to the significance of its direction, which is likewise verified by science. Thus, in Our treatment, We shall, as it were, be listening from afar off to a concert of the immense universe, which nevertheless has a voice strong enough to be heard singing ' the glory of Him Who moveth all that is '. (*Paradiso,* 1. 1).

THE FIVE WAYS: SOME PHYSICAL PRINCIPLES

CHANGE

10

Various kinds of change are observed in gross matter

At first we marvel, and rightly so, to see the reign of mutability extended both in the great world and in the small—the macrocosm and the microcosm—according as science advances, as though the new observations served to confirm the theory of Heraclitus: 'Everything is in a state of flux': *panta rhei*. It is well known that everyday experience reveals a multitude of changes of various kinds going on in the world around us, both close at hand and far away, notably the movement of bodies. In addition to mechanical changes—so-called local motions—we notice physical and chemical changes taking place in the world. As examples of physical change we have those which occur in water when it passes through the phases of steam, liquid, and ice. We know, too, that extensive chemical changes are produced by fire, for instance —indeed, this knowledge goes back to prehistoric times—and by the weathering of rocks, and by the decay of vegetables and animal matter. Such knowledge, common to all, is corroborated by the natural sciences, which have taught us that these and other similar changes are instances of combinations and dissociations of the smallest chemical units constituting material bodies, the chemical atom. Further, natural science has shown that physical and chemical change is not confined to terrestrial substances, as the ancients believed, but holds for all bodies in the solar system and throughout the great universe: the telescope, and still more the spectroscope, have demonstrated that heavenly bodies are composed of the same kinds of atoms as matter on our earth.

11

Changes are also observed in microscopic matter

Nevertheless, although mutability was undeniable in inanimate nature, the question of what happens in the unexplored microcosm remained open. It seemed, indeed, that unlike the organic world, inorganic matter was in a certain sense immutable. True, its smallest units, the chemical atoms, did in fact combine with one

another in most various ways; but they appeared to be endowed
with the privilege of eternal stability and utter indestructibility,
since they always emerged unaltered from every chemical analysis.
A hundred years ago, the atoms of the chemist were still regarded
as simple indivisible and indestructible. The same idea prevailed
about the amount of matter and energy in the universe, being
enshrined in the fundamental laws of the conservation of mass
and conservation of energy. There were some who went so far as
to consider themselves authorized to formulate in the name of
science a fantastic monistic philosophy, whose sorry memory is
linked with, among others, the name of Ernest Haeckel. But in
the very lifetime of this man, towards the end of last century,
the too simple picture of the chemical atom was shattered. Increased knowledge of the periodical system of chemical elements,
the discovery of radiations from radioactive substances, together
with other facts of similar significance, showed that the chemical
atom is a small world in itself—the microcosm. With dimensions
measured in ten-millionths of a millimetre the atom is a theatre
of constant change, no less than the macrocosm perceptible
to all.

12

Inside the Atom : the electronic domain

It was through the study of electrons that the character of
atomic mutability was first established. Electrons moving in orbits
inside the atom produce rays of light and heat which are absorbed
by other atoms according to the energy level of the orbits. Movements of electrons out of or into these orbits account for ionization as well as for the ordinary chemical and physical
properties of matter. But it remained possible to suppose that
this mechanism, which explained physical and chemical change,
provided one last refuge for immutability, since it left untouched
the core of nucleus of the atom, the seat of its mass and positive
electric charge which determine the place of the particular atom
in the natural system of the chemical elements. Here in the
nucleus, science seemed to have found at last an absolutely stable
and unchanging entity.

13

The Nucleus

But already at the dawn of the new century, observations on
radioactive processes—processes caused by spontaneous disruption

of atomic nuclei—began to exclude such a hope. Yet even here, once science had recognised the fact of instability in the ' deep heart's core' of chartered nature, it appeared that the nucleus was impervious to human control, since all attempts to accelerate or retard radio-active disintegrations were failures. The first successful effort to break down a nucleus—of nitrogen—was very modest and it dates back little more than three decades; but in recent years by bringing into play ingenious methods and prodigious forces it has been found possible not only to smash nuclei but also to rebuild them. Although this achievement—which, in so far as it contributes to the cause of peace, is certainly worthy of record among the glories of our century—represents no more than a preliminary step in the development of the new sciences of nuclear physics and nuclear chemistry nevertheless it provides us with an important conclusion, namely, that while atomic nuclei are much more stable than ordinary chemical compounds yet they, too, are capable of transformation and hence they are mutable.

14

Nuclear changes supply the stars with energy:
Cosmic Radiation

Simultaneously with these developments, it was established that nuclear transformations can play a most important part in supplying the stars with energy. Thus, according to Bethe, in the interior of the sun, at a temperature approaching some twenty million degrees, there occurs a cyclic chain-reaction in which four hydrogen nuclei combine to form a single nucleus of helium; and the process liberates energy which in turn compensates for the heat lost by solar radiation. So, too, in the modern physics laboratory, nuclei are successfully transformed—as for instance in the case of uranium—by bombardment with high-energy particles or with neutrons. As likewise bearing on this subject, mention should be made of the effects of cosmic radiation, which is capable of breaking down even the heaviest of the chemical atoms, thus not infrequently producing whole swarms of subatomic particles.

15

Matter is mutable

We have desired to cite only some few instances, but such as could establish beyond all possible doubt the fact of mutability in the material world, large or small. Mutability is clearly revealed in the numerous changes which the forms of energy undergo. Mutability of matter is seen especially in the chemical changes which are constantly going on in the macrocosm. Mutability is no less evident within the atom itself, right in its very core, affecting the sub-atomic constituents of the nucleus.

16

Mutable matter is not self-explanatory

So, the scientist of to-day, directing his gaze more penetratingly into the heart of nature than did his predecessor a century ago, sees full well that inorganic matter is, so to say, countersigned in its inmost being with the stamp of mutability; and; that, consequently, its origin and existence demand for their explanation a reality of a totally different order, one which by its very nature is immutable.

17

Contrast

Just as in a black-and-white drawing, figures stand out and take on shape and life by contrast with the background, so the Eternal and Immutable Being emerges clear and resplendent by contrast with the restless river of mutability which envelopes all matter whether large scale or small. The scientist who stands dizzy on the edge of the cosmic torrent finds stability and steadiness in God's definition of Himself, ' I am Who am' (Exodus iii, 14), the Absolute, to whom the Apostle gives praise as the 'Father of lights, with whom there is no change nor shadow of alteration.' (James i, 17.)

DIRECTION OF COSMIC CHANGES

18

Energy is conserved but degraded. So there must be a Prime Mover

Modern science has not only sharpened our knowledge of reality and shown the extensive occurrence of change in the material universe; it has, in addition, furnished us with precious indications about the sense of direction which marks natural processes. As late as a hundred years ago, just after the discovery of the law of conservation of energy it was believed that the processes of nature are reversible. So, in conformity with the principles of causality, or, more strictly speaking, physical determinism, a periodic renovation or rejuvenation of the universe was regarded as possible.   But, through the law of entropy formulated by Rudolph Clausius, it was recognised that the spontaneous occurrences of nature are always accompanied by a diminution of free or utilizable energy. In a closed system this entails the eventual cessation of all large-scale processes. Such a fate—from which hypotheses sometimes unduly gratuitous) like that of continuous creation, for instance, have endeavoured to rescue the universe— stands out clearly from the testimony of positive science, and it eloquently demands the existence of a Prime Mover.

19

Even in the sub-atomic world free energy is not being created

In the microcosm, the law of degradation of energy which is statistical in nature, need not necessarily apply. At the time it was formulated, nothing was known about the structure of the atom or the way the atom worked. However, recent advances in atomic science and unexpected progress in astrophysics have produced a number of interesting surprises. Here, we can do no more than allude to the results of such discoveries; they can be summed up by saying that a sense of direction is clearly present in all atomic and sub-atomic transformations.

20

Illustrations from solar energy

To illustrate this fact, it will be sufficient to cite the example already mentioned relating to solar energy. The electronic structure of the atoms in the sun's photosphere is continuously releasing a prodigious amount of radiant energy and discharging it into space. Inside the sun the lost energy is compensated for by the formation of helium from hydrogen. This process manufactures energy at the expense of hydrogen nuclei, a small amount of their mass (seven tenths of one per cent) being converted into radiant energy. Therefore, compensation takes place at the expense of the energy which originally in the hydrogen nuclei existed as mass, or inert matter. So, in the course of millions of years, by a process which is both slow and irreversible, this energy is turned into radiations. A similar transformation occurs in the case of radio-active substances, whether they be natural or artificial. Thus here again, in the world of the small — the microcosm strictly and properly so-called—we find a law indicating a sense of direction in natural changes, a law which is analogous to the law of entropy in the large-scale world. The direction of microscopic processes is always such that the available energy inside the atom suffers a diminution. Up to the present time, science knows no way of countering this tendency; high-energy nuclei are not formed spontaneously in nature.

21

In the future

If the scientist turns his attention from the present state of the universe and considers the future, even the very remote future, he finds himself constrained to admit that both on the large scale and the small the world shows signs of growing old. In the course of millions of years, even the seemingly inexhaustible quantities of atomic nuclei lose free energy; and matter becomes, so to speak, like an extinct and scoriform volcano. Not unnaturally the thought comes: if our actual universe, which to-day so vibrates with rhythm and life, is, as we have seen, insufficient to explain itself, still less can we expect an explanation to be forthcoming from a world which will have fallen a victim to a ' heat-death.'

22

In the past

If we direct our attention to the past, the farther back we go, the more matter presents itself as rich in free energy and a theatre of great cosmic events. Everything seems to indicate that the material universe had a mighty beginning in time, being endowed at birth with vast reserves of energy, in virtue of which, at first rapidly, and then ever more slowly, it evolved into its present state.

23-24

Two questions

This conclusion naturally raises two questions: First, is science in a position to state when the mighty beginning of the universe took place? And, secondly, what was the initial or primitive state of the universe?

The most competent experts in atomic physics, in collaboration with astronomers and astro-physicists, have endeavoured to find answers to these two difficult but extremely fascinating questions.

25

Date of creation

First of all, We shall quote some figures with the object merely of indicating in round numbers how long ago it is since the universe began. Science has a variety of methods at its disposal for making the calculation, each of them more or less independent of the other, and the results converge. We point out a few of them briefly.

26

First method: Recession of the spiral nebulæ

Study of spiral nebulæ, especially by Edwin W. Hubble at the Mount Wilson Observatory, has led to the interpretation—presented with all due reserve—that the galaxies are moving away from one another with such speed that, in the space of thirteen hundred million years, the distance between nebulæ doubles. Tracing this process of the ' expanding universe ' backwards, we find that, from one to ten milliard years ago, the spiral nebulæ were packed into a relatively small space, and at that time the cosmic processes may be said to have had their beginning.

27

Second method: Age of the earth's crust

To calculate the age of radioactive substances present in rocks, we can take approximate data from the transmutation of uranium 238 into an isotope of lead (Radium G), or of uranium 235 into actinium D (another isotope of lead), or of thorium into thorium D (also an isotope of lead). The mass of the helium concomitantly formed can be measured and used to check the other calculations. The method leads to the conclusion that the age of our oldest rocks is about five milliard years.

28

Third method: Age of meteorites

The preceding method has also been used to determine the age of meteorites, and it has given practically the same figure of five milliard years. The result assumes special importance from the fact that today many scientists admit the inter-stellar origin of meteorites.

29

Fourth method: Stability of stellar systems

Variation of gravitational pull in systems of double stars and star groups, along with the consequences of tidal action, limit the stability and life of such systems to a period of from five to ten milliard years.

30

Results not revolutionary

Although these figures may appear stupendous, they involve no new idea even for the simplest of the faithful. They introduce nothing different from the opening words of Genesis, '*In the beginning* God created heaven and earth . . .—' that is to say, at the beginning of things in time. The figures We have quoted clothe these words in a neat and, as it were, mathematical dress. From them there springs forth a new source of strength and consolation for those who share the esteem of the Apostle for divinely-inspired Scripture, which has its uses 'to instruct us, to expose our errors, to correct our faults, to educate us in holy living'. (II Tim., iii, 16.)

31

State of primitive matter

Besides enquiring into the age of the universe, men of science have with equal earnestness and freedom directed their intrepid genius to the other problem previously mentioned, a harder problem: what was the nature and condition of the first matter in the universe? The answers given differ considerably from one another according to the theories on which they are based. Yet, there is a certain amount of agreement. It is agreed that the density, pressure and temperature of primitive matter must each have touched prodigious values. (Cp. A. Unsöld, Director of Kiel Observatory: *Kernphysik und Kosmologie*, in the *Zeitschrift für Astrophysik* 24B, 1948, p. 278.) Only under such conditions can we explain the formation of heavy nuclei, as well as their relative frequency in the periodic table of the chemist's elements.

32

Questions

The mind of man in its pull towards truth rightly persists in asking how matter could have reached a state so unlike anything seen or known in modern experience. It also wants to know what went before. In vain do we seek answers from natural science, which frankly declares itself baffled by these problems. Such questions demand too much from positive science. Equally, it is certain that minds trained in philosophical reflection penetrate more deeply into problems of this sort.

33

The creative spirit

Yet, when a mind, enlightened and enriched with a knowledge of modern science, weighs the question calmly, it undoubtedly feels itself impelled to abandon the idea of self-sufficient matter —whether eternal or self-made—and ascend to the notion of a Creating Spirit. Clearly and critically, as when it examines facts and passes judgment on them, it perceives the work of creative omnipotence and recognizes that its power, set in motion by the mighty *Fiat* of the Creating Spirit billions of years ago, called into existence with a gesture of generous love and spread over the universe matter bursting with energy. Indeed, it would seem that present-day science, with one sweep back across the centuries, has succeeded in bearing witness to the august instant of the primorial *Fiat Lux*, when, along with matter, there burst forth from nothing a sea of light and radiation, and the elements split and churned and formed into millions of galaxies.

34

Limit of natural science

It is true of course, that the facts established by men of science up to the present are not an absolute proof of creation unlike the proofs drawn from metaphysics and Revelation concerning simple creation and from Revelation concerning the fact of creation. The pertinent facts from natural science, to which We have referred, need to be extended before they can provide a sure foundation for arguments which of themselves are outside the sphere of positive science.

35

The idea of creation is not repugnant to modern science

Nonetheless, it is worthy of note that modern scholars in these fields regard the idea of creation as quite compatible with scientific conceptions, and that they are even led naturally to such a conclusion by their researches. Only a few decades ago, any such 'hypothesis' was rejected as quite irreconcilable with science. As late as 1911, the celebrated physicist, Svante Arrhenius, declared that 'the opinion that something can come from nothing is at variance with the present-day state of science according to which matter is immutable'. (*Die Vorstellung von Weltgebäude im Wandel der Zeiten*, 1911, p. 362.) In the same vein we find the statement of Plate: 'Matter exists, nothing can come from nothing; hence matter is eternal. We cannot admit the creation of matter.' (*Ultramontane Weltanschauung und Moderne Lebenskunde* 1907, p. 55.)

36

Confirmatory quotation from Space and Spirit

On the other hand, how different and much more faithful a reflection of limitless visions is the language of an outstanding modern scientist, Sir Edmund Whittaker, a member of the Pontifical Academy, when he speaks of the above-mentioned inquiries into the age of the world:

'These different estimates converge to the conclusion that there was epoch, one to ten billion years ago, on the further side of which the cosmos, if it existed at all, existed in some form totally unlike anything known to us: so that it represents the ultimate limit of science. We may perhaps without impropriety refer to it as the Creation. It supplies a concordant background to the view of the world which is suggested by the geological evidence that every organism ever existent on the earth has had a beginning. If this result should be confirmed by later researches, it may well come to be regarded as the most momentous discovery of the age; for it represents a momentous change in the scientific conception of the universe, such as was effected four centuries ago by the work of Copernicus.' (*Space and Spirit*, 1946, pp. 118-9.)

37

Modern science and God

What, then, is the importance of modern science in the argument for the existence of God based on change in the universe? By means of exact and detailed research into the large-scale and small-scale worlds it has considerably broadened and deepened the empirical foundation on which the argument rests, and from which it concludes to the existence of an *Ens a se*, immutable by His very nature. It has, besides, followed the course and the direction of cosmic developments, and, just as it was able to get a glimpse of the final state towards which these developments are inexorably moving so also has it pointed to their beginning some five billion years ago. Thus, with that concreteness which is characteristic of physical proofs, it has confirmed the contingency of the universe and also the well-founded deduction as to the epoch when the world came forth from the hands of the Creator.

38

Creation and Creator

Hence, creation took place. We say: therefore, there is a Creator. Therefore, God exists! Although it is neither explicit nor complete, this is the reply We were awaiting from science, and which the present generation is awaiting from it. It is a reply which bursts forth from mature and calm consideration of only one aspect of the universe, namely, its mutability. But this is quite enough to make the entire human race, which is the peak and the rational expression of both the macrocosm and the microcosm, become conscious of its exalted Maker, realize that it belongs to Him in space and in time, and then, falling on its knees before His sovereign majesty, begin to invoke His Name:

> 'Rerum Deus, tenax vigor,
> Immotus in te permanens,
> Lucis diurnae tempora,
> Successibus determinans.

> O God! all things' sustaining power,
> Remaining in Thyself unchanged,
> Who hast the flight of every hour,
> By daylight's altered gleam arranged.'
> —Hymn for None.

39

Beyond science

The knowledge of God as Creator, now shared by many modern scientists, is indeed the extreme limit to which human reason can attain. Nevertheless, as you are well aware, it does not constitute the last frontier of truth. In harmonious co-operation, because all three are instruments of Truth, like rays of the same sun, science, philosophy, and, with still greater reason, Revelation, contemplate the substance of this Creator Whom science has met along its path, unveil His outlines and point out His features. Revelation, above all, makes His presence, so to speak, immediate, vitalizing and loving, like that presence of which either the simple faithful or the scientist is aware in his inmost being when he recites simply the concise terms of the Apostles' Creed: "I believe in God, the Father Almighty, Creator of Heaven and Earth."

40

Today's need

Today, after so many centuries which were centuries of civilization because they were centuries of religion, the need is not so much to reveal God for the first time, as it is rather to recognize Him as a Father, revere Him as a Lawgiver and fear Him as a Judge. If they would be saved, the nations must adore the Son, the loving Redeemer of mankind, and bow to the loving inspirations of the Spirit, the fruitful Sanctifier of souls.

41

Faith crowns science

This conclusion, taking its remote inspiration from science, is crowned by a Faith which, being ever more deeply rooted in the consciousness of the people, will truly be able to assure basic progress for the march of civilization.

42

Vision of the whole

This is a vision of the whole, of the present as of the future, of matter as of the spirit, of time as of eternity, which, as it illumines the mind, will spare to the men of today a long tempestuous night.

43
Prayer

It is this Faith which at this moment inspires Us to raise towards Him whom we have just invoked as *Vigor, Immotus,* and *Pater—Father, Unchanging Strength*—a fervent prayer for all His children entrusted to Our care:

> ' Largire lumen vespere,
>   Quo vita nusquam decidat '—
> ' Bestow thy light on us each evening
>   That our lives may never fail.'

—light for the life of time, light for the life of eternity.

2. *Commentary and Notes*

Modern science. "Modern science," writes the philosopher, Karl Jaspers, " is one of the deepest incisions ever made into human history." It brings rapid changes to the manual of history and to the map. It is the greatest dissolvent of cultures the world has ever seen. It has accelerated communications, enlarged cities, brought about an alarming jump in world population. It has changed the character of warfare. It depletes the earth of its fruits at a dizzy rate. Under its impact, the very texture of human life has altered, and men see life with a new eye. Professor Butterfield in *The Origins of Modern Science*, stresses the part played by science in the making of our civilization. He believes that the scientific revolution which led to the eclipse of Scholastic philosophy and the destruction of Aristotelian physics, " outshines everything since the rise of Christianity, and reduces the Renaissance and the Reformation to the rank of mere episodes ". Further, this remoulding of scientific thought " looms large as the real origin both of the modern world and of the modern mentality ".

The chief effect on the individual is a change in his way of looking at things: the force of authority and tradition has lessened, and there is an increased respect for facts. There is still plenty of wishful thinking, but the appeal to facts is seen more and more. The effective leader no longer like the lord of the manor orders people about, but he tells them why he believes they should do as he suggests. Modern science has created leisure for the individual, and more people have more time for thinking. Through her daughter, technology, and the increased need for skilled labour, science has created a new middle class, the skilled workers, who are not a proletariat but men sensitive to argument. But the argument they ask for must place emphasis on facts, familiar facts, on what can be seen and accepted more or less immediately.

Today more than formerly, seeing is believing. The modern mind eschews abstractions. It demands the specific, the definite. It is habituated to the rapid and effortless presentation of the films, television, the comic strip, the funnies, the illustrated newspapers, the advertisement hoardings, the neon signs. It feels that a picture is worth many words, unless they are fashionable or magic words, *clichés*, emotional phrases, slogans, invented to by-pass thinking. The cinema, television, and the various other visual aids in education affect us all. We find it hard to deal nimbly with abstract notions however essential they may be to our welfare. High-placed moulders of public opinion and culture are unable to sustain a logical process. It is easier for us than for our forefathers to fall victims to alert exploiters, to the power-greedy, to the ideologist. It is all too easy to surrender the mind to the loose visual or emotional analogy. It has become harder than ever to do our own thinking, particularly when it involves abstract ideas.

THE MAN OF SCIENCE. Division of labour and specialization, with their correlatives, concentration and application, are required for progress, as well as for efficiency, but they can be overdone; and when the balance is upset they may be positive dangers. Our civilization is the witness. On all sides we see how the individual is suffering from lop-sided development, brilliantly educated in some matters and neglected in others. Woe to the specialist—he is not always an expert—who digs too deep and narrow a salient into the unknown and loses touch with his fellows, with himself.

The man of science is first and foremost a man. Being a scientist he does not cease to be a family man, a social being, a creature with *duties to himself, to his neighbour, and to his Creator*. Madness has seized him if in the glow of scientific and technological achievement he forgets the basic fact, that he is a man, a rational creature, who has not the reason of himself within himself.

The cold abstract scientist of fiction is a fiction. The scientist in real life is not a robot or an electronic brain: he is like anyone else, and has similar rights and duties, but greater responsibilities than many others because of his calling and opportunities. He is not dispensed from reasoning as a man, from reflecting on life and seeking answers to the perennial questions: Whence came I? Whither go I? Why?

DEMONSTRATIONS OF GOD'S EXISTENCE. (a) *Nature and classification of the proofs.* The arguments for God's existence which satisfy the ordinary man are fundamentally the same as those which convince the philosopher, but there is not the same degree of apprehension and certitude in the two cases. The one sees and adheres to truth at a deeper level than the other. The arguments are not a brilliant guess by St. Thomas or some lone thinker. They have grown by the cumulative insight and experience of millions of men. The proofs are profound and subtle, but at the same time a sure knowledge of God is easy and comes natural to the human mind. The philosophical reasoning is just an extension of common sense.

KANT'S CLASSIFICATION. The demonstrations have taken many forms, and Kant has reduced them to three groups. In what he called the *ontological* proof, one argues from the concept of God to His existence. There are two well-known instances of the argument, one due to St. Anselm, and the other due to Descartes. The former runs this way:

God is the greatest conceivable being.

He must exist.

For if not, we could conceive a greater being, namely, one that possessed existence in addition to the other great qualities.

Descartes' form of the argument can be put thus:

God is the being who possesses every perfection.

But existence is a perfection.

Therefore, God exists.

The ontological argument seems to be purely *a priori*. In the view of St. Thomas and many other philosophers, it begs the question. Today, it is regarded as ingenious rather than solid.

The second class of proof Kant called *cosmological*. Here one starts with some instance of *contingent* being in the world, and one ascends by the principle of causation to the Necessary Being.

The third class of proof starts with a particular aspect of nature, such as its orderliness or signs of purpose in things, and rises to the Cause of this apparently directed, or remotely controlled, behaviour. Here we have the so-called *teleological* argument, or proof from final end. Kant considered it should be cited with reverence as the oldest and clearest demonstration of God's existence.

ANOTHER CLASSIFICATION. There are strong objections to Kant's method of classification, and it has been proposed to classify the proofs for the existence of God according to the nature of the contingent fact from which they *start*. This would give three kinds of proof, namely, *physical* proofs starting from a fact of Nature; *moral* proofs, based on a moral fact such as duty or the universal sentiment of mankind about the existence of God; and *metaphysical* proofs, taking their origin from a conception of the mind. Besides the ontological arguments already mentioned, Plato's proof, based on the existence of eternal truths (and subsequently much used by Leibnitz, Fénelon, and Bossuet), would belong to the last category.

The moral proofs are very powerful. To many people, especially those of artistic temperament, they are more telling than the physical proofs, which appeal in their full force rather to men of science and philosophers. But since one and the same proof may be classed as moral and physical, this system is not wholly satisfactory either. The physical proofs originate in a fact of nature (including moral nature) and their power arises from the principle of sufficient reason and the insufficiency of the naturalist creed (which requires that nature be self-explanatory). The five ways of St. Thomas originate in an observation and study of nature. After that, they proceed on the more abstract philosophical plane.

(But here, as elsewhere, we are up against the difficulty of seeing —in the sense of understanding—the exact nexus between the abstractive and the concrete faculties of the human mind, the power the mind of man possesses to pass from individuals to universals, and *vice versa*. This is at the root of knowledge, and especially of scientific knowledge, this wonderful power to unite and unify intuitions of the concrete with intuitions of the abstract.)

(b) *The five ways outlined.* We speak of natural philosophy and of mental philosophy. In both these senses the five ways are philosophical. They partake of both natural and mental science. They do not proceed from a mere conception of the mind. They involve something more than deductive reasoning. They are founded in experience, in the concrete world. They start with a fact observed in nature and they arrive at their conclusion by means of a philosophical principle.

The relevant facts of nature can be viewed under one of five aspects, and the arguments built on them constitute the five ways.

First way: we see that some things in nature *change*. Hence we argue to the existence of the Changeless One, the Immutable and External, the Prime Mover, God.

Second way: we see that some things in nature are *caused*.

Hence we argue to the existence of the Uncaused Cause, the First Cause, God.

Third way: we see that some things in the world are *contingent*. Hence we argue to the existence of the non-Contingent or Necessary Being, God.

Fourth way: we see that some things in the universe are *less or more perfect*. Hence we argue to the existence of the *Absolutely Perfect Being,* God.

Fifth way: we see that some things around us are *orderly*. Hence we argue to the existence of the Supreme Norm, Rule and Ruler, God.

Clearly, each of the ways presents a different aspect of the Infinite Being, just as theology and Revelation bring out facets which are undreamed of in philosophy.

THE PERSONAL GOD. The God of the Five Ways is a god for philosophers, abstract and remote. It is the generally received opinion that any philosopher, who has made a sincere effort to find Him by the exercise of his powers of reasoning, will usually discover in law itself, and in individual religious experience, as by Revelation, quite new and different aspects of the First Cause and Prime Mover from those made evident by metaphysical considerations. He will become aware of the qualities of the Personal God Who can speak to each man in the heart, the Heavenly Father Who is " Our Father ", the Father Who can turn up a miracle of grace for the prodigal son, the Heavenly Father Who loves His creatures and made His Son incarnate for them, the Heavenly Father Who consoles His children in times of great trial by the presence of the Holy Spirit. At some time or other in life every earnest searcher after truth gets personal experience of the Living God.

THE CHANGING WORLD AND THE FORM OF THE PROOFS. We live in a changing world, and in a changing world there are bound to be confusions. In a time of transition values are unstable. Some confusions in science are due to writers who mix up mathematics and natural philosophy, not to say logic. This is natural when a subject is growing rapidly and luxuriantly. Also, ideas are more plentiful than words, and an old word is used in a new sense without care. Thus we are told that space and time no longer exist but only their union in space-time. We are told that the principle of causality has been upset by the principle of indeterminacy, and so on. These are instances of changing a word from its traditional meaning and then denying a principle containing the altered term.

Some mathematicians, for instance, take the word " space ", change its meaning and talk of space of " n " dimensions, and challenge people to imagine it. (Space in four or more dimensions has nothing to do with physical reality: it is purely an invention like the square root of minus one, useful to the mathematician in his work, but otherwise a figment of the mind.) Similarly, the principle of causation is in no way affected by developments such as statistical mechanics or by other confessions of technical failure in mathematics or quantum theory. (Mathematics, contrary to popular belief, has severe limitations in physical science.) The traditional arguments for God's existence are as much affected by such developments as human nature is affected by changes in fashion.

THE CHANGING WORLD AND THE SUBSTANCE OF THE PROOFS. Apart from the verbal confusions which are likely to occur in a period of activity and originality—confusions which settle themselves eventually—modern discoveries and new conceptions may have affected the substance of the proofs of God's existence. Perhaps some of the discoveries show that matter is eternal, that the universe is a perpetual motion machine, that somewhere energy is being renewed or remade? Perhaps modern science reveals that nature is self-explanatory? If so, some of the classical demonstrations of the existence of the Creator would require to be re-examined and recast or scrapped.

The Holy Father assures us that there is no need to fear revolutionary surprises. The subject-matter of natural science is well defined. It is nature. Nature has various moods and aspects. From the point of view which interests us here, its various moods and aspects can be reduced to five. These have received their classical expression in St. Thomas's five ways. Now, a close examination of modern discoveries and a competent discussion of new conceptions will show that far from being weakened by recent developments in natural science, traditional arguments are strengthened, especially those depending on *change* and *order* in nature, the first and fifth ways of St. Thomas.

THE FIVE WAYS: THE PHILOSOPHICAL PRINCIPLES. THE BASIC PRINCIPLE: THE INFINITE REGRESS. The form of the argument in each of the five ways can be reduced to a fact of nature and an application of the principle of sufficient reason.

The latter may be stated thus: *What is not of itself is of another which is of itself.* There may be intermediaries, of course, and so the basic principle involves a subsidiary one to the effect that *there cannot be an infinite chain of intermediaries;* or, to phrase it less tautologically, there cannot be an infinite regress. This is fundamental in realist philosophy, as in real life, as in physics. There is no such thing as an infinite series in nature.

What about infinite series in algebra? Zeno long ago showed it would require an infinite time to " add up " an infinite series. Some mathematicians in their popular writings have confused an *infinite* series with an *indefinite* series. Number is *actually* finite, that is, when applied to things in nature or to a concrete operation in algebra: it is only *potentially* and *conceptually* that number is unlimited. The mathematician's "infinite" number is really an indefinite number. There is a definite quantity of energy, of matter, in the world: however much it is, there is just that much and no more. The term "infinite quantity" is really meaningless. The quantity of matter in the universe is neither unlimited nor indefinite. Likewise, the term "infinite sum" has no meaning. (Mathematicians like Sir James Jeans tend to confuse a *limit* or *limiting value* with a *sum.*) No mathematician could live long enough to add up an infinite sum. Energy cannot be infinite in amount because it is an actuality, it is physical. Time can be infinite only in the sense of *possibility* of events, not in the sense of *actual* events. Actual events are and must be finite in number.

A MODERN FORM OF THE ARGUMENT. The kind of reasoning employed in the five ways may be illustrated by the story of " The Big Boss ". A certain American one day became acutely conscious that he was not his own master, really, although he was a full citizen of the great democracy. He was being " pushed around ". The man who pushed him around was his boss. Then he found that his boss was pushed around by another man. Then he wondered who pushed around the boss's boss. He followed this up and discovered there was a chain of bosses pushing other bosses around. The final boss was pushed around by an idea. Who had planted that idea and started the pushing-around chain? And so back. There was a start somewhere, for neither men nor ideas had been going on forever. So there must be someone or some thing not pushed around by anyone else, who begins the chain of chains. Our investigator concluded that there was an ultimate, final, boss, the Great Pusher Around, the Unpushed and Unpushable. Our philosopher rejected, as unreal and outside his knowledge of nature, both the possibility of an infinite regress, and the possibility of a circular chain. He equally excluded theories of millenary renewal or secular re-creations.

FIRST WAY: THE ARGUMENT FROM CHANGE. Some confusion is caused by calling this argument the argument from *motion*. It would be no more misleading to call it the argument from emotion, since both are equally instances of change but not necessarily in the sense of " becoming ". Change is to be understood as " becoming " in this argument.

We all know what change is until we try to define it. It is then we begin to appreciate the difficulties of the philosopher when he attempts a profound analysis. We recall the historical sophism of Zeno who argued that change is impossible, because it requires a thing to stop being what it is without yet being what it will be. In reply to this piece of dialectic, it may be pointed out that a thing can be intermediary between what it was and what it will be. Change, indeed, is a continuous process with union of different elements. The least unsatisfactory theory of change is probably the Aristotelian one.

Aristotle explained change in terms of potency and act. Change, he said, is the passage from potency to act, potency being the *possibility* of acquiring a perfection, act being the *possession* of the perfection. Change consists then in the passage from a state of privation to a state of possession.

From these preliminaries—which are necessary in order to grasp its force and beauty—we may go on to state the argument from change. It may be formulated thus: It is certain from sense knowledge that some things in the world change. But what changes is changed by another. And an infinite series of changes is impossible. Hence there must be an unchangeable Being, a Being without potency Who is Pure Act, the Source of all change. This is the immutable Prime Mover.

The basic principle *what changes is changed by another* follows from the principle that *a thing cannot change itself* in the sense of converting its own potency into act. A thing cannot actualise itself. It cannot give itself actually what it possesses only potentially. You cannot give what you have not got. It is no objection to say one does not need a black eye in order to give one, as a black eye is not a perfection.

The argument from change was first formulated by Anaxagoras (500-428 B.C.), one of the most eminent Ionic philosophers, taken up by Plato, developed by Aristotle, and refined by the Scholastics, especially St. Thomas, who considered it the clearest of the five ways.

St. Thomas's proof may be put as follows: :
Since there are things that come to be in various ways (change

of colour, growth, and so forth), and since what comes to be cannot make itself come to be, there must be, *now* some being that makes things come to be without itself changing.

SECOND WAY: THE ARGUMENT FROM SECONDARY CAUSES. If something happens we naturally ask, what caused it? We never believe that a cup or glass " broke of itself". Every event has a cause. Such is the plain man's way of putting the principle of causality or causation. He does not say that night is caused by day because it follows day. He knows there is a special intimate connection between cause and effect, and he can point to instances in the world around him, in the physical, moral, economic, political and other orders. The ordinary man knows that cause and effect make a distinctive sort of " contact" with each other: they are always together but they are not the same, they are separate but not apart.

Some people have the habit nowadays of assigning their own erroneous meaning to a fundamental principle and then saying that the principle has ceased to be valid any longer. Persons who would never attempt to lift themselves by pulling up their socks do not show the same respect for the laws of thought. Some of them misinterpret the principle of causality to mean: every event has a known or ascertainable cause. And since in statistical studies we cannot follow all the individual events, they say the principle of causation has broken down. This is of course not logical. There is a clear distinction between an event and our ability to know it. Things do not go out of existence when we close our eyes or ignore them.

When we consider an event in nature we remark that it is not isolated but that it is connected with other events by a cause-effect relation. We are all struck by this inter-connectedness of things in the world: it makes the natural sciences possible. There is subordination or a hierarchy among natural causes. A thing cannot be the efficient cause of itself, for this would require it to exist before itself, a contradiction. Again, its existence cannot be explained by a series of efficient causes, whether linear or circular. Suppose a linear series, even one prolonged indefinitely. In an ordered series of efficient causes, the first term causes the intermediaries and an intermediary causes the last, so that if the first cause is removed all the intermediaries and their effects disappear.

Suppose a circular series. Then two elements will have to be both cause and effect at the same time. For example, if the series consisted, say, of 4 terms, A B C and D, so that A produces B,

B produces C, C produces D, and D produces A. Here A produces D by remote action and is also produced by it; that is, A is both the cause and the effect of D. Which is absurd.

Hence no natural event is efficiently caused by itself or by a series of natural causes, so that we must postulate a first cause which has no cause, namely, the uncaused cause, with existence of itself, God. As Bacon remarks, we must hang the chain of secondary causes from the throne of the First Cause.

THIRD WAY: THE ARGUMENT FROM CONTINGENT BEING. A contingent being is one that can be or not be. If a thing ceases to exist or can cease to exist it is contingent. In the world around us we see that beings are born and die. We see things cease to exist, and we see things come into existence. Consequently the world contains contingent beings. According to men of science there was a time when there were no rational creatures, no brute animals, no plants on the earth. According to the nebular and other theories the heavenly bodies did not always exist in their present state. Such contingent things have not a sufficient reason for existence in themselves. They presuppose a necessary being, a being which exists of itself and must exist. They are of another Who of Himself has being. This Necessary Being is not (a) a collection of contingent beings, because a multiplication of contingent beings—even prolonged indefinitely—leaves the collection contingent. Nor is it (b) an intrinsic law of contingent beings, since the law itself would be contingent and require a lawgiver. It is a Being different in nature from contingent being, it endures without cease.

This argument is much the same as Kant's cosmological argument, and we shall find a reference to it in the concluding portion of the Papal allocution. Modern science in fixing a date for creation thereby proves that the world is contingent.

FOURTH WAY: DEGREES OF PERFECTION IN THINGS. No formulation of the five ways does them justice, for they lose some of their force when put down on paper. They have to be pondered, they have to be lived, the fourth way more than the others.

THE GIST OF THE ARGUMENT. We all have a sense of values, and we can all distinguish degrees of perfection in things and in creatures. We see that some things are truer or better or nobler than others. But such grades of excellence imply a best, a noblest, a most perfect. The existence of goodness, truth, nobility in varying degrees implies a Pattern and Source of Perfection, God.

ILLUSTRATIONS. The argument makes use of the three orders, the physical, the moral, and the philosophical. Hugh Dormer's diaries present a modern illustration. Hugh was a young air-man who lost his life in the war, but not before learning " to appreciate the myriad beauty of humanity and the universe as the creation of God." His diaries let us see the curious solidarity among fighter-pilots in war, a solidarity above prejudice and tragedies and transcending racial antipathies, enabling them to recognize and pay tribute to degrees of excellence in one another. The solidarity was born of the pride of flying men that in their dog-fights in the sky their tussles were clean and altogether different from the fighting on the ground, in the mud, against the din of crawling tanks. They had feelings of disgust when they were ordered to less noble fighting, as, for instance, to shoot up trains. They tried not to think of the shrieks of terror, they tried not to see the shells smashing through the wood, the windows shivering in fragments, the engine-drivers writhing in jets of steam, the white-faced people trapped in the coaches. They could rise above all this and salute a brave enemy pilot who had just died. He belonged to them, he was part of the world where there was no hatred, where there was a sense of comradeship with something noble as its foundation. In spite of their handicaps and immaturity, these youths formed ideals, learned to see the beauty of creation, and raised their minds to the Creator. " Ideals", wrote Hugh, " are romantic and noble at a distance, and they shine through men like light through alabaster", even though they may have origi-nated in earthy conditions.

Another instance of the same kind is the chivalrous Commander Crabb, " the prince of frogmen", who disappeared on the night of April 19, 1956, when diving in Portsmouth harbour near the cruiser *Ordzonikze* which had carried Bulganin and Khrushchev to England. It was said of Lionel Crabb in the House of Commons that Britain would be the poorer but for men like him, a man who liked to talk, not about his own exploits, but about those of the Italian frogmen who were technically his enemies and later became his friends. When the Italian Lieutenant Visintini was killed by a chance shot from a shore battery, it was Crabb who saw to it that Visintini was buried at sea with naval honours.

MORE FORMAL TREATMENT. We argue to the existence of an Infinitely Perfect Being from Whom all imperfect beings derive their degree of perfection, however limited. The possession of a limited degree of perfection is not self-explanatory, it must come from another. The other is either infinitely perfect or not. If the former our case is made; if the latter, then this other derives from another, and so on till we reach the Absolutely Perfect Being, the Source of the various grades and kinds of perfection.

We note that the argument is totally different from the ontological argument, which is based in its entirety on an *idea*. The fourth way starts from *real* grades of perfection in the world. (St. Thomas's treatment differs from that just given, which is a modern version.)

FIFTH WAY: ARGUMENT FROM PURPOSIVE ORDER. There are two kinds of order apparent in the world which we may call mechanical order and purposive order. Purposive order is just as strongly opposed to chance or caprice as mechanical determinism (according to which all actions are determined by prior conditions) can be. Purpose combines unity of aim with variety of means. The purposive systems we know best are human beings: in them mechanical levels operate alongside the levels of consciousness though they follow quite different laws. The causes which *produce* a purpose are different in kind from the secondary causes which *result* from a purpose. If a gun is fired, we find a set of secondary causes reaching all the way from the purpose of the gun-man to the completed process. The sequence of secondary causes such as the squeezing of the trigger through motion of muscles directed by nerve impulses, the detonation, the discharge of the bullet, the impact, and so on, do not really explain the action. Only the purpose of the gun-man does so. A good illustration of how experience can be orderly and yet non-mechanical is found in moral experience, where we see character expressing itself in action. In constant and constantly developing character we observe an order which is flexible but not capricious.

THE ARGUMENT FROM ORDER. Aristotle, perhaps the most intelligent man who ever lived, remarked that the absence of chance and the conduciveness of everything to an end are to be seen quite clearly in the works of Nature. We see objects without intelligence operating in a regular and habitual manner. They behave or function as if they were guided or were under remote control. But this they could not do unless they were ruled by some supreme intelligence distinct from the world.

As to the fact, the various sciences are impressive witnesses. Who has not marvelled at the wonderful order of the solar system, at the regularity of its movements? at the unity and variety of the animal world? at the complex organism that may develop from a cell? at the marvel of the human body and its parts, each so fitted for an end, the foot for walking, the eye for seeing, the hand for many purposes? Over and above the mechanical order present in these instances there appears a purposive order, as if there were knowledge of a goal and of the means to be used in order to reach it.

Order of such a kind proceeds (a) from chance, or (b) from Nature itself, or (c) from a supramundane and supreme intelligence. But not from chance. Whoever reads a poem of Homer or Shakespeare recognises intelligence in it; and there are organic and inorganic bodies in the world more highly organised than any poem of poet. Not Nature in the sense of (1) the whole collection of mundane beings which lack intelligence; since things which are of themselves diverse and inert, cannot of themselves reduce to a unity of order, and that in a habitual and stable manner. Not Nature in the sense of (2) an intramundane intelligence, such as man, since orderly things undoubtedly existed on the earth before man himself. There remains, therefore, the Being outside and above the world, the Supreme Intelligence, Who appoints all things to their end, instils the sense of direction, orders and directs, the Supreme Ruler.

The argument goes back to remote times. It was employed by Plato and Socrates, who took it from Anaxagoras. Aristotle said of the latter: "When a man comes and says there is in Nature an Intelligence which is the cause of the arrangement and order of the universe, this man alone appears to have held on to reason in the midst of universal foolishness". Voltaire's version of the argument runs:

'L'univers m'embarrasse et je ne puis songer
Que cette horloge existe et n'ait point d'horloger'.

The world puzzles me, for I cannot see
How there is a clock and never a clock-maker.

Science discovers order where no order was seen before. With the advance and growth of the natural sciences, the fifth way of St. Thomas is constantly being enriched with fresh illuminating instances of cosmic law. If God really is, we should expect the heavens to declare His glory and the firmament to show His handiwork. What a wealth of illustration is afforded by the physical and biological sciences, and by their numerous and ever increasing offspring?

It may be of interest to note that the key word employed by St. Thomas in his fifth way, " gubernatio rerum "—steering of things—survives in the French word " gouvernail"—the rudder of a ship—and in the English word " government". It also reappears, almost in its original Greek form, in the name of the new science, "cybernetics", which deals with self-correcting machines, the so-called servo-mechanisms, used to prevent errors in electronic computors and selfguided missiles.

THE COSMOS. The Greeks contrasted cosmos with chaos or chance, the former being a world or system characterized by order and beauty, the beauty of law and regularity. We perceive order of this kind around us whether we put our eye to a telescope or to a microscope, whether we study the large scale world, the macrocosm, or the world of the minute, the microcosm. Man is often described as the mean between two extremes, the great and the small (both in space and in time). He is the measure, but he is also the measurer of his surroundings—a point not infrequently forgotten in recent publications. Only he can know a galaxy or an atom. (No nebula, however immense, is capable of knowing a man.) By this knowledge he shows himself the summit of creation, and justifies the poet's words: " What a piece of work is a man! how noble in reason! how infinite in faculty! in action how like an angel! in apprehension how like a god!"

OLDER CONCEPTION OF THE UNIVERSE. To appreciate what modern science has done in the way of enlarging our conception of the universe, of its immensity and detail, of its unity amid variety, of how one and the same kind of law applies and holds enduringly throughout its length, breadth, and profundity, one would require to pass in review and keep in mind former conceptions of the world from earliest times to the present day. The history of civilization is to some extent the story of man's ideas about his surroundings. Up to three centuries ago it was believed that a special kind of law reigned in the heavens. The heavenly bodies were regarded as made of different stuff from mother earth. Also they operated differently and were subject only to mechanical but not to physical or chemical change. Further, their mechanical changes were always of the " perfect " kind, motion in a circle : the heavenly bodies could never move in a straight line. The universe consisted in a baby-size and ill-conceived solar system enclosed within an absurdly tiny sphere which carried the fixed stars.

MODERN VIEW OF THE UNIVERSE. It is instructive to cast a rapid glance at the modern view of the macrocosm. We take the sun as our unit, a ball of very hot metals and gases, a million times the size of the earth. In bulk and condition it is an average star. It is one of the stars of the Milky Way, one of a hundred milliard. If the galaxy, the Milky Way, could be viewed from a great distance, it would appear like the spiral nebulae first seen through the Rosse giant telescope at Birr last century. The Milky Way, our home-galaxy, is in fact a spiral nebula (in shape rather like a currant-bun, the currants, of course, corresponding to the stars), at its greatest spread a quarter million light-years across, an island in the universe, itself a universe. The known universe consists in two millions of such islands. One and the same kind of law is believed to operate throughout the immense region in which they move and have their prodigious being. A ball kicked along the ground obeys the same laws of motion as a pair of stars circling round each other in an " island-universe " a million light-years from the earth.

No less striking than the extensiveness and intelligibility of the macrocosm is the extent by which knowledge of the microcosm has been advanced by modern science. Knowledge of the minute world has grown with great rapidity through a variety of methods and at the hands of all kinds of specialists. Chemists, physicists, biologists, metallurgists have all helped. Since the microscope of Leeuwenhoek, methods have included chemical analysis, new kinds of spectroscopic analysis, examinations by X-rays and by positive rays, ingenious use of electric and magnetic fields, and lately the electron microscope has been added. In the new domains of mole-cule, atom, and sub-atom thus revealed, in the ceaseless motions of the particles discovered by Brown, as in the structure-patterns of matter made visible by the penetrating eye of Roentgen or other radiations, the reign of law—the same type of law as in the macrocosm—stands out amazingly.

Modern research has extended the reign of law not only in space but also in tife. Ussher's figure of 2,369 years from the date of Creation to the death of Joseph in Egypt has been multiplied by a million, and the period during which mechanical law is con-ceived to have operated has been increased in like proportion. The range of the survey in space has its counterpart in time. Particles —components of cosmic rays—which endure for no longer than the millionth of a second have been " snapped " as they flash in and out of existence.

THE RESTLESS UNIVERSE. It is a matter of common knowledge that changes are always going on in the animate world, where creatures are born and die, where life is a series of perpetual trans-formations. The activity of the inanimate world is not so obvious.

The sciences, however, reveal the mutability even of the apparently inert world, and show that profound and continual alterations are always taking place in it.

Gross matter—in the form of bodies which may range from twinkling stars to specks of dust dancing in the sunlight—is constantly observed to change its position: this is *mechanical change*.

A more intimate form of change than the one just mentioned is *physical change*, of which examples are given in the text. (We have to be on our guard about the term " physical change " which is here employed in a technical and narrow sense to describe those changes studied in physics.) Physical change does not involve any change of chemical substance. Or, to put it another way, the chemical substance of a piece of matter remains unaltered in a physical change.

Refined examination of matter by chemical means has shown that matter consists of 101 varieties (1957), the so-called *chemical elements*. Metals like the precious metals platinum, gold and silver, and the commoner metals, iron and copper, are chemical elements. Also mercury, carbon, hydrogen, oxygen and nitrogen. The smallest amount of a chemical element that the chemist can come at by his methods is the *atom*. It cannot be cut up or subdivided by chemical techniques. It is a chemical unit. If we exclude the new man-made varieties, we find there are 92 sorts of chemical atoms, ranging from the lightest, hydrogen, to the heaviest in nature, uranium. The size of atoms is such that a million of them end to end would make only a hundredth of an inch, the breadth of a fine hair. The combinations of chemical atoms produce chemical compounds. Thus, water is a chemical compound. A drop of water is a collection of units, each of which is made up of two atoms of hydrogen and one atom of oxygen.

Chemical change involves change of substance. In *nuclear physics* we meet a class of substantial change which is even more intimate and more profound than chemical change, as we shall see later. In *nuclear change*, the inmost structure of the atom undergoes alteration.

Structure of the atom: nucleus and electron. Broadly speaking, the atom can be regarded as a solar system in miniature: its core, its massive part, corresponds to the sun, and light electrons, speeding in orbits around the core, are the counterpart to the planets. The core is named the *nucleus*: it contains nearly all the mass of the atom, and it is charged with positive electricity. The latter is equal in amount to the negative charges on the planetary electrons, so that the atom as a whole is electrically neutral in the normal state. When this state of neutrality is upset, the atom is said to be ionised, that is, it has become a carrier (Greek, *ion* from *eimi*, go) of electricity of one kind.

Apart from the neutrino, believed to have been detected in 1956, the *electron* is the smallest bit of matter that has been isolated. It is nearly two thousand times lighter than the lightest of the atoms, the hydrogen atom. It is charged with negative electricity, the amount being the smallest ever isolated. The electron may well carry the limit of physical division in electricity. In that case it would be a true and ultimate unit. Its name is due to the Galway Professor, G. J. Stoney, who foretold its existence. Its properties of tiny mass and small electric charge make it an unique entity. It is the most wonderful instrument, at once delicate and powerful, in the hands of the modern scientist and technician, and has led to wireless, radar, television, the electron microscope, amazing calculating devices, servomechanisms, and in general to the vast and growing developments known as electronics.

COSMIC RAYS. Cosmic rays are rays of energy—radiant energy —of very great penetrating power, capable of giving measurable effects after passing through hundreds of feet of water or a score of feet of lead. They come to us from all directions in space, but their origin is unknown. It has been suggested that they originate in the union of electrons with positive particles when elements are being synthesised in nebulæ far outside the Milky Way. Of the total radiation-energy received on earth from all the stars, with the exception of the sun, one-tenth part consists of cosmic radiation. Every second of time, these cosmic radiations break up a score of atoms in each cubic inch of air at sea-level, and disintegrate hundreds of thousands of atoms in our bodies. According to one guess, they are a cause of cancer. It is cosmic rays which ionize the upper atmosphere, and they cause the most carefully-insulated electrically-charged body to leak and lose its electricity. The energy of the rays is relatively enormous. How prodigious such energy may be—exceeding that of fission or fusion in nuclear bombs, even—is indicated by work in Professor Leprince-Ringuet's adventurous cosmic ray laboratory high up in the Alps.

WAVE MECHANICS. The whole development of physical science from Leucippus and Democritus to Hamilton and Schrödinger has been along two fronts, the atom front and the wave front. Or, to put it in another way, the models which have inspired fruitful ideas always derive from our notions of particles and ripples. (The mathematician would of course phrase it differently and say that the material universe is glimpsed under the apparently opposed but really complementary aspects of continuity and discontinuity). The particle or corpuscular model presents a picture of matter as consisting in lumps, discrete entities; while the wave model considers matter as continuous, no two parts of the universe being cut off or in physical isolation from each other. Material science began with the particle picture. Astronomers saw the stars as points of light, discrete bodies, with forces between them. Eventually their observations and studies led to dynamics as a science, to Newtonian mechanics, applicable to all matter. The wave conception developed later, and at first, in opposition as an enemy. It was developed to explain strange events in the radiation of light rays, to explain for instance how light added to light could produce darkness. The wave theory was highly successful in elucidating what were called interference effects. There was confusion when it was found in more recent times that sometimes radiations behaved as if they were corpuscular and at other times as if they were waves. The position became unsatisfactory when one had to regard light rays as particles on odd days of the week and as waves on even days. In 1924, a formal and purely mathematical bridge was constructed to unite the two inimical models of radiation and of matter. The chief founders of the new formalism, which is called wave-mechanics, are de Broglie, Heisenberg, Schrödinger and Dirac.

The dual aspect of matter as waves and particles can be summed up in the quantum formula for radiation, according to which the smallest amount of energy that can function in a physical event depends on the colour or wave-length of the radiation. This, so to speak, atom of energy, or quantum, is a tiny but exact multiple of the wave-length, a whole number of waves and never a fraction. The quantum of energy is then like a particle, a sealed-off packet, but the colour of the radiation is wave-like, and is conceived to result from a vibration being propagated much as waves spread out when you paddle your feet in water. A further and more nebular refinement or development is to suppose with some mathematicians that matter waves are not really material but only probability functions representing where in space-time there is a chance of finding matter.

ENTROPY. Of all the conclusions reached by centuries of careful research in science, one of the most revealing, as well as thought-provoking, is that which points to the degradation of energy. The notion of the progressive devaluation of energy, which finds expression in the Second Law of Thermodynamics or Law of Increasing Entropy, has been known for a hundred years, but we have been amazingly slow to see its philosophical implications.

The Law of Entropy must be understood in conjunction with the First Law of Thermodynamics, or law of conservation of energy. According to this principle—which was formerly distinguished from the principle of the conservation of matter but is now united to it, as will be explained later—the amount of energy in the world is fixed and cannot be increased or diminished unless by the Creator. The amount put in at creation has not altered one whit throughout the succeeding billions of years down to our time. The law of entropy or Second Law of Thermodynamics qualifies the First Law and states that while the total energy in the universe remains unchanged, it is continually passing into a spent or useless form. Whenever anything happens of itself, like a stone falling to the ground, there is a conversion from one form of energy to another, and there is always a loss of useful or employable energy. The *amount* of energy never alters, but less of it remains available for work, for doing things. The useful energy of the world is being all the time used up. Because there is incessant dissipation, and because there is no *addition* to the total energy—theories of continuous creation are gratuitous and have no foundation or support in science—we foresee a final state of absolute stagnation. The law of increasing entropy points precisely to this.

Entropy itself is a mathematical construct based on experiment. It is an index of a system's disorderliness or state of disorganization. It measures the degree of chaos in a body or a closed system. The idea is not *a priori* but has been adapted by mathematicians from experience to make calculations easier. The notion is many removes away from sense perception, since it is a ratio, namely, the ratio of the heat lost or gained by a system to the temperature at which the loss or gain takes place.

The law of entropy is a generalization of the observation that heat of itself never passes from cold to warm bodies, but only in the opposite direction. In other words, in some physical processes there is by the very nature of things one-way traffic only: certain processes in nature are uni-directional and cannot be reversed—they are irreversible, like the arrow of time. The significant point is that if *any* processes in nature are irreversible, and if nowhere in the universe energy is being created (created in the strict sense of the term, that is, being made out of nothing) then the ultimate end of matter must be uniformity without differentiation, that is, a state of inertness.

It is easy enough to *imagine* and conceive how the law of entropy can fail in limited regions of matter, non-living matter (it is in flat contradiction with organic evolution which supposes that more highly ordered or organised beings develop from simpler structures). For instance, the great physicist, Clerk Maxwell, whose researches led to wireless, showed how spritely little demons could, without the expenditure of any energy whatever, separate the fast bits of a gas from the slow, and thus set up a temperature-difference capable of producing activity and power.

ILLUSTRATIONS. In all physical systems we observe a levelling tendency, as if nature had democratic leanings. Water seeks to level itself. The radiator sends its heat into sealed surroundings until a uniform temperature is attained. Nature behaves as if it abhorred, not a vacuum, but differentiation and concentration of energy. The stars radiate away their store of energy and the energy never returns. So far as we know, stellar radiation is a one-way process, and it tends to even out the distribution of energy in the world. This promotion of levelling is called the "increase of entropy". As the degraded or useless energy increases, the useful energy lessens by an equal amount. Entropy is the ratio of the heat exchanged to the temperature of the exchange, and it expresses the proportion of useless to useful energy. The law of entropy states that the ratio is always increasing: which means that the amount of energy available for the processes of nature is ever growing less. The reason why we can get work from a waterfall is because there is a difference of level. The waterfall is useful because the water can fall. If the water were all at the one level, all work would be at an end. Likewise we get work out of a steam engine so long as there is a temperature difference, and no longer.

THE LAW IS CERTAIN. Though the law (more correctly, principle) of entropy is in part a matter of speculation—the conclusion is large in comparison with the field of observation—the conclusion arrived at is far from fanciful. Indeed, no less a physicist than Sir Arthur Eddington called this law the most certain and the best grounded of all the laws of physics. Emile Meyerson, eminent student of physical theory, wrote that it " is a fact, and by far the most important fact, of all science ". On the basis of present work, there appears to be no rational escape from the prospect of an ultimate dissipation of all the energy in the universe. This means not only the " death " of our particular solar system, but of any and every physical system. (The prospect has seemed to furnish Bertrand Russell and others with grounds for a rhetorical display of despair.)

COROLLARY I. It seems quite clear from the Second Law of Thermodynamics that the physical world, so well known to us through the labours of the men of science, is something which not only will have an end, but is something which had a beginning. If the universe is running down like a clock, the clock must have been wound up at a definite date. If the world is to have an end, it must have had a beginning. This follows strictly from the fact that the law of entropy is irreversible. A clock which is running down and is never re-wound cannot have been going for ever.

(We note that a sequence of changes is *reversible* if on carrying out the whole sequence in the reverse order, we find that every operation is exactly and perfectly reversed. This is impossible if at any stage there is friction or loss of heat to cooler surroundings. Other less obvious conditions are also required for reversibility.

We note further that strictly speaking we should not say the world began in time, since time only began with the world.)

COROLLARY II. The chief philosophical significance of the law of entropy consists, not in evidence of a beginning of the universe —important as that is—but rather in the evidence that the *natural world is not self-explanatory*. Energy by the very nature of things loses its power. It cannot then be self-sufficient. Without something outside nature, there would be no energy capable of deterioration. *Nature points beyond itself for an explanation of itself*.

The Second Law of Thermodynamics is thus a finger-post to the Creator as an explanation of the world. The reasoning reproduces more or less that of the cosmological argument for the existence of God. It is a blend of the second and third ways of

St. Thomas, and the heart of the argument is the necessity of a First Cause, because of the impossibility that a series of secondary causes connecting up contingent beings should be infinite.

THE ARGUMENT. The changes which we know in the world of nature are all dependent changes. Changes in plant growth we attribute to changes in soil or weather, and these changes are referred to still other changes, and so on. At each step there is degradation of energy. No single step in the process would even occur apart from the other steps on which it depends. (This dependence has nothing to do with succession in time.) Therefore, the entire chain of causes presupposes the existence of a power which is truly originative, able to account not only for others, but also for itself. If we take the law of entropy seriously, the only conclusion we can come to is that the material universe needs an explanation *external to itself*. We must say that the universe as we know it by the light of modern natural science could not have begun without the action of a creative, extramundane Source of energy. But a creative Source of energy outside the natural order is God.

It is no valid reply to say with Hume's critic that the necessary being which accounts for all the contingent parts of the world may be nothing other than the *world as a whole*. It is just the whole that most requires explanation. There is no line of evidence which makes this more manifest than that which leads to general acceptance of the law of entropy among men of science and philosophers.

MASS-ENERGY. According to Einstein's relativity theory, there should be an equivalence between mass and energy; in fact, mass would be condensed or solid energy, " frozen " energy, so to speak. The first satisfactory confirmation of this idea by experiment took place in the classic researches of Cockroft and Walton (1932), for which they were awarded a Nobel prize. The sequel of the theory and of analogous experiments was the atom-bomb. In such transformations of mass into energy, a minute amount of mass disappears and is replaced by a prodigious amount of energy. Mass is thus really a form of energy, and when a transformation occurs there is a constant rate of exchange or exact equivalence between the two forms. Hence the two hitherto distinct laws of conservation of mass and conservation of energy can now be subsumed under a single law, the conservation of mass-energy.

In mass-energy changes, there is no violation of the law of entropy, so far as we know. The amount of available energy is not increased at the expense of degraded energy; on the contrary, the indications are that these processes degrade energy and are irreversible.

THE AGE OF THE WORLD: HISTORY AND METHODS. The history of efforts to date the earth's origin and fix its age is a long and lively one, and falls into three main chapters. The first serious attempt to make exact estimates is found with the geologists who made use of mud layers and fossil imprints. Next came the evolutionists, prominent among them being Darwin and Wallace. Lord Kelvin, the Belfast-born physicist, was the first to introduce really exact methods of dating great periods, and the two reliable kinds of method mentioned in the Papal allocution, the physical method and the astronomical method, may be said to owe their origin to him.

The astronomers have two time-scales for the age of the universe, a long and a short. One set of facts in astronomy seems to require a relatively long period while another set of facts, or rather, their interpretation, appears to demand a much shorter period. The two astronomical methods mentioned in the text, dealing with nebular recession and stability of star-groups, indicate that the short period is correct. This indication is confirmed by the results of a physical method, the radioactive method, applied to terrestrial rocks and to meteorites. The radio-active method is the least objectionable of all the methods hitherto devised. It is very striking that it gives the same value both for minerals—located on the earth—and for meteorites, some of which are believed to come to us from interstellar space, that is, altogether outside the solar system. The results mean also that the age of the earth is of the same order of magnitude as that of the universe, quite an interesting and unexpected conclusion. It is of course most remarkable that the methods, so different from each other as the astronomical and the physical, should give results which agree so well together.

The general conclusion is that the age of the earth and of the universe is some billions of years. The date of Creation is 5 billion B.C.! The degree of accuracy to be accorded such a statement is of the same order as that of the earlier attempts in the 17th century to measure the velocity of light.

THE BILLION. We must say a word about the unit we employ for measuring the age of the earth. It is the Irish-American billion, which has the same value as the French milliard and denotes a thousand million. (The English billion is a thousand times bigger.) In these days of rising prices an astronomical unit of this magnitude is beginning to make sense in several spheres. With a thousand francs to the pound sterling, a French milliardaire is no better off than an old-fashioned British millionaire. An Irish-American billion is the number of seconds you have put behind you on your thirty-third birthday. If you wish to count the number of people on the earth, two and a half of these units will be enough. About five of them, as we shall see, will measure the age of the universe. The number of cells in your brain is represented by almost a dozen of them. But you need a gross or a dozen dozen if you want to tot up the stars in the Milky Way or in any other galaxy.

THE EXPANDING UNIVERSE. The Louvain mathematician, the Abbé Lemaître, who is a member of the Pontifical Academy of Science, has shown from a consideration of Einstein's theory of relativity that a universe of a certain size is not stable but must expand: all the things in it must rush away from one another with high velocity. The conclusion is of great interest because for some years it has been thought that the distant spiral nebulae are receding from one another at terrific speeds.

The speeds of recession have been deduced by an application of what is known as Doppler's principle. It is a matter of common knowledge that the warning whistle of an express train rises in pitch and then falls as the train approaches you and recedes. The same thing is observed with the noise from the klaxon of a passing motor-car. On the same principle, the light emitted by a nebula as it recedes from us appears redder than that emitted by an approaching body, colour in light corresponding to pitch in sound. By accurate measurement of the shades of colour, the astronomer with his spectroscope can discover whether a body is approaching us or rushing away, and also the speed of the motion.

Dr. Hubble (in 1924, a landmark in the history of astronomy), from his study of the question at the famous observatory of Mount Wilson in America, concluded that individual nebulæ are rushing away from the solar system at speeds proportional to their distances from us, as they should be if Canon Lemaître's inference from the theory of relativity is correct. If we trace the implied motion backwards, we find that all the nebulæ in the universe must have been crowded into the vicinity of the sun a few thousand million years ago. This suggests we live in an expanding universe which started to expand some few billions of years back.

ISOTOPES. All Eskimos are not the same weight. But when we begin to think of them, or of any other race of men with whom we are not familiar, we do not at first advert to this difference of weight, we think of the qualities which are the same for all the individuals of the race.

When chemists first studied, say, hydrogen, which is among the chemical elements what a particular race is among men, they thought all atoms of hydrogen had the same weight. Closer study revealed that the weights of hydrogen atoms vary: in any sample of hydrogen gas there is a small proportion of the atoms which are twice the weight of the others, and are therefore abnormally heavy. If we collect these heavy atoms together we get heavy hydrogen. (Most of us are familiar with the term " heavy water ". It owes its name to its constituents being rich in heavy hydrogen.) Heavy hydrogen atoms have the same chemical properties as ordinary hydrogen, just as heavy Eskimos have the same racial characteristics as their lighter compatriots. Heavy hydrogen and ordinary hydrogen are said to be *isotopes*. They occupy the same place (Greek, *isos-topos*) in the chemist's table of the chemical elements. *Isotopes* are varieties of elements which are distinguished by their atomic weights, but not by chemical qualities. The different kinds of lead, among them uranium-lead or radium G, actinium-lead, and thorium-lead, are isotopes.

RADIOACTIVITY AND DATING THE PAST. In radioactivity we see one of the dreams of the alchemists being realised. Radioactivity is natural alchemy. It is a spontaneous transmutation of a chemical element accompanied by energetic radiations, and hence the name. (it has nothing to do with wireless.) It is seen in action in the luminous dials of watches and clocks. It arises from instability in the heart of the atom leading to disintegration or explosion, with ejection of fragments of the nuclear mass or energy. The change goes on at precisely the same rate no matter what the external conditions are, or the age of the atom. Variations in pressure or temperature make no difference. The rate of transmutation never alters.

Radioactivity is due to the fact that the two heaviest chemical elements in nature, uranium and thorium, are not quite stable. Occasionally an atom of uranium breaks up and forms a new atom with different properties. In the instance we are considering, the process is very slow—it would take about four and a half billion years for half the uranium to transform. The new element is itself more unstable than uranium and changes spontaneously into still another radioactive element. So the process goes on stage by stage through a series of daughter elements until finally the original atom of uranium becomes an atom of lead. The lead is perfectly stable and the radioactive process is at an end. Radium is the best known member in the radioactive family just described. By way of illustration, it may suffice to say that the rate of transmutation is such that 5 per cent. of any given quantity of uranium changes into lead in 370 million years. It is easy to see that this allows us to date, for instance, a sample of rock containing uranium and uranium-lead.

Apart from the recently discovered neptunium series there are three great radioactive dynasties, and all three end in an isotope of lead. We have referred to two of these families implicitly in mentioning uranium. There are two kinds of uranium, known as uranium 238 and uranium 235. The former originates the radium family, and the latter is the founder of the actinium dynasty. Finally there is the thorium series of radioactive elements which begins with the heavy element, thorium 232, and after many transformations terminates likewise in lead. The rates of transformation have been measured carefully for all three families so that from the proportion of radio-lead and parent-substance present in a specimen, we can tell how long ago the radioactive element first appeared in that mineral or ore.

We are thus provided with natural clocks, radioactive clocks, we may call them, perfect time-keepers. They enable us to tell the time somewhat after the manner of an hour-glass, though of course the latter measures short intervals while the former are for long periods. In the ordinary hour-glass, sand falls from an upper compartment to a lower one: the longer the interval since it was set, the more sand you will find in the lower compartment and the less sand in the upper storey. If you take a mineral containing uranium, say, pitchblende, the uranium is turning into lead at a known rate. With the passage of time, the lead in a given ore increases and the uranium diminishes. Thus, if we measure the relative amounts of lead and uranium in a piece of rock, we can calculate what period has elapsed since the rock was formed or crystallised. A careful analysis by Holmes of the radio-active minerals in the crust of the earth (1946) led him to the value of three and a third billion years for the age of the earth's surface. This compares extremely well with the astronomers' figures of five billion years for the age of the universe. Let us proceed to consider more of their methods for estimating how old is the world.

STAR GROUPS AND THE AGE OF THE WORLD. Every one is familiar with the Pleiades, the group of stars in the constellation of the Bull (Taurus), which sparkle on a clear night like finest diamond dust. They form a cluster of some 200 stars, and like star-clusters constitute a rather lonely and isolated group in space. In a star-cluster the individual motions are as random as those of flies or midges in a swarm, and the star concentration varies from point to point in the group. In consequence the gravitational force on a star varies. The cumulative effect of variations over a long period of time causes stars to escape from the group, and thus leads to dispersal or " death " of the cluster. Accordingly we can calculate the " expectation of life " of a star cluster. From observation of a particular star group, we can say whether it is old or young or at its prime—in short, what is its age. There are many clusters similar in type to the Pleiades. Examination of them suggests that they have been in existence some three billion years.

A study of stars which are found grouped in pairs, the so-called binary or double stars, furnishes us with yet another estimate of the age of the universe. In this case the gravitational forces due to the neighbouring stars are different for the partners constituting the binary group. In the course of time the difference causes the partnership to be dissolved. An application of this idea leads to the conclusion that existing binary systems are about five billion years old.

COSMOGONY: LEMAITRE'S PRIMEVAL ATOM. A paper of Canon Lemaître's, published by the Pontifical Academy of Science and referring to the origin and development of the world, is of interest at this stage. Unlike some recent theories, which have gained notoriety, Canon Lemaître's speculation is both vivid and based on science. Lemaître pictures the universe at the moment of its birth as consisting in a " radio-active atom " of monster size. The primeval atom would be an immense " particle " containing the total mass of the universe. Being radioactive it would be unstable. At the instant of creation it breaks up. This is the beginning of space and time. The laws of thermodynamics now operate to produce a succession of disintegrations, with the formation of a gas consisting of high-energy particles, some of which are still bombarding the earth as cosmic rays. Unevenness in the density of the gas gives rise to the formation of the nebulæ. When two clouds of this primitive gas collide, a solar system may result.

The theory may throw light on the complex problems of cosmic radiation. There is good agreement between the figures calculated from it and the values observed by astronomer and astro-physicist. Its weaknesses are that it cannot explain the stable existence of electrified particles, and that it is based on the general theory of relativity, which is now under suspicion. Its strength is that it is still the least weak in the field.

PART TWO

THE CHURCH SPEAKS ON SCIENCE

I   *THE PAPAL ADDRESSES*

1. Timely documents.

    2. The august author.

        3. The Pontifical Academy.

1. *Timely Documents*

T RUTH should not oppose truth, yet it is quite easy to have a quarrel, and often a bitter one, between scientists and theologians, as we all know from the history of Western civilization. We also know that the conflicts were really between false science and theology, or between science and false theology, or—fiercest of all—between extremists on either side. There is no lack of partisans and false scholars today. But timely reminders of the basic truth, that truth never really contradicts truth but eventually confirms it, no matter the source, are to be found in the remarkable series of addresses delivered by the Holy Father on a variety of occasions to men of science.

It is not infrequently said that the Church is illiberal and obscurantist, the opponent of enquiry and enlightenment. How little substance there is in the charge will be seen by those who take the trouble to read the papal allocutions for themselves. Several of them present us with an astonishingly vivid and comprehensive picture of the latest, and sometimes obscure and highly technical, ideas and inventions of science. They clearly proceed from one who is well informed.

The documents are timely because at a moment when our culture appears to be on the verge of collapse, when there is unease in the minds of many that our civilization is crumbling to the dust, and that science or its daughter, technology, is chiefly to blame—here is one who never despairs, never drifts, never hesitates and never blames science or its offspring. Here is one who has an unclouded vision of the end and the means. Here is the witness of God, the depository of truth. In a disordered world that stumbles by the way, here is one whose words inspire confidence and impart sublime consolation. He reassures the timid as he says: Have faith, trust in your heavenly Father.

The timely publication of these documents would indeed seem to confirm the theory of some historians that outstanding occupants of the chair of Peter suit their times. When the Church was called on to civilize the barbarian, Gregory the Great appeared. At a crisis in the history of feudalism, Gregory VII was present to wear the tiara. Innocent III held the keys when spiritual rights were challenged by rampant nationalism. In more recent times, the great social Pontiffs shot shafts of light into a dark and troubled world. Now, when science and its applications seem to be on the point of going wrong so as to endanger humanity, appears the Pope who is a poet of science, a beacon amid the wilderness of the earth, a " pledge of certitude writ bold across the winding scroll of time", a man with both depth of intellect and sensibility, clearly a depository of the authority to teach.

These documents are not only for men of science, but for many others besides, for all those who have retained the common touch. First, they are so clearly directed to students that there is no need to embroider the statement. Also, they are useful for those, who, having read about " so many brilliant young scientists being Communist " feel that modern science leads somehow or other to atheism and dissolves the foundation of religion. (Such people have, of course, an erroneous idea of science. They are human in being misled, but their inference is quite illogical. As well say that if your grocer turns Communist, there is something about the grocery business that leads to a disbelief in the Creator.)

There are people who reach wrong and dangerous conclusions in a less illogical way. The papal allocutions are helpful to both these kinds of people. Then there are extremists both inside and outside the fold who will derive benefit from the documents. The one accuse the Church of being obscurantist, the others— ultra-conservative and die-hard elements within the Church itself— are the ground of the allegation.

The documents should also bring comfort to those who are timid by nature and somewhat fearful of the expansive and adventurous period we live in. Likewise, they should be helpful to such people as are always ready to suspect or condemn the new, not because it is unsound, but because it is strange. The Holy Father says to them: The world is young again, do not fear, have courage and exploit it. Finally, there are the few who always talk and occasionally act as if knowledge had ceased to grow since the thirteenth century. It may profit them to reflect how the Head of the Church can accept, for what they are worth, the most recent theories of cosmology and natural science.

With the growth of leisure and education, more people come to discuss the things that really matter. As the circle of discussion widens, more people are called upon to give a reason for the faith that is in them: they are called upon to confirm the belief handed down to them from the cradle—a belief by tradition—and turn it into a belief by conviction. The papal discourses represent a powerful modern means of confirming one's Faith, while they serve to keep one in touch with the mind of the Sovereign Pontiff regarding the events and problems of the day.

2. *The august author*

HIS HOLINESS POPE PIUS XII, the august author of these addresses, is not merely the head of the Church and a ruler deeply loved by his subjects (with an affection that in itself is an index to his greatness and a measure of his influence over his flock) but he has shown himself the champion of human liberties. An unwearied opponent of materialism in all its forms, he has always been alert to defend the dignity and the rights of man. When in 1939, the clouds of war hung black over a doomed world, he strove tirelessly to avert the tragedy. In the years of stress and sorrow that followed, he gave himself to the task of softening the afflictions of mankind; and he constantly reminded the nations of the principles on which a just and lasting peace could be built. Men of every creed and colour looked to him for guidance and listened for his voice.

In the farthest corners of the earth that voice has been heard as he broadcasts in Italian, English, French, German, Dutch, Spanish or Portuguese. To send his messages to the peoples of the world, he employs every modern means from the screen to radio. Providence has fitted him exceptionally well for his heavy burdens. His training and experience as a diplomat brought him to know at first hand the problems of many countries and races. His intellectual powers and learning developed a mind of wide understanding. A scholar and a diplomat by upbringing, he remains a simple fatherly priest; and all who are privileged to meet him, the farmer from Donegal as the oil magnate from Texas, the child and the grandparent, the girl and the boy, come away from an audience with an enduring memory of an unique experience.

His broad outlook, wide sympathies and interests, along with his remarkable spiritual and intellectual gifts, have earned for him an outstanding place in the scientific world of our time. No one doubts that through his addresses he has made a direct impact on world opinion and on the specialists who mould it. In his allocutions he strives to let each expert see his own special work and function in society as a lasting thread in the weaving of an abiding tapestry.

Surveying the existing state of knowledge within a particular field, he shows how it is related to a world scheme which derives from the Creator and is instinct with moral law; and he goes on to reveal how ethical principles apply to its activities and future development.

The range of subjects covered by this luminous personality is very striking, including as it does such disparate disciplines as psychiatry, genetics, the press, television, the cinema, sport, industry and history, not to speak of the whole integrated spectrum of the sciences, physical, moral and theological.

No less remarkable is the thoroughness with which he keeps in contact with the experts, and thus is always informed about the latest developments and the burning questions in diverse spheres.

The extent and degree in which Pope Pius XII makes use of allocutions represents a marked advance on the practice of his predecessors. Future historians are likely to stress the rôle played in the formation of world opinion by these addresses. A papal allocution is really a lecture delivered by the Pope personally on a subject of topical interest. While the three previous Popes of the twentieth century employed this medium from time to time, they did so only on rare occasions. Pope Pius XII has not only vastly increased the number of papal addresses delivered by a single individual, but he has created a new type in the allocution which develops a single theme, analyses its principles and applies them to recent developments in the sciences and to problems of a fast changing world. Each year sees him giving one after another expositions of moral themes, expositions which are invaluable as authoritative statements of the Church's teaching on pressing and complex questions.

3. *The Pontifical Academy of Science*

MANY of the addresses we publish were delivered to the Pontifical Academy. The Pontifical Academy of Science traces its origin to the earliest of all modern scientific academies, the *Academia dei Lincei,* founded in 1603. It took its name from the lynx to indicate the keenness of its study of nature. In the beginning it concentrated on physics and mathematics, and later it added philosophical pursuits. It thus promoted studies which were little cultivated at the commencement of the seventeenth century, and so offset the prevailing bias towards purely literary interests. In the end it devoted itself almost exclusively to the exact sciences, and became their chief centre in Italy. It was the forerunner and model of the great scientific academies of Paris, London (the Royal Society), St. Petersburgh, Berlin, and Dublin (the Royal Irish Academy).

The *Lincei* lapsed and was revived on several occasions. A turning point in its history occurred in 1847 when Pius IX resuscitated it under the title *Pontificia Accademia dei Nuovi Lincei* as a centre of study for physical science. In 1936, Pius XI reconstituted and revitalised it: he gave it its present name, *Pontificia Accademia delle Scienze* (literally, *Pontifical Academy of the Sciences*) along with a new constitution. Membership of the academy is restricted to seventy Fellows, who receive their appointment from the Holy Father himself. The academicians are of all nations and religions, and from amongst the most famous men of science the world over. The directors of the Vatican observatories are *ex officio* members. The academy publishes scientific papers, promotes discussions, and organizes researches, both theoretical and experimental. When we glance over the roll of members the thought strikes us that there is no other learned body in the world with so high a proportion of its Fellows who are Nobel laureates.

As an example of the level of scientific work done by the Pontifical Academy, we may refer to the stately *Spectral Atlas* of Gatterer and Junkes (1937-1951). This is a product of the astrophysical laboratory of the Vatican observatory. It has superseded all other spectral atlases, and it is more than likely that it will dominate the field for the next half century at least, as the standard publication on the subject of chemical identification of substances by means of spectra. Its power and detail so far surpass anything heretofore available that it has given the spectroscopist increased confidence in the infallibility of his almost magical or "wizard" methods. W. F. Meggers of the Bureau of Standards, Washington, says of the atlas: "It is truly a monumental publication, outstanding, superb, an indispensable reference work for all spectroscopic laboratories." These are big words coming as they do from a man of science in a very responsible position.

II *SCIENCE AND THE COSMOS*

1. The expanded universe.

2. Terrestrial physics.

3. Space flight.

1. *THE EXPANDED UNIVERSE.*

(*Discourse to Astronomers, September* 7, 1952.)

[The address of Pope Pius XII in September 1952 to the astronomers is an instance of the Sovereign Pontiff's gift for presenting the conclusions of modern science with lyrical eloquence. He illustrated his theme with vivid word-pictures of galaxies and light years and other impressive symbols of the infinite and eternal.

Persuasively he shows that ' the spirit of man which bold and unafraid confronts and conquers the unimaginable cosmic immensities' must be of a higher order than matter: for, as he points out, the human mind can reach up to the Divine Spirit, ' the breath of all '.

This argument should satisfy those, who, having learned about the physical immensity of the universe, immediately conclude that it reduces the status of man to insignificance. Man is physically insignificant, of course: but, belonging to a higher order than brute matter he transcends the physical world however enormous its stretch in space and extent in time. One should always keep in mind the great difference and veritable gulf there is between quantity and quality, even in these democratic times when we tend to abolish or ignore natural differences and hierarchies.

One is naturally impressed by quantity when there is enough of it—*e.g.,* the Niagara Falls, which, after all is only a lot of water falling down. It is natural to be struck by the tremendous impact of great massiveness whether appearing as momentum or stunning sound or any other material form. But while the mind of man has come to know much of the vast universe and its laws, no part of all that vastness or unmeasured energy of matter has any knowledge of itself or of man. (It is of course curious that we should be impressed, sometimes to the point of dizziness, by a lot of empty space; it is strange that our senses should reel because of—nothing).

In this allocution the Holy Father makes graceful reference to great astronomers of the past, including Copernicus and Galileo. His remarkable tribute to Copernicus and Galileo as founders of modern astronomy is an important *amende honorable* for events of three centuries ago. Hence, this discourse is an event of the first magnitude in the history of relations between the Church and science.

The discourse is further evidence of the Church's great interest in modern science; and its teaching shows with an astonishing depth of doctrine—theologic, philosophic and scientific—the perennial freshness of moderate realism, indicating how the rational movement of the creature to God (the *motus rationalis creaturae ad Deum* of St. Thomas), reinforced by the fresh successes of science, goes on with renewed vitality.

The address, a document of some 3,000 words, was delivered to a gathering of 650 astronomers on a Sunday. The Holy Father, speaking rapidly in French for 26 minutes spoke with much scientific detail on the advances of astronomical knowledge in the last half century. He referred to the spiritual ideas suggested by contemplation of the universe, and showed how they are exemplified in the latest work of the world's astronomers who have charted the undreamt of depths of space.

After the audience, four Russian delegates jo'ned the other astronomers in an inspection of the Vatican Observatory, led by the Director of the Observatory, the Irish Jesuit, Father Daniel O'Connell.

A commentary which followed the papal discourse, entitled *The ways of science,* by F. (Alessandrini) will be found in *l'Osservatore Romano,* September 12, 1952.

The address itself is in three sections which deal with 1. the cosmic panorama, 2. the human mind, and 3. the creative Spirit.]

THE COSMIC PANORAMA

1

THE NEW PICTURE OF THE WORLD

T HE presence of so many eminer ₁ astronomers from all over the world brings to Our mind, gentlemen, the picture of the universe that has resulted from your brilliant researches of the last half century. There are several reasons why We should be grateful to you, and not least because your study of the cosmos evokes in Us, as in yourselves, reflections of the highest order. They direct the mind to the Power That, surpassing all understanding, leaves the imprint of Its seal on all creation: ' The divine love that moves the sun and all the other stars '. (Dante: *Paradiso, XXXIII, 145.*)

2

COSMIC SPACE

W E are conscious of addressing an elite, better versed in this subject than We are; but We cannot restrain Ourselves from reviewing rapidly the fascinating progress made in astronomical science in recent years, since this progress suggests sublime and inspiring thoughts. In the first place, to-day we begin to appreciate the true meaning of what can be called cosmic space. Thanks to theoretical and practical investigations, science now holds in its hands a gigantic compass that daily widens its sweep and embrace of the far-flung universe. Your unceasing researches have thrust aside the barriers of distance and carried man's knowledge a thousand million light-years out into the immensity of the galactic spaces.

3

STELLAR DISTANCES

L AST century saw the first steps taken in this vast exploration when Bessel, Struve and Henderson measured stellar parallaxes. [Stellar parallax, the angle subtended at a star by the earth's orbit, permits us to calculate the star's distance.] They succeeded so well indeed that by the end of the century the distance of some 58 stars, distant 30 to 40 light years from our sun, had been determined with certainty.

4

THE CEPHEIDS

T HE year 1912 presided at the birth of a new method for searching out cosmic remoteness. In a certain type of star that is continually waxing and waning, the cepheids, Miss Levitt found a relation between the period of their variation and their brightness or magnitude. So, wherever in the heavens you saw a cepheid, from its variation in luminosity you could infer its absolute brightness: comparing the latter with the apparent brightness, you could easily calculate how far off the star is from us.

5

PROGRESS

Meanwhile, by making photographic emulsions more sensitive and by improving the telescope, scientists multiplied the power of the human eye many million-fold and enabled it to penetrate the cosmic mists to depths never before thought to exist.

6

STRUCTURE OF THE GALAXY

The next step (bringing us out beyond the nearer stars) was accomplished by the astronomer Shapeley. His classical researches on the distribution of globular clusters gave us a new conception of how the galactic system is constituted. The new idea was perfected by other developments, such as those relating to stellar motions and the absorption of light by obscuring matter in space. As a result, it is now certain that the Milky Way of the ancients, the inspiration of so many myths, is an immense assembly of about 100 billion stars—some bigger some smaller than our sun—shot through with great clouds of gas and cosmic dust. The whole system, too, obeys the law of universal gravitation, and rotates in a gigantic orbit around a point situated in the great star clouds of Sagittarius. Shaped somewhat like a huge magnifying glass, but alive with motion, it has a breadth of some 100,000 light-years and in the centre a thickness of perhaps 10,000 of the same units. As for us and our solar system, we are not, as was formerly thought, at the hub of this prodigious wheel of stars, but some 30,000 light-years off-centre; and though we rotate with a dizzy speed of some 150 miles a second, we take 225 million years to complete a full round.

7

GREAT TELESCOPES

With legitimate pride can the astronomers of our century boast that they have analysed the structure of the galaxy. To this great triumph succeeded another, bringing knowledge beyond the Milky Way, the home galaxy, out into the further depths of space among the external nebulae. We owe it to the great telescopes of Lick, Yerkes and Mount Wilson that this pioneer step was taken.

8

EXTERNAL NEBULAE

IN the years 1917-19, Ritchey found some *novae* in the Andromeda Nebula: the notion that they were stars belonging to extra-galactic nebulae, hundreds of thousands of light-years away, met at first with a cool reception among scientists. It was only when Hubble, with the aid of the 100-inch reflector of Mount Wilson succeeded in resolving the outer parts of the Andromeda Nebula into distinct stars and globular clusters, and in finding some cepheids, that opposition to the idea waned. Gradually it became certain that these, the spiral nebulae, are really vast stellar systems [or "island universes"] similar in make and size to our home galaxy, the Milky Way, but so far off that they appear to the eye to be no more than tiny wisps of luminous fog. In fact, the distance of our nearest neighbour outside the Milky Way, the Andromeda galaxy or nebula, is found to be 750,000 light-years, while the distance of the one in the Triangle is slightly greater.

9

SMALL NEBULAE

UNREMITTING in their efforts, the astronomers next considered those nebulae which appear to be smaller than the galaxies. Here, too, they were successful. By comparing apparent diameters and luminosities with those of the nearest nebulae, they succeeded in making estimates of positions.

10

HUMASON'S LAW

FINALLY, Humason's studies led to a new law, to the effect that rays of light from a nebula or galaxy are reddened in a way that depends on the distance of the nebula from us. This law permits us to say how far off a particular nebula is, provided it emits rays strong enough to furnish us with a measurable spectrum.

11

DISTRIBUTION OF NEBULAE

As a result of such studies, it was concluded that if one considered sufficiently vast regions of space, there was a uniform distribution of the external nebulae in all directions, with no sign of a fall-off in their number anywhere. Within the range of the Mount Wilson telescope, it was estimated there are some 100 million galaxies occupying a sphere a billion light-years in diameter, each galaxy or nebula consisting in an assembly of perhaps 100 billion stars similar to our sun.

12

SOLAR SYSTEM

After this rapid trip of the imagination through space, let us return to our tiny planet, the earth, which at times seems to us so vast and mighty, with the mass of its mountain chains, the boundless expanse of its ocean, the violence of its hurricanes, and the terror of its volcanic irruptions and seismic motions. And yet a ray of light can circle the earth in the seventh of a second; in a little more than a second, in the twinkling of an eye, it can reach our neighbour, the moon; in just over 8 minutes, it could arrive at the sun; and in $5\frac{1}{2}$ hours Pluto, the most distant planet of the solar system, could be touched by a beam of light from the earth.

13

GALACTIC DISTANCES

But the nearest stars, many of which on clear nights seem to be within reach of our fingers from the mountain tops, are seen by means of rays that set out on their journey a few years ago; while light from the hub of our home galaxy comes to us only after completing a voyage of 300 centuries. The light from the Andromeda Nebula which we now see left there 750,000 years ago; and the luminous images, barely discernible on photographic plates after long exposures in our most powerful modern apparatus, are photographs of galaxies that lie between 500 and 1,000 million light-years away.

14

THE FUTURE

W HAT figures, what dimensions, what magnitudes in space and time! And yet astronomical science is still far from having arrived at the end of its thrilling adventure. Who can say what further frontiers will be opened to us in the very near future by the work going on with the 200-inch telescope at Mount Palomar or in the rapidly-growing branch of radio astronomy.

15

MAN

H OW small man himself appears in this majestic expanse of space and time, apparently as insignificant as a microscopic piece of dust in the immensity of the universe. And yet!

THE PROBING MIND

16

THE HUMAN SPIRIT

T HE outstanding feature in the foregoing picture of the universe (the fruit of long and laborious enquiries, not of just a single individual, but of generations of scholars from every clime) is not the gigantic masses involved, nor their harmonious courses in space, but the marvel of the human mind which has succeeded in unveiling the vast panorama. Man is really a captive within the narrow confines of his own body, yet he has broken out beyond the barriers of the senses; and with the aid of his intelligence he has apprehended the universe in its vastness and complexity.

17

INGENIOUS APPARATUS

A WORK of prodigious effort, this scaling of the heavens, if one thinks how it began, conditioned as it was by the human senses which are generally imprisoned within their immediate layers of space and time. The spirit of man first broke down its prison walls by inventing and constructing ingenious apparatus to extend the capacity of the senses: the telescope to swallow up the enormity of space between the eye and the far-off stars (making the observer almost feel them); the photographic plate to receive and record faint beams of light from the farthest nebulae. The mind of man made use of the extended senses to know better the order of nature, inventing a thousand skilful ways to detect hidden and subtle phenomena. Thus, by adding up minute effects in constant operation, a perceptible total was obtained; or, again, by inventing instruments, like the photocell and the Wilson cloud-chamber, men were enabled to explore the most delicate happenings of radio-activity, cosmic radiation and other atomic processes. Pressing home his attack, the mind of man discovered the laws behind energy-exchanges; and so came to control forms of energy outside direct perception—such as electric waves and ultraviolet and infra-red radiations. He transformed them and made them amenable to the senses and to precise measurement.

18

BOLD AND UNAFRAID

THE mind of man interrogates nature in the laboratory, and deduces laws which are provisional and valid only within the limits of experiment. Not yet satisfied, the spirit of man experiments further, and extends the range of law beyond the domain of the laboratory by means of astro-physical observations. Knowledge of molecular or " band " spectra allows his insatiable spirit to venture into the thick atmosphere of the outer planets; and infer their composition, density and temperature. With the aid of spectroscopy, he lifts his gaze to the fixed stars and detects the chemical com-position and physical condition of their mysterious envelopes. He employs the modern theory of *quanta* to read the riddle of strange spectral lines long before they are reproduced in the laboratory. The interior of the sun itself does not escape his penetrating gaze; for he follows the dissociation of matter, and becomes, so to speak, an assistant at the nuclear processes that go on in the sun and compensate for the heat lost by radiation over countless ages. Bold and unafraid, the human spirit confronts and conquers even the cataclysm of a *nova* or *supernova*, measuring the gases as they explode and tracing their prodigious speeds to their source. He tracks the galaxies as they move through the heavens, infers what paths they have travelled in times past, and so becomes in a manner of speaking a spectator of the cosmic events that happened on the very morning of creation.

19—20

WHAT IS MAN?

WHAT thing is this, then, the spirit of man, microscopic man, physically lost in the ocean of the universe, daring to enquire from his puny senses, what is the shape of the boundless cosmos, what is its story? and finding answers to both questions.

There can be only one reply. It is this: the spirit of man belongs to a higher order than matter, even though the latter is immeasurable, immense, unbounded.

THE ENDURING CREATIVE SPIRIT

21

QUESTION

IT is natural to enquire: will the path of knowledge, so honourably laid bare by the curious spirit of man, remain open to him? Will he tread it tirelessly until he has found and solved the last problem of matter? Or, on the contrary, is the riddle of the universe so stupendous and so hidden that the human mind, succumbing to its own frailty, must fail to find the key?

22

REPLY

THE reply of those hardy spirits who have most studied the physical universe is modest and cautious. We are, they say, only at the beginning. There is still a long way to go, and it seems that the quest will be endless. It is quite unlikely that even the most gifted enquirer will succeed in recognising, (and much less in solving) all the mysteries locked up in the cosmos.

23

THE DIVINE SPIRIT

SUCH mysteries point to the existence of a Spirit of an infinitely high order, the Divine Spirit Who is the Creator of everything that exists, Who conserves it in being, and governs it. With supreme insight He knows and scrutinizes His own handiwork, to-day as

at the dawn of Creation: "*Spiritus Dei ferebatur super aquas*"—
And the spirit of God moved over the waters " (Genesis: 1. 2.).

24

HAPPY ENCOUNTER

HAPPY and sublime the meeting born of a creature's contemplation of the material universe—between the spirit of man and the Divine Creative Spirit.

25

TRULY DIVINE

SPIRIT truly divine, not a sort of world-soul (as imagined by the pantheists). The world of our experience is opposed to the latter idea, and reveals itself as a complex, in spite of a unity of action. Also, besides its undeniable beauty and harmony, it displays shortcomings which are inconsistent with divine fulness of Being.

26

CONTINUALLY PRESENT

DIVINE SPIRIT, distinct from the world; yet not outside the world, as if He has retired into disdainful solitude, abandoning creation to its fate (as theists would have it). On the contrary, He is continually present in the world as loving Creator, conserver, and all-powerful principle of order, to Whom the world is bound intimately, in being and in action; and on Whom the world by its very nature depends.

27

NO ABSENTEE GOD

GOD is no absentee in the world He omnipotently made. To the mind of the scientist, who knows how to find a meaning in things, the Divine Spirit reveals Himself. He reveals Himself, not as the cold cosmos but as the breath of goodness and love that pervades all and explains all. In a special way He reveals Himself in the human spirit made to His own image and likeness.

28

DIVINE LOVE

Hence it is that the Divine Spirit does not disdain to make man the constant object of His love and of His ineffable works, as when He redeems him through the mystery of His Incarnation.

29

NEW OUTLOOK

Thus, the new conception of the universe has rightly swept away the old notion that the earth and man constitute the centre of things. The new outlook on the physical world has reduced our planet to the insignificance of star dross, and has shrunk man to an atom on this speck of cosmic sludge, relegating both to a corner of the universe. But nothing in this expanded conception of the universe (in spite of what is sometimes claimed in discussing the mystery of the Incarnation) can cast doubt on the Creator's love for man; or on the omnipotence of Him Who is pure Spirit, and, as such, transcends matter, however immense it may be in terms of space, time, mass and energy.

30

WISH

And so, gentlemen, besides Our deep esteem for all the sciences, and for yours in particular, another motive of higher and more general level urges Us to formulate this wish: May the modern conception of astronomical science, the goal of so many great men in the past, like Copernicus, Galileo, Kepler, and Newton—contrive to bear fruit and promote fresh advances in celestial physics. And may the astronomers' vision of the universe, through friendly collaboration (of which the International Astronomical Union is a shining example) approach ever closer to completeness and perfection.

31

INVOCATION

And, in order that the enduring light of God may guide and illuminate your labours (whose aim is to trace His perfections and re-echo His harmonies), We invoke on all those present the grace of Heaven; in pledge of which, We call down on you Our Apostolic Blessing.

2. TERRESTRIAL PHYSICS

(*Address to Geophysicists, September 25, 1954*)

[In the morning of Friday, September 15, 1954, the Sovereign Pontiff graciously received in audience members and their families attending the Tenth General Assembly of the International Union of Geodesy and Geophysics (I.U.G.G.) organized by the National Council of Research.

The audience took place in the Swiss Hall where more than 900 persons of 50 different nationalities gathered to hear the papal address. The Union is made up of seven International Sections dealing with geodesy, seismology, meteorology, terrestrial magnetism and electricity, physical oceanography, vulcanology and hydrology. Plans for the coming geophysical year, 1957-58, were prepared and commented on at the sectional meetings.

The discourse traces the history and growth of the I.U.G.G., and refers to the importance of the forthcoming Geophysical Year.]

1

APPRECIATION

GENTLEMEN, it has gladdened Our heart to receive a request for an audience from the International Union of Geodesy and Geophysics on the occasion of its tenth General Assembly, and We rejoice that We are in a position to tell this impressive and learned gathering how deep is the interest which We Ourselves, as well as the Church at every available opportunity, take in the progress of scientific research. Indeed, the invitation you kindly extended to the Vatican City State to come and share your labours, shows that the world of science itself recognizes full well and appreciates the regard which the Church has for men's efforts to advance knowledge.

2

GEOPHYSICS

THE renown of the seven international bodies constituting your Union, the great number of delegates who have arrived in Rome, and the interesting subjects to be discussed at your meetings, all combine to mark your Congress as an event in the calendar of science. All of you are united under one head by the subject Geophysics, a science which demands that your various efforts be grouped together and organized on a world-scale. Specialization is the key-note of modern science, which tends more and more to restrict fields of enquiry so as to achieve higher precision and more trustworthy results. The branch of science which studies the earth, its shape and size, together with the atmosphere, the earth's crust, and the oceans, must needs possess a chain of observatories spread over the whole globe, where men of different tongues, cultures and countries, and perhaps inspired by different motives, may each explore a domain that is necessarily limited. It would be almost impossible to obtain an integrated view without some organization which could lay down broad lines of enquiry, undertake works of an international character outside the scope of private institutions, make suggestions for uniformity of procedures, and invite unattached observers to take part in the common efforts. It is for such reasons that your Union unites seven separate societies, namely, the international associations of geodesy, seismology, meteorology, terrestrial magnetism and electricity, oceanography, hydrology and vulcanology; and convenes and brings them together in this tenth General Assembly, at which there are also present the Special Committee organizing the Geophysical Year 1957-58, and the Fourth Commission of the International Society for the Study of Photograms. [Refined study of certain astronomical photographs.]

3

THE INTERNATIONAL UNION

IN a sense, the International Union of Geodesy and Geophysics is the culmination of a movement that has been going on for over twenty centuries, since geodesic measurements had their beginnings as far back as Eratosthenes (276-196 B.C.). The early workers, whose names and labours are enshrined in history, employed methods which seem crude beside those now in use. But it would be wrong to despise them or laugh at them, for they had the same incentives as you have today; they had a disinterested intellectual curiosity, they desired to make quantitative studies of specific phenomena, and they aimed to deduce general laws of natural happenings by the aid of reason.

4

THE DEGREE OF ARC: ITS HISTORY

BY extending the triangulation process of the surveyors so as to determine the distance between two places of given latitude, Snell led to an effective method for measuring lengths on the earth's surface. In a short time, his method was followed in England, France and Italy. Then in the 17th century, through the discovery of centrifugal force and the principle of universal gravitation, scientists ceased to regard the earth as a sphere, but rather as an ellipsoid. They tested the new idea, and succeeded in measuring the flattening of the poles, a measurement destined henceforth to be a major objective in geophysics. By 1670, improved telescopes fitted with micrometric attachments brought a ten-fold increase in the sensitivity of surveyors' methods and produced a corresponding increase in the precision obtainable in measuring angles. There ensued several determinations of the degree of arc on the earth's surface. It pleases Us to recall the Roman-Rimini degree, measured by the great scientist, Roger Boscovitch, at the command of Our Predecessor, Benedict XIV, the base chosen being along the Appian Way, near the tomb of Cecilia Metella. We recall also the degree measured by the French geophysicists towards the end of the 18th century, to fix the length of the metre. Profiting by these measurements, each European State set about surveying and mapping its territory in a truly scientific way.

5

THE GEOID

IN 1891, in order to collate the various European surveys and so achieve a more precise measure of the degree, there was founded the International Association of Geodesy, subsequently called the "Internationale Grad-messung" (the "International Degree-Measure"). Finally, after the 1914 war, the present body—the International Union of Geodesy and Geophysics—came into existence: it carries out extensive surveys, and so provides the precious figures needed for determining the shape and dimensions of the geoid [the ideal terrestrial ellipsoid used for reference purposes in geodesy]. It was on the occasion of your second General

Assembly, in 1924, that the parameters of the geoid were settled upon, and all geodesic services were asked to employ these values in their future calculations. In such manner, the road has been smoothed for geodesy to continue its march towards its perennial goal: namely, the ever more accurate determination of the size and shape of both the earth and the geoid.

6

HIGH VALUE OF GEOPHYSICS

I T is not feasible for Us to enter into the separate histories of the many new branches of terrestrial physics, whose distinguished representatives We have the honour to receive in audience; but, Gentlemen, be assured that We set a high value on each of your disciplines and appreciate its contribution to the circle of knowledge.

7

THE GEOPHYSICAL YEAR

T HE Geophysical Year 1957-58 merits a special mention. It is the third of its kind. The International Polar Years of 1883 and 1932-33 produced such a splendid harvest for science that experts have been stimulated to plan for this coming international year simultaneous observations over the whole globe, the Arctic and Antarctic regions being particularly provided for. The project is immense and it has little chance of success unless many countries come together and act in unison. It is to be hoped not only that the looked-for benefits will be in proportion to the vast expenditure of effort and funds, but also that this notable instance of collaboration and good will between nations will advance the cause of world peace.

8

EXHIBITION

T O help it onwards towards its goal, physical science has fortunately at its disposal observing and recording equipment of high precision and fidelity. Since good apparatus makes for speedy readings and accurate results, it is important for workers to know of the improvements constantly being achieved by the instrument-makers. So, in addition to the display of publications from various institutions and observatories, you have organized an exhibition of the most recent instruments available in geodesy and geo-physics.

9

TRIBUTE

Y ET, one should keep in mind that scientific progress, while owing much to the existence of national and international bodies as well as to improvements in measuring apparatus, depends more especially, not on machines or societies, but on such factors as human endeavour, and the personal initiative and persevering courage of the individual. Is it not touching, Gentlemen, to see with what steadfastness a scientist in a distant and lonely station, will, in the absence of competent replacement, remain at his post, day and night, for months or years, in order to ensure the proper working of the apparatus entrusted to his care? It is thanks to him that there is no gap in the records, and it is thanks to him that satisfactory data for statistical and comparative studies are col-lected. One must also refer to the explorer who with fortitude investigates harsh and almost inaccessible regions of the earth, braving cold and heat as well as isolation from his fellows and unforeseen dangers: he sometimes runs the risk of losing his life in campaigns demanding great self-denial and self-sacrifice, and a successful conclusion is often as much a tribute to his character and resoluteness as to his scientific ability.

10

FUNDAMENTAL QUESTION

A LL the same, however greatly endowed he may be with fine qualities of head and heart, the scientist is not worthy of the name who does not occasionally rise above his technical cares and his immediate problems to put to himself the basic question which gives a meaning to life.

11

THE ULTIMATE TRUTH

EVERY thoughtful mind has an inner urge to search out the principle that unifies all branches of knowledge. The finest thing in the world around us is not the wonderful harmony of the laws of Nature, but rather the power and force of the human intellect which is able to master the hardest problems and plumb the inmost secrets of the universe. The enquirer who halts at the first stage has a legitimate satisfaction, no doubt, but it is a deceptive one unless he goes on to embrace the wider perspective. For the mind of man, as talented as you please, is in itself and in its functions subject to the supreme Lawgiver, its Creator, God. Let the enquirer recognize that God the Creator is also the Truth without which there can be no consistence. It is his duty to serve Him, for science severed from the rest of life is not only futile but noxious. The man of science is first and foremost a man, face to face with his destiny: more than others he will have to render an account of the good or evil he may have done.

12

ENCOURAGEMENT

WHETHER you devote yourselves to pure or applied science, your efforts are terms in an infinite series of endeavours to help on humanity towards the goal laid down for it by its Author. Let each one with courage and integrity do the task that has fallen to his lot; let him work with the desire to serve the community generously in a useful and meritorious manner. Our mind follows you in your labours, gentlemen. We congratulate you and give voice to Our encouragement, while from Our heart We accord you, to you yourselves, to your families present in Rome or elsewhere, and to all dear to you, Our paternal Blessing.

3. *SPACE FLIGHT*

(*Address to Astronauts, September*, 1956)

[This address, which was delivered to members of the Astronautical Federation, outlines the rise and development of clubs interested in promoting devices to realize artificial satellites and ultimately space travel. The allocution shows clearly how the Holy Father is vividly aware of, and warmly sympathetic towards, even the most venturesome and apparently fantastic phase of modern life.

Truly, to borrow an expression from science, he is in sympathetic resonance with every human aspiration.]

1

ADMIRATION

ON the occasion of your gathering here in Rome this year for the seventh Congress of the International Astronautical Federation, you have desired Us to be in some way connected with your activities. We are happy to be associated with you, and We avail Ourselves of this opportunity to express Our admiration for your tireless labours. In the past fifty years you have taken one progressive step after another in a strange territory.

2

AMAZEMENT

TO be perfectly candid, the first time one hears of your aims and efforts, the natural reaction is a feeling of incredulity. For the word itself, ' astronautical ', conjures up fantastic journeys through space under conditions that must wreck the human organism venturing outside its native element. To many people, the very idea of space travel would suggest that it originates in an unrealistic mind, full of whim and fancy, and impatient of fact. Yet, by the beginning of the century, the theoretical principles of astronautics had received clear and logical consideration, and had been put on a sound footing. It was seen that by developing sufficient acceleration in a moving body, escape from the pull of gravity would be possible. It was further seen that the required power for this purpose could be produced from rockets. In a short time, one began to speculate on the feasibility of transporting human beings by such means.

3

ROCKET POWER

W HILE it was already something to have given utterance to
such ideas, it next became necessary to show how they could be
realized. Since rocket-power afforded the only method for achieving space flight, it was immediately clear that a host of obstacles,
technical and instrumental, would have to be overcome if great
altitudes and high speeds were to be attained. The experimental
phase began in the second quarter of the century, and by 1926 the
first liquid-fuel rocket had been launched in America.

4

SPACE FLIGHT

E UROPEAN enthusiasts were not idle. The *Verein für Raum-
schiffahrt* was founded when it became evident that astronauts must
combine their efforts to cope with the complexity of their undertaking. Other countries soon followed the lead given by the German group. In 1930, the American Interplanetary Society, later
called the American Rocket Society, was formed; and in a short
time it did much to popularize the idea of space flight and promote experimental investigation. The British Interplanetary
Society, founded in 1937, likewise lost no time in familiarizing its
members with astronautical problems and how to deal with them.

5

THE V-2

O THER and more powerful forces came into existence. The
threat of world war drew the attention of rulers to the new strategic
weapon, and the outbreak of hostilities imparted weight and seal
to research on guided missiles. The well-known ' V-2 ', first
launched in 1942, created a sensation and instituted a landmark
in the development of the liquid-fuel rocket. Happily, the return

of peace allowed the invention to be applied for scientific purposes, for example, to the investigation of the stratosphere. Thus, with the aid of rockets, we have been able to measure stratospheric pressures and densities and degree of ionization, as well as to make a more thorough study of solar and cosmic radiations.

6

INTERNATIONAL ORGANIZATION

WHILE rocket-power serves the purposes of pure research, such use is for you only a step on the road to the more ambitious goal of space travel. In 1944, the Gesellschaft für Weltraumforschung and the British Interplanetary Society proposed the formation of an International Astronautical Congress. At a meeting of this body held in Paris in 1950, a resolution was passed in favour of setting up an international organization to study and promote interplanetary flight.

7

WORLD CO-OPERATION

A SECOND congress, held in London in 1951, presided at the birth of the International Astronautical Federation and initiated some details of organization. This was really the first effective move to achieve world co-operation among specialists in astronautics. The Federation grew in numbers and influence year by year.

8

ARTIFICIAL SATELLITES

AT this congress, also, the question of projecting artificial satellites from the earth was considered—it was the main theme of the scientific discussions. The idea was canvassed in the years that followed. Consideration was given to the advantages such a project would have for astronautical science, for electronics and nuclear research, as well as for biology and cartography. The problem received clear formulation when in 1954 the special committee set up for the International Geophysical Year recommended that a small test satellite be constructed. Finally, on July 29, 1955, the United States announced it would launch such a satellite during the Geophysical Year.

9

DIFFICULTIES

Y OU have made it clear that the present Congress attaches special importance to this experiment. Besides the man-made satellite, many other rockets for exploring the upper atmosphere will be launched during the Geophysical Year. Such extensive collaboration at international level, along with the desire to carry out a task so rich in promise of beneficial results, must be inspiring. Of course, the difficulties confronting you are both numerous and formidable. Taken as you must meet them, one by one you hope to overcome them with the help of the powerful resources of science and modern technology. A precious aid will be the electronic computor which marvellously slashes the time required for elaborate computations.

10

INTERSTELLAR FLIGHT

O VER and above, you are mindful of the general problems raised by space travel. Indeed, as appears from the documents you have sent Us, some of you have actually worked out the theory of interstellar flight—the ultimate goal of astronautical endeavour.

11

MORAL ASPECTS

W ITHOUT entering into detail, We would ask you to remember that a project of this kind has intellectual and moral aspects that should not be ignored. It involves a definite conception of the world, of its meaning and destiny. Our Lord God, in placing an insatiable thirst for knowledge in the heart of man, put no bound to his attempts at conquest when He said "Subdue the earth". He has put the whole of creation before us, leaving it to the human mind to penetrate its mysteries, and so come to see ever more clearly the infinite greatness of the Creator.

12

REFLECTION

UP to recently, man has felt himself, so to speak, shut in on the earth. He has had to be content with the scraps of information that came to him out of the universe. It seems that now the possibility is being offered to him of removing the barrier and having access to new truths and new knowledge which God has spread in profusion throughout the world. Something more than intellectual curiosity or a spirit of adventure will be needed to sustain a task of such magnitude and lead it to fruition. Faced with this alluring invitation and opportunity to enlarge the scope of the human understanding, man ought to reflect and take stock: he ought to examine closely his knowledge of himself and of God so as to judge correctly the import of his actions and take his proper place in the scheme of things.

13

SENSE OF BROTHERHOOD

THIS common effort of men to effect a peaceful conquest of the universe should bring with it a sense of brotherhood and solidarity, thus instilling in us a deep conviction that all mankind constitute God's great family, and that all men are children of one and the same Father. But in order to grasp this truth and have it brought home to our minds, we must have respect for all kinds of truth, as we have respect for facts, for courage and for scientific research. The boldest ventures into space will only lead to divisions and contention if they are not accompanied by moral reflections and a spirit of altruism.

14

GOOD WISH

IT is Our sincere desire that the present Congress may serve to advance the aims of the Federation, and We should like to see its labours crowned with spiritual rewards no less than with scientific achievement.

15

BLESSING

CALLING down on your heads the protection and grace of God Who has created the universe for man and desires through it to make Himself known and loved, We impart to you, to your families, and to your collaborators Our Apostolic Blessing.

III *SCIENCE APPLIED AND MISAPPLIED*

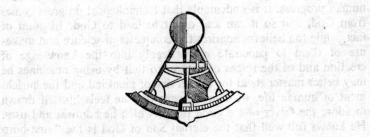

1. *The Technological Spirit*

[Extracted from the Papal message to the world, December 24,
                    1953.]

MANY people are dazzled by the passing splendour of human
achievements. Their vision goes no further than the bounds of
creation, and they seem incapable of raising their eyes to the
Creator Who is the beginning, the continuation and the final end
of all things.

TECHNOLOGICAL PROGRESS. These men whose spirit is in darkness We call upon to turn and gaze towards the great light
radiating from the manger, and We ask them to reflect on what it is
that is making them blind and insensible to things divine. Is it not
an excessive esteem for what is called progress in technology?
First imagined as a universal panacea, as it now advances to the
most daring conquests, triumphant technology has at length
imposed itself on many minds as the final end of life and appears
as a substitute for every ideal, religious and spiritual. Gradually
we begin to see that its extravagant exaltation has so blinded our
understanding, that some of us have become an example of those
whom the Book of Wisdom castigated in its time (Wisdom xiii, 1)
—persons incapable of learning from the visible world of Him Who
is, incapable of seeing the worker in His work. So today, there is
an eclipse of the supernatural, and in particular an eclipse of the
work of Redemption, which is above nature and was accomplished
by Jesus Christ.

TECHNOLOGY COMES FROM GOD AND OF ITSELF LEADS TO GOD.
Nevertheless, the above false consequence need not follow, nor is
Our present criticism to be understood as a condemnation of
technological progress in itself. The Church loves and favours
human progress. It is undeniable that technological progress comes
from God, and so it can and ought to lead to God. In point of
fact, while the believer admires the conquests of science and makes
use of them to penetrate more deeply into the knowledge of
creation and of the forces of nature, so that by using machines he
may better master them for the service of mankind and the enrich-
ment of human life, it often happens that he feels himself drawn
to adore the Giver of the good things which he admires and uses.
He knows full well that the eternal Son of God is the " first-born

of every creature, because in Him were created all the things in Heaven and on earth, both visible and invisible " (Col. i, 15, 16). Far then from any thought of disavowing the marvels of technology and its lawful use, the believer may find himself more eager to bow his knee before the Child come from Heaven. He may become more conscious of his debt to Him Who gives all things, and imparts the ability of mind to understand them. He may be more disposed to see the place of the works of technology in the chorus of the angels as expressed in the hymn of Bethlehem: " Glory to God in the highest " (Luke ii, 14). He will even find it natural to place beside the gold, frankincense and myrrh, offered by the Magi to the infant God, these modern conquests of technology: machines and numbers, laboratories and inventions, power and resources. Furthermore, to present such an offering is as though to offer to Him the work which He Himself once commanded to be done and which is now brought to realisation though it has not yet reached its term. " Dwell on the earth and bring it to subjection " (Gen. i, 28), said God to man as He handed creation over to him as a legacy for a time. What a long and hard road from then to the present day, when men can at last say that they have in some measure fulfilled the divine command!

PERFECTION OF MODERN TECHNOLOGY. Technology has in fact brought man's domination of the physical world to a pitch of perfection never known before. Modern mechanisation allows a mode of production that replaces and multiplies a hundredfold the human capacity for doing things. Today's machine is independent of organic assistance and it ensures that the utmost is made of resources. As We take in with a glance the results of this development, nature itself seems to nod approval and to beckon man on to further enquiry and exploitation. So it would appear that every investigation of natural forces, in which technology fulfils its function, is at the same time a search for new laws, and a discovery of the greatness, the wisdom, and the harmony of God. Looked at in this way, there is nothing to disapprove of or condemn in technology.

DANGER OF THE " TECHNOLOGICAL SPIRIT ". Nevertheless, it can hardly be denied that technology (which in our century has reached the height of its splendour and fruitfulness) is the occasion of grave spiritual dangers. For it gives to modern man, prostrate at its altar, a sense of self-sufficiency, and it satisfies his boundless thirst for knowledge and power. In its varied uses, in the robust confidence it inspires, in the extraordinary possibilities that it promises, modern technology opens up to man so vast a vision, that many confuse it with the infinite itself. In consequence, it is allowed an autonomy to which it has no right, and so it is translated in the minds of some into a false conception of life and of the world under the form and name of the technological spirit.

In what exactly does the spirit of technology consist? In this: that what is most highly prized in human life is the advantage that can be drawn from the forces and elements of nature. Whatever is technically possible in mechanical production takes precedence over all other forms of human activity, and in it is seen the perfection of earthly culture and happiness.

IT TENDS TO RESTRICT MAN'S GAZE TO MATERIAL THINGS. There is an underlying error in this distorted vision of the world. The huge panorama unfolded before the eyes of modern man, however extensive it may be, is yet but a partial projection of life. It merely expresses the relationship of life with matter. Accordingly, it is a deceitful panorama, for it ends by shutting up as in a prison those who are too intent on the power and immensity of technology. The view is wide indeed; nevertheless, it has limits, and in the long run it cannot be accepted by man's inmost eye as complete. For his vision, far from roaming over infinite reality as he anticipated (reality embraces more than the material), soon feels chafed by the barriers which matter necessarily sets up. From this arises the sore anguish of modern man who has lost width of vision because he has wilfully cloaked himself with a mantle of heavy darkness.

IT BLINDS HIM TO RELIGIOUS TRUTH. Much more serious is the spiritual damage done to the man who is intoxicated with the spirit of technology. This is the darkness to which the Evangelist St. John alludes, an opaque veil that impedes understanding of the mysteries of God which the Incarnate Word came to dispel.

Not that technology demands the denial of religious values. On the contrary, as We have said, logically it is led to acknowledge them. But the technological spirit puts man into a state of mind that is unfavourable for seeking, finding, and accepting truths of the supernatural order. The mind, which has let itself be led astray by the concept of life connoted by the technological spirit, remains uncomprehending, uninterested, and hence unseeing in the presence of the mysteries of the Christian faith, which are also God's works but are in kind totally different from technology. The remedy for the defect (consisting in a redoubled effort to arouse in the soul an interest in supernatural truths) is made ineffective right from the start by the technological spirit itself. This way of looking at life deprives men of their sense of values and blinds them to the remarkable unrest and superficiality of our time. Here we have a defect which even those who approve of technological progress must, unfortunately, recognize as one of its consequences.

Those who are saturated with the technological spirit find with difficulty the serenity and the inwardness needed for discovering the path that leads to the Son of God made man. They will even go so far as to belittle the Creator and His work, saying that human nature is a defective product, because the natural limitations of the human brain and other organs impede the fulfilment of technological plans and projects. Still less are they fit to see and value the deep mysteries of life and of the divine economy in which the union of the Eternal Word with human nature brings into play realities and marvels quite other than those of technology. Their thought is on different planes and follows other patterns, under the one-sided influence of the technological spirit which recognizes and reckons as real only what can be expressed in mathematical formulae and utilitarian calculations. They think that thus they are engaged in analysing reality, but their knowledge goes no deeper than the surface of things and is limited to a single aspect.

It is evident that whoever adopts the technological method as the sole way of seeking truth, must give up any idea of a deep insight into the bases of organic life. This is even more true of the realities of the spiritual life, the living realities of the individual person and of human society, since such cannot be resolved into quantitative relationships. How can one ask, of a mind so formed, assent and wonder in the presence of the awe-inspiring reality to which we have been lifted by Jesus Christ through His Incarnation and Redemption, through His Revelation and Grace?

Even leaving aside the religious blindness which comes from the technological spirit, a man who is possessed by it is arrested in his intellectual life. Yet it is precisely in that life that man is created to the image of God. God's intellect is infinitely comprehensive, whereas the technological spirit makes every effort to restrict in man the free expansion of his intelligence. The technologist, whether master or pupil, who would free himself from this limitation, needs a mental formation that entails depth of knowledge. Above all, he needs a religious education, for, by its nature and in spite of what some say, it is the thing most apt to safeguard thought from the evils of one-sidedness. The narrowness of his knowledge will then be broadened: creation will then appear before him in a light that reveals all its dimensions, especially when before the Crib he makes an effort to comprehend " in all its breadth and length and height and depth the love of Christ " (cf. Eph. iii, 18, 19). Otherwise, our technological era will go on to produce its monstrous masterpiece, namely, a man who is a giant in the forge of matter but a pigmy in the realm of the supernatural.

REPERCUSSIONS OF THE TECHNOLOGICAL SPIRIT. Such is not the only harm done by technological progress when it is conceived as an end in itself. No one can fail to see the dangers of a purely technical approach to things. The technological spirit regards life as consisting solely in technological values, and sees life as nothing more than an element or factor in technology. This attitude has its repercussion both on the way men now live and on their mutual relationships.

Consider for a moment how this spirit already operates among the people. See especially how it has changed the traditional conception of work, and what influence it brings to bear on legislation and administration. The people have welcomed (and rightly so) technological progress because it eases the burden of toil and increases production. Yet it must also be admitted that if such a way of thinking is not kept within bounds, the human and Christian concept of labour will necessarily suffer. With a distorted idea of life (and therefore of work) men come to consider leisure as an end in itself, instead of looking upon it as a time for reasonable recreation, bound up with the rhythm of an ordered and natural life. In the latter, rest and toil alternate in a single pattern and blend into unison. More evident still is the influence of the technological spirit applied to labour, when Sunday loses its uniqueness as the day devoted to the worship of God and to physical and spiritual rest for the individual and the family. It becomes, instead, merely one of the free days in the weekly round; days which can be different for each member of the family, according to the greater profit one hopes to derive from such a mechanical distribution of material and human energy. Likewise, professional work can become so dependent on, and subordinate to, the efficiency of the machine and to the efficiency of the tools of labour, that the worker is rapidly exhausted; one year's work at his trade uses up the same energy as was consumed in two or more years of normal life.

INFLUENCE ON PERSONAL DIGNITY AND ON WORLD ECONOMY. We refrain from showing at greater length how this system causes a waste of material resources and of higher sources of energy, among which man himself must be included. We might show how in the long run it would prove a costly burden on world economy. We must, however, call attention to the new form of materialism which the technological spirit introduces. It empties life of meaning, since it affects the spiritual and material values connected with man's nature and personal diginty. Wherever technology reigns supreme, there human society will be transformed into a colourless mass, into something impersonal and unenduring, contrary to the clear designs of nature and the Creator.

INFLUENCE ON THE FAMILY. Undoubtedly, large sections of mankind have not yet been touched by such a technological concept of life. But, it is to be feared that wherever technological progress penetrates without safeguards, there the aberrations referred to above will not be long in showing themselves. With particular anxiety We consider the danger threatening the family, which is the strongest unit and firmest principle of order in society. For the family is capable of inspiring in its members innumerable daily acts of service, binds them to the home and hearth with the bonds of affection, and awakens in each of them a love of the family traditions by working to produce and preserve what is good and useful. But wherever the technological notion of life penetrates, the family loses its personal bond of unity and is deprived of its warmth and stability. It remains united only in so far as mass production requires, and such production is more and more the object of man's endeavours. No longer is the family a joy to serve and a haven for souls. It is rather a desolate store which, according to circumstances, can be depended upon to supply either manpower for mass production, or consumers for the material goods that have been produced.

THE TECHNOLOGICAL CONCEPTION OF LIFE IS A PARTICULAR FORM OF MATERIALISM. The technological idea of life is therefore a particular form of materialism, inasmuch as it offers a mathematical formula and mere utility as if they were the final words on the question of existence. Because of this, modern progress seemingly aware of being lost and having gone astray, is showing uneasiness and anxiety. This is evident in those who engage in a feverish search for industrial methods ever more complicated, ever more hazardous. A world carried on in this way cannot be said to be illuminated by that light, nor animated by that life which the Word, the splendour of God's glory (Hebr. i, 3), by becoming man, came to give men.

GRAVITY OF THE PRESENT HOUR. As Our eyes scan the dark horizon in anxious search of some sure sign of approaching dawn, there meets them the sombre spectacle of a still unsettled Europe, where the materialism of which We have spoken, instead of solving, only serves to accentuate the prime problems, involving peace and order throughout the whole world.

Truth to tell, our continent, however, is not more seriously threatened than other regions of the world. Rather, We think that countries which have been slow to make use of the rapid progress of technology, are more exposed to the dangers indicated, and are more vitally disturbed in their moral and psychological equilibrium. The reason for this is that imported progress, which is not a steady growth but proceeds spasmodically, does not meet with any strong walls of resistance, of counterpoise, of adjustment, either in the maturity of individuals or in traditional culture.

Nevertheless, Our fears for Europe are augmented by the repeated disappointments which the sincere desire for peace and for a relaxation of tension a desire cherished by the nations has for years encountered. Our dread arises also from seeing a materialistic approach to the problem of peace. We are thinking particularly of those who judge that the question of peace is technological, persons who consider the lives of individuals and of nations exclusively from a technico-economical standpoint. The materialistic idea of life threatens to become the rule of conduct of certain busy peace agents, and the mainspring of their pacifist policy. They think that the secret of the solution lies in bringing material prosperity to all nations through increase in productivity and in the standard of living. A hundred years ago similar formula aroused the confidence of statesmen: "With free trade, lasting peace."

THE ROAD TO PEACE. Materialism, however, in any form, was never apt to establish peace. For peace is, above all, a state of mind, and only secondarily an equilibrium of non-mental forces. So it is foolish in principle to hope for peace from a system that corrupts the core of man and stifles his personal and spiritual life. Experience teaches the same lesson, for it shows that the more or less equal distribution of technical and economical resources between two parties causes reciprocal intimidation, from which results a peace based on fear, an uneasy peace, but not the peace which gives security for the future. We must repeat it again and again, and persuade those who are easily deceived by the mirage of tranquillity through an abundance of temporal goods, that secure and lasting peace is above all a question of spiritual unity and of moral dispositions. This peace demands, under pain of further catastrophes for mankind, that there be discarded an unwise autonomy of material forces (which today scarcely differ from war potential). The present state of affairs will not improve, unless all nations recognize the common spiritual goal of mankind: unless they help one another to attain it and, in consequence, unless they agree to eliminate the cause of division reigning among them in the discrepancy between the standard of living and the standard of production.

2. *Expedients of Propaganda*

(*Letter, July* 22, 1955)

[THE XDII Session of the "Semaines Sociales de France" began at Nancy on July 22, 1955, and the following letter was addressed to Mr. Charles Flory, President of the assembly, by His Excellency the Right Reverend Monsignor Angelo Dell'Acqua, Deputy of the Secretariate of State. It contains the directives of the Supreme Pontiff to the meeting which was to discuss the general theme: "Technical expedients of propaganda in contemporary civilization"].

MR. PRESIDENT:

Year by year those attending the "Social Weeks of France" take up and consider the great questions of the day, economic and social as well as political and cultural; and, squarely, without shirking difficulties, try to solve them in the light of Christian principles. This year, likewise, your association is to discuss an important topic, namely, the techniques of propaganda employed in contemporary civilization. It is the outstanding subject in the programme of the Social Week at Nancy, and the very mention of it conjures up various feelings and thoughts. While raising fair hopes, it at the same time causes anxiety; it affords a prospect of culture and unity for the human family, but it also brings before the mind a picture of enslaved peoples and the spectre of men with degraded consciences.

Without entering upon a discussion of the problem peculiar to the press, the cinema, sound broadcasting or television, you will study the aspects common to these different techniques, and your work will constitute one of the first organized researches by French Catholics on this subject. I am happy, therefore, on the eve of these meetings in Lorraine, which will be held under the high authority of the Bishop of Nancy, to voice the warm encouragement of the Holy Father and to convey his fatherly good wishes for the success of the gathering.

The kindly interest of His Holiness in your labours is no surprise to those who know the keenness with which he follows the rapid growth of propaganda techniques. One recalls among others the masterly discourse delivered by him during the Holy Year to Catholic journalists on the Christian idea of public opinion, as well as the directives he sent recently to the International Congress of the Catholic Press in Paris. On many occasions he has reminded the clergy and laity, parents and children of their duty in regard to the cinema; and again, only the other day, in an important discourse he showed his concern, as he expounded in a constructive manner the fundamental principles underlying a good film. Finally, in 1954, His Holiness, who himself makes use of wireless, and latterly of television, as a means of communicating with his children everywhere, spoke of the latter to the Italian episcopate in unambiguous terms. Thus the head of the Church, in close touch as he is with the advances of science in this domain as in so many others, has spoken out clearly and forcefully. He has asked Catholics to take an active part in the development of the techniques of propaganda, and also to guard them from the abuses to which they are liable. The lecturers of the Social Week at Nancy will appreciate the opportunity now offered of pondering on the advice and directives of the Holy Father.

That the constantly improving instruments of propaganda (whether designed to spread information, entertainment or culture) can be used for good or for evil has been often established, and it is not necessary to go over the evidence again. The rapid and marvellous discoveries of science, which are the source of the techniques, are good in themselves. They redound to the praise of the Creator.

Scientific progress is valuable of itself even though in the hands of man it may be used for conflicting purposes—either to make known the true, the good and the beautiful, or to serve to corrupt the individual and the group. Far from rejecting it, the Church readily acclaims such progress: She teaches her children to make good use of it for their own ends, and invites them to develop the marvellous possibilities thus placed at the service of mankind for the spread of God's word.

Nevertheless the development of techniques of propaganda in the XXth century has raised a new and very serious problem. It is not only the use good, bad or indifferent that man and society can make of the means now at their disposal; it is also a question of the power which the instrument, by escaping from the control of its author, tends to acquire over human beings. More dangerous even than the advance of mechanization in the last century (of which nevertheless it could be said that it ennobled material at the expense of the workman) the new processes of propaganda threaten man's spiritual independence. By the pressure of controlled information, by the insidious attraction of pictorial illustration, and by the compelling demands of skilful publicity and advertising, the combined action of the press, the cinema, wireless and television are now reaching the point where they can mould the conscience of the individual without his knowing it. Propaganda gradually encroaches upon his mind and determines modes of behaviour which are thought to be spontaneous. Present-day life offers, unfortunately, many examples of this danger: it weighs heavily upon the young, who are so easily influenced, it reaches even remote country villages, and the intellectual *élite*, though best armed against it, is by no means immune to its attack.

In one of his Christmas messages, the Holy Father denounced the technological spirit, which ruins the person in his interior life, restricts the free expansion of his intelligence, and reduces the society wherein it reigns to a characterless and confused mob (cp. p. 208, *Papal Message*). With much greater reason the excesses of technology are dangerous if they succeed in corrupting the art of propagating thought and thus have a profound influence on the psychology of the individual and of society. Acute observers have seen in this phenomenon signs of a renewal of human relationships and of traditional forms of civilization.

Further, the Holy Father invites you to discuss and try to determine what the attitude of man should be in the face of the increasing domination of the techniques of propaganda. How is he to survive the contemporary crisis of civilization?

The first task of Catholics, in this connection, is to note there are moral laws governing propaganda and to see that they prevail. Quite recently His Holiness issued a warning against the pretension of science and the arts to be emancipated from ethics because of their independent methods, and insisted on the principle that " the order willed by God embraces the whole of life, including all aspects of public life." (*Broadcast Message*, March, 23, 1952. AAS (1952) 277.) The processes of propaganda come under this law. Their morality depends not only on what is advocated but also on how it is advocated, i.e., the manner of presentation. This point is nowadays of capital importance.

It is not without reason that, in his analysis of the ideal film, His Holiness put in the first place respect for man and for the full exercise of his faculties, to the point that the cinema should tend "to strengthen and ennoble man and make him conscious of his dignity " (*Discourse, June* 24, 1955). Now, one fails in this respect if one employs propaganda to do violence to an imperfectly trained mind, to impose upon it a ready-made judgment, to arouse in it unhealthy passions, to abuse its confidence by an erroneous or tendentious presentation of facts. Have the millions of readers or listeners who, every morning, judge events from their newspaper or the wireless news-bulletin, any awareness that they are being restricted or, better still, educated in the free exercise of their personal judgment? To be moral, propaganda must seek to serve man, not to enslave or exploit him.

One should not overlook what may be called the professional obstacles in the way of achieving unblemished morality in propaganda. The difficulties peculiar to the trade itself are increased by financial constraints sometimes of a very powerful nature, a restrictive dependence on press-agencies whose objective presentation is not guaranteed, the weight of competition that is often unscrupulous, and also, it must be said, the pressure of the impatient demands of a public difficult to satisfy. These conditions of operation open up a wide field to the co-operative apostolate of Catholics, who could aim at purifying the practice of the professions concerned, of freeing them, as far as possible, from pernicious domination and of directing all technical resources to the genuine service of mankind.

Nevertheless, the public authorities are partly responsible for the moral issue now under consideration. " If the civil and moral inheritance of the people and their families is to be effectively guarded ", said the Holy Father, " it is right that the public authority should intervene, as far as is necessary, to prevent or check the exercise of dangerous influences " (*Discourse,* June 24, 1955). In her sphere the Church exercises this right by the censures which she reserves to herself, and also by the warnings which she issues through the moral assessments of films drawn up by commissions delegated for the purpose. The civil power is carrying out its function of promoting the common good when, while encouraging a lawful freedom of the press, it restrains the excesses of those who go so far as to use such media as the newspaper, wireless, the cinema or television for an attack on public morality, the propagation of dangerous errors, the spread of calumny, the defamation of persons, or to arouse popular passions.

Furthermore, the rapid advances in techniques have so affected social life, that it now seems necessary to devise a corporative plan, and enquire into the legislation best adapted to the wide range of problems recently raised. In this also, the principles of Catholic social teaching will point out a mean between exclusive

State control and an undue domination by private commercial bodies. Experience has brought to light disorders arising from an intolerable pressure generated at times by such groups. Yet, on the other hand, how many governments experience the temptation to abuse the direct or indirect control they have over the means of publicity to bring pressure to bear upon public opinion, to create it and direct it according to their pleasure? Not to mention the indescribable outrages committed against the masses which are peculiar to totalitarian régimes, it remains true that the authorities responsible for the common good must be the first to give an example of respect for opinion; that they should enlighten it without constraining it, that they should preserve it without smothering it, that they should listen to it without being its slave; in a word, that they should encourage its progressive education.

The truth, in fact, is that the surest protection against modern mass-publicity methods or, better, the best means of co-operating with their advance, consists in a sound education of public opinion. In an impressive discourse, the Holy Father, after declaring that the lack of public opinion in a country is a social disorder, urged Catholic journalists to foster it so as to give men, as he said, " their strict right to their own judgment and to their own convictions " (*Discourse*, February 17, 1950, AAS (1950), 256).

It is the natural tendency of the press, the cinema, wireless and television to favour mass reactions and to try and reduce public opinion to a blind and submissive uniformity of thought and judgment. Yet it is possible—and, indeed, imperative—that in the hands of men conscious of their responsibilities, these means of propaganda should become instruments to impart a sound training for the personality of the reader, the listener or the viewer. It is no exaggeration to say that the future of modern society and the stability of its inner life depend in large measure upon keeping a proportion between the power of publicity processes and the capacity for personal response of the citizens of the State. God grant that the citizens may become, in large numbers, such as the Holy Father would wish them to be: " men who know how to look at God, the world, and all events, great and small, in the light of the central principles of life and in the light of their own strong convictions ", men who build up " brick by brick, the solid wall against which the meaning of events strikes, and rebounds spontaneously " (*Ibid.*, p. 252).

All this points to a task that must engage the attention of active Catholics, in union with all men of goodwill who feel the urgency of safeguarding personal values in present-day society. The Holy Father is aware of the efforts already made to this end in your country, and readily supports them. Yet, as in every work of education, it is youth that must undertake the task. It is important, these days, that the critical sense of the young should be developed before they enter upon civic and social life. Not, of course, that you should flatter their taste for criticism—the young are only too prone to it—or encourage their spirit of independence. Rather, they should be taught how to live and think as men in a world where the methods for spreading news and ideas have attained a compelling power of persuasion. Ability to read a newspaper, to judge a film, to criticise a play; in a word, the power to preserve the mastery of one's judgment and emotions in the face of all that tends to strip manhood of its personality, has become a need of our times. Parents and teachers, then, must take care to protect the rising generation from the new illusions that threaten to seduce them. So will they effectively safeguard the future of society.

These considerations sufficiently stress the importance of the Social Week. His Holiness has no doubt of the attentive reception that will be accorded to the teaching of your staff of lecturers. He is pleased to learn of the active presence at Nancy of competent groups of those engaged in Catholic Action. He prays that all may receive a generous bounty of divine grace, and, in pledge of his goodwill towards a work so deserving, he grants you from his heart a fatherly Apostolic Blessing.

Please accept, Mr. President, the assurance of my devoted esteem.

(Signed) ANGELO DELL' ACQUA,
Surrogate.

3. *Concerning Television*

(*Exhortation to the Italian Episcopate, January* 1, 1954)

THE rapid strides which television has already made in many countries draws Our attention closer to this marvellous instrument which science and technology offer to mankind. It is bound to exert a profound influence for good or ill on public and private life.

In Italy, too, television is about to begin regular transmissions. The project already in hand of a vast network of stations throughout the country, foreshadows a remarkable development of this new and powerful means for expressing views and ideas and spreading news and culture.

No one can fail to recognize the importance of the event. It raises a whole series of delicate and urgent problems, and creates the necessity to be watchful and to organize in a new field.

It is a great comfort to Us, Venerable Brothers, to know that you share Our anxiety about the new mass-medium, and We thank you sincerely. Convinced, therefore, that the matter is weighty, We think the moment has come to address you concerning it, to exhort you to persevere in your praiseworthy efforts, so that your combined action, with this, Our guidance, may be timely and effective, and bear lasting and wholesome fruit.

Let Us fully acknowledge, Venerable Brothers, the worth of this splendid conquest of science, for it is another manifestation of the admirable greatness of God, " which He reveals to man in order to be honoured in His wonderful works " (Eccl. xxxviii, 6). So television, too, calls forth our gratitude, a duty which the Church never wearies of stressing to her children every day in the Holy Sacrifice of the Mass, telling them that " It is really worthy and just, right and salutary, always and everywhere to give thanks to God " for His gifts.

Such were Our thoughts, Venerable Brothers, when We were able to use this medium for the first time at Easter, 1949, to communicate with Our children. While Our voice reached them, their eyes could see Us personally. Our words, even then, were:

" We hope that television will play an important rôle in making truth ever clearer to minds sincerely seeking it."

Indeed, it is not difficult to realize the innumerable benefits of television, if it be used for man's betterment, as We confidently hope it will.

In recent times the cinema and sport, not to mention the dire necessities of daily work, have increasingly tended to keep members of the family away from home, and thus the natural blossoming of domestic life has been hindered. We must be glad, then, that television contributes, in effect, to restoring the balance, by providing the whole family with an opportunity for honest diversion together, away from bad company and dangerous places.

Neither may we be indifferent to the benefits which television can bring in social matters, in relation to culture, to popular education, to teaching in the schools, and in the international life of peoples. It will certainly help the nations to a greater mutual knowledge and understanding, and promote more cordial feelings and better co-operation.

Nevertheless, it is on the part which television will play in spreading the Gospel message, that We wish to dwell especially. In this respect, the consoling results which have accompanied the industry of Catholics, in countries where television has existed for some time, are known to Us. But who can foresee the nature and magnitude of the new fields opened to the Catholic apostolate, when television stations, established all over the world, will make possible a still closer view of the throbbing life of the Church? It is Our earnest hope that the spiritual links which bind the great Christian family will then be drawn still tighter, and that a greater knowledge, a deeper understanding, and a wider extension of God's reign on earth may follow the use of this marvellous instrument in spreading the luminous message of the Gospel in men's minds.

Such considerations, however, should not make one forget another aspect of the delicate and important question. If indeed television, when well regulated, can be an effective means for a sound, Christian education, it is also true that it is not free from dangers, because of the abuses and evils to which it can be perverted by human weakness and malice. These dangers are all the more grave as the power of suggestion possessed by this invention is greater, and its audience wider and more indiscriminate. The theatre and the cinema limit their plays to those who attend of their own free choice, whereas television is directed especially to family groups, made up of persons of every age, of both sexes, of different education and moral training. Into this circle it brings the newspaper, the chronicle of events and the drama. Like the radio, it can enter at any time, any home and any place, bringing not only sounds and words, but the vivid detail and action of pictures; which makes it more capable of stirring the emotions, especially of youth. In addition, television programmes are made up in great part of cinema films and stage productions, too few of which, as is known from experience, can fully satisfy the standards of Christian morality and the natural law. Finally, it should be noted that television finds its most avid and rapt devotees among children and adolescents, who, because of their very youth, are more apt to feel its fascination, and consciously or unconsciously, to translate into real life the images or phantasms they have absorbed from the lifelike pictures of the screen.

It is easy, therefore, to realize how television is intimately bound up with the education of youth and even the holiness of life in the home.

Now, when We think of the incalculable value of the family (which is the very cell of society) and reflect that within the home must be begun and carried out the physical as well as the spiritual development of the child—the precious hope of the Church and of the nation—We cannot fail to proclaim to all who have any position of responsibility in television, that their duties and responsibilities are most grave before God and society.

Public authorities, especially, have the duty of taking every precaution that the atmosphere of purity and reserve which should pervade the home, be in no way offended or disturbed; in this connection, the wisdom of the ancients, inspired by religious feeling, declared:

> " Let no improper word or sight cross the threshold of this home . . . for the child one must have the utmost reverence " (Juvenal, *Satires*, XIV, 44, 47).

We have constantly before Our mind the painful spectacle of the power for evil and moral ruin of cinema films. How then can We fail to be horrified at the thought that this poisoned atmosphere of materialism, of frivolity, of pleasure seeking, which too often is found in so many theatres, can by means of television be brought into the very sanctuary of the home? Really, one cannot imagine anything more fatal to the spiritual health of a country, than to rehearse before so many innocent souls, right within the family circle, those lurid scenes of forbidden pleasure, passion and evil, which can undermine and bring to lasting ruin a solid foundation of purity, goodness and healthy personal and social upbringing.

For these reasons, We think it timely to make the point that the normal vigilance that must be exercised by the authority responsible for public entertainment is not sufficient, in regard to television programmes, for securing broadcasts which are unobjectionable from the moral point of view. In television, where there is question of pictures that will penetrate into the sanctuary of the family, a different criterion of judgment is necessary. Hence the groundlessness, especially in this field, of the pretended rights claimed for absolute freedom in art. Equally baseless is recourse to the pretext that there must be freedom or unrestricted access to all sources of information and of thought, since here higher values are at stake and they must be safeguarded. Those who offend against them cannot escape the severe sanctions threatened by the Divine Saviour:

> "Woe to the world because of scandals . . . woe to that man by whom scandal cometh " (Matt. xviii, 7).

We cherish the earnest hope that the noble sense of responsibility of those who have authority in public life, will avail to forestall the deplorable occurrences which We have deprecated. In fact, We should like to hope that, as far as programmes of cinema or drama are concerned, sound standards will be forthcoming so that television will serve as a healthy recreation, and contribute in every way to the education and moral improvement of the people. But, if these desired measures are to achieve their full effect, all must be alert and on the watch.

To you, Venerable Brothers, We turn first of all, and to all the clergy, in this matter, making Our own the words of St. Paul to Timothy:

> "I charge thee, before God and Jesus Christ, who shall judge the living and the dead, by his coming and his kingdom: preach the word; be instant in season and out of season; reprove, entreat, rebuke in all patience and doctrine" (II Tim. iv, 1-2).

But no less urgently do We turn to the laity, whom We wish to see in ever greater numbers and in closed ranks around their Pastors, also in this holy crusade. Particularly, let those whom the Church, through Catholic Action, calls to work at the side of the Hierarchy, understand the need for timely effort, to make their presence felt. No one has the right to look idly on at the rapid developments in television, when he realizes the extremely powerful influence it undoubtedly can exercise on the national life, either in furthering good or in spreading evil. And when there are abuses it is not enough for Catholics to deplore them; the abuses should be brought to the notice of the public authorities in precise and documented particulars. Indeed, it must be admitted that one of the reasons, less noticed, perhaps, but none the less real, for the spread of so much immorality, is not the lack of regulations, but the lack of reaction or the weakness of reaction on the part of good people, who have not known how to make timely denunciation of violations against the laws of public morality.

However, your efforts would still be far from satisfying Our desires and Our hopes, if they should be restricted simply to setting up safeguards against evil, and did not result instead in a vigorous accomplishment of good. The goal We wish to point out to you is this, that television should be not only morally irreproachable, but it should also become an instrument of Christian education.

In this connection, the wise considerations which Our predecessor of happy memory, Pius XI, addressed to the motion picture industry, are to the point:

> "Just as the advances in art and science, as well as in technical perfection and industrial production, are true gifts of God, so also they must be directed to the glory of God and

the salvation of souls, and must contribute, in a practical way, to the spreading of the kingdom of God on earth, so that, as the Church bids us pray, we may profit by them in such a manner as not to lose the eternal good:

'Let us so employ the good things of the present as not to lose those of eternity'" (Encyclical *Vigilanti cura*).

In order to attain this aim, it is easy to understand how important is the preparation of the programmes to be televised. Certainly, in a country of such age-old and profound Catholic traditions as the Italian nation, We have every right to hope that Catholicism will have a place in television in proportion to the importance which it occupies in the national life.

To this end, We know well and praise highly the provisions already made, in the dioceses where there are transmitting stations, for designating one or more laymen or priests, whose duty it will be to take an interest in the preparation of programmes of a religious character. We hope, however, that this preparation, in order that it may prove more beneficial, may be developed and co-ordinated on a national scale, directed by a competent Central Office, which will have the function of imparting uniformity to the activity of individuals. The Office will profit by the fruitful experiences met with in various parts of the world. It would gather together observations and advice, especially of pastors of souls; and at the same time it could represent in the proper quarter the voice and even the mind of the Italian Episcopate. With an activity of this kind on the part of the Bishops (who interpret the desires of the saner part of the nation) as well as of the majority of those who use television, it certainly will be easier for those charged with the choice of programmes to resist criteria and ratings which are not wholly satisfactory, no matter from what source they may come. So also, projects that have to do with culture or organization or other matters, promoted in the various localities, could be centred in the above-mentioned Office. In the busy hum of modern life, which receives such a powerful impulse from the spirit of organization, it is necessary to proceed with unity and harmony; in this field especially, the union of Catholics constitutes their power.

At the same time, it is more than ever urgently necessary to form in the faithful a right conscience with regard to their Christian duty in the use of television: a conscience, namely, that knows how to forewarn against eventual dangers, and accepts the judgments of ecclesiastical authority on the morality of televised programmes. In the first place, parents and teachers should be enlightened, so that they may not have to weep, when it is too late, over the ruins of lost innocence in the souls of their charges. We could not, therefore, praise highly enough, as true apostles of good, all those who, as far as they can, will aid you in this beneficial undertaking.

The work which awaits you, Venerable Brothers—why hide the fact?—is vast and arduous. May you be encouraged, however, by the thought that you are fighting for the preservation of Christian morality in the midst of your flocks; and may your efforts be made fruitful by the Immaculate Virgin, to whose motherly protection, particularly during this year dedicated to her, We entrust the success of your holy undertaking. And just as the first steps of television here in Rome, maybe a favourable omen, contributed in rendering more solemn the inauguration of the Marian Year, so may its further development help in the succeeding triumphs of Jesus and Mary, making more radiant in the souls of all men of goodwill " the light which enlightens every man that comes into the world " (John i, 9), and bringing into every home and every gathering, wherever this instrument penetrates, " all that rings true, all that commands reverence, all that makes for right; all that is pure, all that is lovely ". The cause of civilization, of religion, and of peace will be benefited thereby, and " the God of peace will be with you " (Phil. iv, 8-9).

That Our hopes and Our prayer may find a generous response in the souls of all: to you, Venerable Brothers, to the faithful entrusted to your care, and to the conscientious and prudent men who work for television, with fatherly affection We impart the Apostolic Blessing.

4. *Address to Technicians*
(*To the first Congress of the International Federation of National Associations of Technicians, October* 9, 1953.)

We have no hesitation, gentlemen, in considering as an important event this first Congress of the International Federation of National Associations of Technicians, which brings you together in Rome, to discuss various questions concerning the general training of a technician, and also his social duties. The interest of the subject itself, as well as the outstanding qualifications of the members, gives every reason to hope that your work here will be fruitful in many ways. We are therefore happy to welcome you, and to tell you how closely Our solicitude coincides with your own.

The subjects you treat of during your sessions, in fact, touch closely upon one of Our constant preoccupations, for they impinge upon certain typical aspects of modern society, aspects which will affect its future. It is not Our intention to add new considerations to those which you have already authoritatively and competently developed; but rather to dwell on certain points which seem to Us worthy of particular attention, both because of themselves and their consequences.

The present session undeniably marks an epoch in the growth of Technicians' Associations and in their collaboration on an international level. No doubt there is already a tendency towards unification on the European plane, not only of political and economic, but also of professional and cultural activity. Nevertheless, your present motives, and the significance you attribute to your studies here, justify hopes of very fruitful results. Far from restricting yourselves to the problems relating to the technician's training and professional functions, you go on to consider the part he plays in the national economy, in public life, in the social structure of the nation, and even in the aggregate of the professions and in the framework of the whole of Europe. We are pleased to see with what sincerity and conviction these complex subjects have been undertaken by the various lecturers. Through careful study, you have been able to ascertain the state of each group in the different countries, what are its convictions and hopes, as well as its needs and manner of seeking remedies. Even if it be not possible to enter into these solutions in detail, even if such solutions do not depend entirely on you, at least you have come to know the general data of the situation and the steps to be taken for its improvement. You have, above all, enlivened the community spirit which unites you all, far above all local variations, in a basic agreement in which like tendencies and points of contact are far more numerous than differences. You know that you are a power in the professional field and even more so in the moral domain; such a power, unified and well directed, can in turn draw in its wake many individuals and groups who are still undecided, and without well-defined programmes of study and action. These will now feel the attraction of your movement and of the ideas which it promotes.

Those are the reasons why your Congress cannot fail to exercise a deep and enduring influence, at least if you are faithful to the motives which inspire your actions, keeping them in harmony with principles already established, and whose practical value you have learned to appreciate.

THE TECHNICIAN. More than once, your lecturers have regretfully indicated the paradoxical place apparently assigned to your profession. In fact, the technician occupies, without a doubt, an eminent position among those who have built up and who still develop the modern world. Present day civilization is marked by an extraordinary evolution of man's powers, his ability to observe phenomena, to manufacture tools for transforming matter, to build engines capable of conquering distances, and to establish speedy and secure means of exchange between various countries. All these results are the fruit of technical research, and of long, painstaking calculations. In spite, however, of his very extensive contribution, the technician becomes aware of the fact that the place allotted to him in the organization of society is inadequate, and that he rarely attains to positions of command. Though ever ready to collaborate in carrying out the projects of others, he can seldom have the direction of those economic, administrative, and political forces on which the progress of public institutions depends. You have pointed out several causes of this state of affairs; We shall turn Our attention to one of them, which seems to Us more significant than the reṣt.

It has been justly remarked how well the training of the technician, based on the study of mathematics and the experimental sciences, qualifies him to observe concrete realities, and evalue the forces and resources of nature, besides the possible means of using them. The building of machines and instruments demands the greatest precision, both in preliminary calculations and in making and assembling the various components. Even minute defects are quickly detected, and the reward of success or the punishment of failure is not long in coming. Constant practice of a profession entailing such keen demands accustoms the technician to concrete problems and to solutions which must be practical. This is the price of technical progress: an invention becomes outmoded as soon as a cheaper, more efficient process is discovered. Thus, through being continually employed in solving practical questions, the technician may yield to the temptation to neglect somewhat the scientific aspect of his career, and to prefer empirical procedure to scientific solutions. Since he is often obliged to bow to administrative and economic considerations, he runs the risk of having his intellectual view of problems shrink little by little. He may become too absorbed in a group of immediate interests, to the detriment of higher considerations which are, perhaps, less immediately useful, but more universal, and consequently of wider import. You are right, then, to insist on the need for a general scientific culture which will allow the technician to surpass the limits of his specialization and the overnarrow conditions of his ordinary occupations, in order to interest himself in collateral studies and profit by their resources. His creative power will thus be intensely stimulated, as well as his efficiency in his own line.

But one must have the courage to go even farther. If new techniques have greatly increased economic prosperity and extended well-being to wider classes of the population, this does not mean anything more than partial achievement. We might say it is a first phase, on which all the others must be based, but which cannot suffice of itself. History shows us that eras of discovery and invention generally give rise to a more or less profound crisis in institutions and manners. A kind of intellectual and spiritual revolt upsets men's minds and their way of life. A certain period is then needed before society can become once more stable, before it can master the new forces placed in its hands, and achieve a balanced growth of all branches of culture. In this connection, it may be said of the technician that he fulfils the task of precursor, that he is a forerunner in pursuit of new achievement and a continual extension of technical potentialities. This, however, is not enough. In order to influence, as he earnestly hopes, the age in which he lives, he must, as it were, look back and measure his action, not by the yardstick of progress in scientific and industrial equipment, but by that of the over-all development of mankind. There is no question here of denying the excellence of technique, the innumerable services it renders, and the intellectual and moral qualities demanded of its adherents. Still, it only satisfies one part of mankind's need. If it be exalted for its own sake apart from all the rest, it becomes harmful, and upsets the present order instead of really improving it.

In other words, if the technician aims at being a guide and pioneer of social progress, it is important that he should have, first of all, well thought-out views on the general aims of human society, and on the elements affecting its evolution. This does not mean that he should be an expert in juridical, economic and other sciences, though they may well afford him useful supplementary information: but that he must acquire for himself a sufficiently exact idea of those natural laws which govern man and rule his actions as an individual, and as a member of the various social groups, particularly of the family and of the nation. For such a purpose, it is not sufficient to consider man as he is to-day; for man must be explained by following his development through the ages which mark the progress of civilization. The meaning of individual elements is better seen by looking at them in the general scheme, into which they fit and, consequently, appear in their true perspective. For this indeed is the mark of true culture, which carefully distinguishes between the essential and the accessory, and sees in the general effect the rôle played by each of its components. We repeat, there is no question of becoming specialists in each of these fields. It is a case of keeping one's mind open to every form of the good and beautiful that has been created by men's initiative and devotedness in our own time or in the past; and of seeing in order of precedence the relations that bind them together.

THE CHURCH. Of such open-mindedness, the Church herself furnishes an example which is too seldom noticed. Under her charge, received twenty centuries ago, to educate man in religious and moral life, she has never neglected his other cares and needs, whether in regard to his material or legal condition, or his education, or family and civic organization. The Church has never shut herself up in a narrow conception of man, because she realizes the complexity of his nature, and knows the condition of man better than anyone else. Her social teaching is an exact reflection of her central position; it strives to obtain due respect for the various needs of man as a whole, in body and soul, as individual and member of society, child of man and son of God. That is why Christian principles are the surest guarantees of the normal happy evolution of humankind.

We have just now praised your efforts to fulfil your social obligations fully. Your post at the very heart of enterprises, as the link between the general management and the workman, demands of you, not only professional ability, but also an intensely human outlook. You have to direct free, intelligent persons. If you strive to keep before your eyes the vision of man as a comprehensive whole of which We have just spoken, you will have no difficulty in noting that the personal problems which affect your life and destiny, touching the most intimate depths of mind and heart, are just as acute, though perhaps less clearly so, for the humblest of your subordinates. You like to be entrusted with responsibility, to be left free to take initiative yourselves; you wish to see the purpose aimed at, and to check as you proceed, the steps which bring you nearer to it; you want to rise above the merely professional framework so as to develop your whole personality, and that is all quite good and lawful. It is likewise desirable that the most modest worker should gradually come to share in it. When he had been too long treated as a tool of production to be used at will, his material condition of life became a subject of anxiety. It is now realized that one cannot stop at partial emancipation. Since work is a necessity for every man, his professional occupations must not be allowed to interfere with his natural and spontaneous aspirations, but must respect his dignity. That is to say, it is not enough to see in him a producer of goods, but he must be treated as a human being, whose work should ennoble him and who is entitled to expect from his superior, even more than from his equals, true brotherly sympathy and understanding of his needs.

The technician, in order to increase his influence and the prestige of his profession, does not have to go outside his own rôle. In a world of ever expanding undertakings, splendid tasks await him, provided he is careful not to allow his field of vision to be narrowed down, or his generosity to wane. Towards that end, let his personal life be well-ordered; let him respect his own highest aspirations, both religious and moral; let selfish interests, the attachment to comfort or wealth, the pursuit of material gain or honour, never stain his ideal, that ideal which you have set before you, in all its nobility, during these days of study.

We wish you that courage and optimism which is never daunted by inevitable set-backs and difficulties. On your path you will encounter scepticism and misunderstandings; but your faith in the real destiny of mankind will remain unaffected. God, Who knows the depths of the heart, approves of your generous intentions. May He give you the strength to carry them out, and may He protect you, your families and your fellow-workers.

5. *Address on Radiology*

(The history and importance of medical radiology, April 5, 1954.)

GENTLEMEN, We are happy to welcome the group before Us to-day, impressive both in the number and quality of its members. Two great congresses, one national, the other international, have gathered you together this year in Rome for the discussion of a notable scientific programme. to which eminent authorities have brilliantly contributed with learned papers and valuable reports.

Radiology is growing more perfect every day, and now holds such a place in general medicine, that the latter can no longer ignore its potentialities, or do without its help. The time is past when it was considered by many a specialization of slight importance. It has won an acknowledged place in the curriculum, thanks to the many improvements, and, at times, revolutionary changes, that it has introduced into traditional conceptions. Thus, for example, as a result of radiological examination of the living subject, both anatomy and physiology have made noteworthy progress. It is now possible to diagnose rapidly and confidently congenital or acquired diseased states, hitherto distinguished only with difficulty or too late. The same means of observation has made it possible to show the interrelation and repercussion of localized abnormalities. This has led to the discovery of suitable treatment, it has promoted earlier medical attention, and afforded precious help to all branches of medicine.

Radiology is not merely diagnostic, it is also therapeutic. Its practical applications are numerous and beneficial, especially in the case of inflammations and in the domain, so vast, alas! of tumours of all kinds.

How many technical and scientific problems have been solved since 1895, date of the first discovery of Roentgen, down to the marvellous radiological apparatus of our own day which is capable of rendering sensible what is not so in itself. How amazing the intuitions and workings of the human mind which can proceed by hypothesis whenever the direct observation of phenomena is impossible; and constantly succeeds in inventing new means for detecting and measuring quantities outside the normal range of our senses. The apparently simple problem of how to eliminate heat in X-ray generators is complex and highly technical. The conditions to be fulfilled in order to obtain fidelity in a radioscopic or radiographic picture are hard to satisfy. Yet, astonishingly, a solution is found for all these problems in one and the same piece of apparatus, namely, the tube with revolving anticathode, now in general use.

If we turn to the question of the medical effects of X-rays on living matter, we are again faced with a number of problems, this time concerning the nature of the disturbance produced in a cell by bombardment with high-speed small particles. The electron microscope does not enlighten us about the immediate and remote consequences of lesions, nor does it tell us about the possibility of restoring healthy tissue that has been injured in the treatment of tumours. We know, however, that parasitic and pathological cells are much more sensitive to X-rays than natural and healthy cells. The whole radiotherapy of malignant tumours is based on this observation. Its use and its limits are defined by the knowledge of the dose which the surrounding tissue can bear. One must endeavour to focus on the tumour, whatever its depth, a dose of irradiation, sufficient to destroy it completely while sparing the healthy region. The vital problem is to determine in each case what the organism of the patient can stand at that precise moment. Time is often not available to await remote reactions, whilst on the other hand, the disease must be cut short before it spreads. One easily perceives how extensive is the knowledge required to use X-rays. Two of the themes of your Congress are devoted to it; others study new radiographic techniques relating to the kidneys or the physiotherapy of sport.

But the fruits of a Congress are far from being exhausted by the enumeration of official lectures and discussions. Personal relationships and meetings often comprise their most noteworthy attraction and benefit. Deep friendships, based on mutual respect, invite or nourish valuable collaboration. Who does not suspect what patience and devotion are required by the research-worker, so that he may not rest content with a vague approximation, that he may not exaggerate the results of his work, that he keep constantly and to the end that integrity without which there can be no scientific progress. A single individual may tire, or give up. If he be stimulated by the example and encouragement of faithful friends, there is more likelihood that he will bring his laborious efforts to a successful conclusion.

Radiology has given doctors a new instrument, fruit of a new and bold science, which as yet, perhaps, gives only a glimpse of the wealth of its future applications. The rosiest hopes seem justified, but such a prospect might beget among some a harmful reaction; over-confidence, and its almost automatic corollary, discouragement, when failure follows. Every technique applied to restoring or safeguarding health is necessarily limited. A process may heal one ailment and retard another, but it will never completely suppress sickness, pain and death. When the doctor ponders this truth, it is with difficulty that he avoids a feeling of bitterness, especially when he has placed his faith in the capacities of a new technique, one capable of splendid development. Yet he would err in giving in to this feeling and abandoning the struggle. For, in bringing to other specialists a valuable collaboration, in developing constantly the possibilities proper to your own field, you will succeed, perhaps, and we ardently desire it, gentlemen, in triumphing over ills hitherto judged incurable.

But there is still another objective, more worthy and more desirable. Do you not admire the sovereign ease with which Christ healed the sick brought to Him? A look, a gesture, a soothing word, and the sufferer went away, freed from his ailment, but, above all, purified in the depths of his soul and conscience. Should not you, too, desire to extend your action to the moral level? The meaning of a human destiny is not limited to the enjoyment or recovery of perishable health; it extends indefinitely, even to the unspeakable realities of the other world. How accept sickness and suffering? how win profit from them so as to purify the heart and esteem more correctly human values? These are the problems which present themselves to every sick person, and whose solution he consciously or unconsciously seeks. If you are willing to help all those who will have recourse to you seeking an answer to these questions, you will not have to fear any more the failure of your efforts in the medical sphere, nor even the misunderstanding and opposition of those who sponsor different methods from yours. Moved by a most sincere charity, you will perform an action which, besides its temporal efficacy, acquires eternal worth.

The scholar who devotes himself to labours such as yours does not serve an idol, but in trying to know the inexhaustible riches of physical and living nature, he discloses a little more every day the treasures placed by the Creator in His handiwork. He is like one who discovers new lands for the glory of his lord. And in the same measure he is also the benefactor of men, his brothers, at whose service he places immediately, or as soon as he can, the results of his research. Gentlemen, you occupy a noble rank amongst those who labour on behalf of humanity, and We readily congratulate you, and offer the encouragement you have a right to expect from Us. Nothing that touches the knowledge and happiness of humankind leaves Us indifferent, and We express the most cordial and sincere wishes for the success of your labours.

May Almighty God, by the Apostolic Blessing received from Our hand shower on you here present, on your families and on all those dear to you, the abundance of His graces and His most precious favours.

6. *Address to Farmer-Industrialists*

[In the Clementine Hall on the morning of May 30, 1952, the Sovereign Pontiff received in audience 800 members from 30 countries attending a meeting of the IX International Congress of Farmer-Industrialists in Rome. The Holy Father spoke to the gathering on the great benefits that accrue to mankind when scientists and technologists work together to promote the progress of the various industries connected with agriculture, especially those relating to the production and distribution of food for the world at large.]

CO-OPERATION. It is with great interest, gentlemen, that We follow the increasing co-operation between scientists and technicians that is promoted by the International Committee of Agricultural Industries. We believe humanity will benefit from this collaboration which forges fresh links to bind man to man, and nation to nation. Mutual dependence, as it grows and is consciously felt by one group after another, both seeks an exchange of knowledge and creates material resources. Today, when many on this earth have not enough food and great areas are exposed to recurrent famine, it is unthinkable that anyone should be so selfish as to keep to himself information that could bring succour to peoples, a succour to which they have a right as human beings. Hence We turn with joy to your beneficent activity which is calculated to advance scientific research and its practical application in agricultural industries.

PROGRESS. What splendid achievements have already been won by science to benefit these industries! Since the first International Congress of Applied Chemistry at Paris in 1894, and the meetings which gave birth to your International Committee, what progress has been made in various fields. For instance, we may mention the study of soils and of the means to preserve and enrich them; knowledge of vegetable nutrition; the manufacture and use of manures; genetics, initiated by the priest-scientist, Gregor Mendel, through his chromosome theory of heredity and leading to numerous improvements in the breeding and rearing of live stock; microbiology which has unveiled a whole world of the infinitely small that is intensely alive. In so far as feeding, reproduction and improvement in live stock are concerned, patient and methodic efforts have been crowned with success. We must refer also to the many additional techniques introduced by your Committee. On all sides, fresh scientific knowledge, fresh sources of energy and new machines have allowed us to transform completely the methods of production and make them more efficient.

FRESH NEEDS. But all this is still not enough, your report tells Us. There is need to make increasing amounts of raw materials available, we must process them to preserve them, we must improve their nutritive value and organize their transport in accord with consumers' wants, we must especially cater for the underprivileged. The basic needs are so great as to impose a kind of moral obligation. For this reason, your studies and aims have a special importance and they interest Us greatly. We ardently hope and wish that you meet with solid support in your attempts to bring science and technology closer together in order to promote the welfare of mankind in this essential matter of nutrition. The various sectional departments set up by the International Committee of Agricultural Industries, particularly those relating to publications and bibliography, are certainly to be encouraged.

SOLIDARITY. In your ninth Congress, you demonstrate once again how an increased acquaintance with nature and her laws provides scientists and technicians with more abundant means to serve their neighbour. The law of work, imposed by God on men so that they may rise to Him and come to conquer matter, also produces spiritual fruits in those conforming to it, and helps them to see in all things the plan—full of mystery and wisdom—of Divine Providence. It lets them understand in some degree the close solidarity that binds all individuals, making them depend on one another to the point that the material life of each is somehow the business of all. May consciousness of this solidarity spread and deepen. May every day see the co-ordination of studies, the professional skill of specialists, the generous disinterestedness of individuals and groups, increase and multiply the exchange and sharing of useful knowledge, experience and resources. To this end you have contributed nobly, gentlemen, and We pray God for you to contribute even more. With this intention We cordially give you and your families Our Apostolic Blessing.

7. Short Discourses, Excerpts and Summaries

[*References to the full texts will be found in the* SOURCES, *p.* 351]

(i) Scientists and a new world order.
(ii) Address to a university mission.
(iii) Address to the American Press.
(iv) Patron of telecommunications.
(v) Address on statistics.
(vi) Christians and nuclear weapons.
(vii) Address to surgeons.
(viii) Responsibilities of students.
(ix) Control of nuclear force.

(i) EXCERPT FROM THE ADDRESS TO THE ITALIAN SOCIETY FOR NATURAL SCIENCE

October 2, 1942.

SCIENTISTS AND A NEW WORLD ORDER. We are confident that the present generation of scientists will be able to employ their intellectual powers and their idealism so as to found a new world order of justice and of peace, with the collaboration of all decent men of every country; an order which will exclude everything extreme, evil and unjust; an order which the Italian people, too, with their deep faith, will be able to welcome with joy. The day on which scientists can take up the immense task of reconstruction in order to serve mankind will be a day of pure and lasting joy.

(ii) *ADDRESS TO A FRENCH UNIVERSITY MISSION*
April 16, 1949.

W E are deeply touched, dear sons and daughters, by your noble mission [to promote international understanding at the highest intellectual levels] and it gives Us much ground for hope. Among the griefs and anxieties which present events cause Us, one, and that not the least, is the disorder of men's minds and their wandering from truth. This brings fear of fresh disasters.

BANKERS OF GOD. You, professors and students of Universities, represent the intellectual *élite* of France. The word *élite* suggests high station, dignity, and above all, mission, duty, responsibility. It is often stated and quite rightly, that those who have material goods and fortune in plenty should look upon themselves as the " Bankers of God ", for to them He has entrusted His Providence for the poor. In the same way, and with all the more reason, those to whom the Father of Lights has given a larger measure of the gifts of understanding and knowledge, have received, as well as these gifts, the mission and duty to dispense them wisely to the many who might otherwise be deprived of them, or might in their folly be in danger of wasting them.

PASSION FOR GENERAL KNOWLEDGE. It is clear that the world today is possessed, more than ever, by a passion for knowledge. Things have changed very much from former times, from those ages wrongly described as primitive, when a man aimed at gaining all the skill he could in his craft and calling, and sought to acquire knowledge of the things needful for a worthy and honourable life on earth and for eternal salvation. Today, everyone would have, or claim to have, a general sort of knowledge which is, in fact, no more than a smattering of widely differing subjects; enough for an empty show of knowledge. Such curiosity, is it good or bad? Whichever it may be, it is a fact, and it has taken hold of the minds of many. It is dangerous, of course. It is also sad to see this absurd longing to throw oneself, without knowledge of essentials and due preparation, into every kind of intellectual pursuit, be it philosophy, social science, or economy, and natural science, chemical or biological. Yet, let Us say it again, there is the fact, that forces itself upon us, and so gives point to your mission and duty.

SUPERFICIAL KNOWLEDGE. This craze for seeming to know everything makes many a braggart (and there are far too many of them) ready to flatter and gratify his foolish ambition with little cost to himself, but great harm to his hearers, and to those who read his writings. There is only one remedy. To satisfy the need and respond to the call of men's minds, one must set before them wholesome food, such as may give them a distaste for heady beverages and tainted fare. The problem is yours and you must deal with it. There lies the beauty and glory of the part you have to play, that part to which you, distinguished teachers, devote a life of toil; and for which you, young students, attracted to such a life by generous and high ambition, are now preparing. Without doubt, it would be easy for you to dazzle the multitude with fine phrases, high sounding, yet empty. Such language would not convey the truth; nay, it would lead people to mistake sophism and falsehood for truth; so credulous are they.

TRUE LEARNING. Your task is far more strenuous; far less easy. It is to store the mind with knowledge, to examine knowledge already acquired, to extend it, to advance the bounds of your own particular sphere. In so doing you will take account of its contacts and interplay with other branches of knowledge. You will tailor knowledge to men's minds and sweeten it to their taste. Thus they may digest it, and, what is more, may find in it nourishment and enlightenment for their spirit.

FRENCH SCHOLARS. In France you have had a splendid roll of men, equally eminent in research and in writing, such as the mathematician Henri Poincaré, the entomologist Henri Fabre, the geologist Pierre Termier, and a host of others, not to mention men of the present day. This combination of scientific and literary worth is a most precious treasure. For what use is it to mankind to have knowledge hidden away in books with pages uncut or scanned only by the expert few? What is the good of a literature that is only an amusement, a pastime, a plaything for triflers, in which the mind acquires no new light, the will no new incentive, the heart no glow of desire, and life itself no new ideal? It would yield little better than a mirage, and point to a goal unworthy of human endeavour.

REVERENCE FOR TRUTH. There is yet another motive which should urge you to loyal and painstaking effort of tongue and pen.

We refer to the motive of dignity and reverence. For what is a scholar, a writer, a schoolmaster, a speaker, an educated man of whatever sort, if he be not in greater or less degree, in some way a man sent from God to bear witness of the light? (John i, 7-8). Keenly aware of the dignity wherewith God has endowed him, he should be full of reverence first and foremost for the Eternal Light, whose rays he has been bidden to shed over all creation. Along with this there must be reverence for knowledge itself, for truth. This he may never alter, maim, or discredit by stating as certain what is only theoretical or probable. Nor may he yield to the sway of passing passion, nor to fear or vainglory. Reverence he must always have, let Us add, for the kind of language needed if truth is to be clad in a robe of light and beauty. Your French tongue is indeed very well equipped for this task. It has often been called *clear, strong* and *satisfying*. Yet it is a tongue not easily handled; it can only be mastered and practised by dint of long and brave effort. As Joseph de Maistre said: " Like steel, the least tractable of metals, but one that takes the best polish when mastered by the craftsman, the French tongue, in the hand of an artist who can use it well, can show the most lasting and brilliant of forms."

You see now, dear sons and daughters, what makes Us so keenly interested in your work, and why We feel for you personally. Being of such mind and heart We pray most earnestly that the Word, the Eternal wisdom, and the Blessed Virgin, your Mother, the seat of Wisdom, may be your guide, and We bestow upon you Our most fatherly Apostolic Blessing.

(iii) *ADDRESS TO THE AMERICAN PRESS*
January 23, 1950.

THIS audience will not, perhaps, be listed in the strict category of Holy Year audiences. And yet while welcoming you right heartily to Our Vatican State, We cannot but reflect. There is a contribution you can make to the attainment of a coveted goal set for this Holy Year.

This year, We fondly hope and pray, will mark a great return of the whole world to God through Christ, and this return, if accomplished, is going to be made along the path of truth. When the individual man is recognized by all in his true stature as image of God gifted with inherent rights which no merely human power may violate. When the State is recognized in its true nature as divinely instituted to protect and defend its citizens, not to enslave them; when the whole world unites in open profession of the inescapable truth of its dependence on God, the universal Creator; then mankind will have made definite strides back to God, and, by the same token, back to prosperity, peace and security.

Truth needs a voice, and the most potent voice reaching the general public is the Press. Who does not know that a journalist can deliberately falsify facts, or by lifting them out of their context can distort their true meaning, or can suppress truth that in justice clamours to be heard? And the net result is that the masses are misled, human tragedy is incurred, and civil strife and even wars are engendered, simply because an unworthy member of your profession for one reason or another has been recreant to his grave responsibility to truth.

Yes, that responsibility before God and man is grave indeed. Never before, We dare say, has it been more exacting than today, when communication has become so easy and far-reaching, and the influence of the ordinary citizen is being felt more and more in the government of nations. That influence, in proportion to its weight, imposes a duty to acquaint oneself with the true facts; and that duty confers a right to be told the truth.

Your present journey through Europe is in search of the truth concerning certain international transactions, because you rightly rate this truth high in importance to your country, and, be it added, to the rest of the world.

We are, then, happy to use this occasion to compliment your profession on many priceless benefits it has brought to the great human family and to encourage each and every one of its members in the resolute purpose to serve with unyielding loyalty the cause of truth in charity. No society that rests on foundations of hypocrisy and falsehood is secure.

As we pray that the blessing of peace and security may descend on the world, We assure you, gentlemen, of Our most sincere good wishes for yourselves, for those who are near and dear to you, and for your large-hearted country.

(iv) *PROCLAMATION OF ST. GABRIEL ARCHANGEL AS PATRON OF TELECOMMUNICATIONS*

January 12, 1951.

TECHNICAL instruments [for telecommunications] it is true, can do a great deal of harm if they are not put to honest use. But clearly they can render precious service when properly employed. They may promote the brotherhood of man and advance human culture.

They may contribute to the spread of the liberal arts and of scientific research throughout the world. They may even serve to impart religious instruction, to carry the voice of the Supreme Pastor of souls from St. Peter's to the farthest corners of the earth, and unite in wondrous manner the hearts and minds and voices of the faithful everywhere in public prayer to the Divine Majesty.

Hence Holy Mother Church has never for a moment opposed the development of this widespread practice. Nay, she has been at pains to foster, stimulate and protect it in the fullest measure possible, and still continues to do so. She has, indeed, good reason to know that every truth, every new scientific discovery must be welcomed as one more trace, as it were, of the Divine Intelligence, and one more token of the power of God.

We believe it to be most opportune, therefore, that these marvellous professions, with their technical staffs and assistants, should enjoy the advantage of a heavenly blessing and a supernatural protection all their own.

We do now, by virtue of these Letters, appoint and proclaim St. Gabriel Archangel to be henceforth and forever the Heavenly Patron before God of the above professions and their members, with all of the liturgical honours and privileges to which principal Patrons of their type are entitled.

(v) *EXCERPTS FROM THE PAPAL ADDRESS ON STATISTICS*

September 10, 1953.

THE SCIENCES OF MAN. In our day, without ceasing to study nature, we are turning more and more towards the sciences of man, and, in particular, towards those which make a study of human society. But on account of the presence of personal and free causes, a great number of the significant facts escape appraisal by the methods of classical mathematics and seem to defy all attempts at rational and systematic explanation.

CONTRIBUTION OF STATISTICS. If you [statisticians] are making a great contribution to the study of present-day society, (whose rapid evolution calls for constant effort to get it into focus and to forecast its trends) the great world problems are also profiting from an application of your methods. In particular, one sees to-day whole populations suddenly introduced to civilization and culture, and clamouring for major improvements in their material and intellectual standards of living. The institutions, whose task it is to help them, stand in need of information that will enable them to make an exact study of the question. Here again statistics intervenes to direct such efforts and here also are you carrying on a work the importance of which We are pleased to emphasize.

STATISTICS AND TRUTH. There is one point on which We wish to insist again since, it might be said, it conditions all the rest of your work. Since statistics proposes to give the most exact information possible within the limits of its own methods, we expect from the person who practises it, besides the professional competence We mentioned above, a loyalty and sincerity which are above suspicion. It is useless to perfect methods if in the end they will serve only to deceive the public more efficiently. Now the temptation is great, when there is a strong desire to support a thesis, to twist results, to dissimulate the truth, or even (for financial gain or propaganda purposes) to falsify embarrassing or damaging figures. Be on your guard and do not give in to this temptation and thus degrade your profession. To the love of truth (which is the very soul of scientific work) unite rectitude of conscience, which rejects all compromise and which—to repeat it once more—is careful to distinguish between statistical data and the results deduced from them.

THE ACT OF KNOWING. Wise men of old were astonished, and rightly so, at the inventive power of the human mind. Still more in our day do we admire the perfecting and constant adaptation of the methods man uses in order to know the world in which he lives. Now the act of knowing consists essentially in bringing the multiplicity of reality to the unity of the mind, in discovering amid the complexity of data the permanent elements which explain them and account for their ordering and then in explaining by synthetic formulae the laws which govern reality. The domain of the natural sciences, wherein reigns the determinism of matter, offers a suitable field for such intellectual activity and lends itself readily to the formulation of precise laws.

(vi) *CHRISTIANS AND NUCLEAR WEAPONS*

[Summary of the Christmas message, December 24, 1955]

IN a message to the world on Christmas Eve, 1955, the Holy Father dealt with the problems occasioned by nuclear weapons. He began by reminding the world that though the tremendous advances of applied science had given mankind great mastery over natural forces and over sickness as well as over the beginning and conclusion of human life, such mastery could not transform the earth into paradise. But because we cannot expect a heaven on earth is not a reason for giving up the effort to better man's lot. At the same time, man's destiny should not be trusted to the tremendous industrial power of the age, for this power is in itself no real bulwark against Communism. Strangely enough, Communism also has a ' superstitious esteem' for technological progress, and thinks security can come from it.

Man's security, however, really rests on the moral order, which alone has a proper regard for true human values. Communism is against the principles of the natural law, and it is unacceptable as a social system in Christ's teaching. To say that Communism is the ' necessary moment' of evolution, directed by divine Providence, is to speak against the truth.

To control and to bring to an end the nuclear armaments race, there should be international discussions. There should be agreement:—

1. To give up experiments with atomic weapons.
2. To give up the use of atomic weapons.
3. To organize control of nuclear armaments.

The Holy Father pointed out in connection with the first proposal, that the effects of multiplying experiments would with the lapse of time increase the radio-active content of the atmosphere, and diffusion would cease to be under man's control. Thus there could arise conditions likely to be highly dangerous, especially through the biological effects that might ensue.

As for the second suggestion, the employment of atomic weapons could result in the generation of prodigious amounts of energy in a short time. Electro-magnetic radiations of fierce intensity could produce high temperatures and massive destruction. The natural consequences would be a pall of death on pulverised ruins, and the inconsolable weeping of humanity.

In connection with the third proposition, the Holy Father insisted that the solution lay not in planes but in control. A world-wide net-work of observation posts, staffed by experts of different countries, protected by solemn international pacts, and equipped with meteorological and seismic apparatus, could control many atomic stations, but not all.

These three precautionary measures should form the subject of an international agreement. This should be regarded as an obligation on the conscience of the nations and their leaders. It is morally binding to set about establishing a true and equal degree of security for all mankind. There is need for frank speech and plain talk, because the nations are accusing one another of a lack of sincerity, and because mutual suspicion is poisoning international discussions in a matter which is fundamental for the fate of the whole human race.

(vii) *ADDRESS TO SURGEONS*
May 24, 1956.

[This is an address of welcome to members of the International College of Surgeons from the United States who took part in a "Continental Clinical Cruise". The wording is as it was given in *L'Osservatore Romano*.]

CARE of the sick is a noble and an ennobling vocation, something more than a profession. It is your vocation, gentlemen, and that also explains your special interest in hospitals.

The French have a word for hospital, and We find it still in use in your New Orleans. It is Hôtel-Dieu. What a beautiful connotation is found in that name! Hôtel-Dieu! Now God is charity. And the spirit that breathes in the halls and wards of a hospital should be charity: a love for God present in His creatures, whose souls have been created to His own image and likeness. Hôtel-Dieu! The proffered hospitality of God. It was such charity that moved Our predecessor, Innocent III, back at the close of the twelfth century, to establish the hospital that is still only a stone's throw away from this Vatican City, Rome's hospital of the Holy Spirit, the Spirit of love; and a like charity has laid their foundations, erected and sustains similar hospitals throughout the world.

Vast improvements have been made since the twelfth century and, We are pleased to note, are constantly being made in the facilities and service, the organization, administration and staffing of the modern hospitals. That is as it should be. Let research and progress in nursing and medical technology continue to move forward. We would only ask that doctors and nurses again and again remind themselves that their patient has a task to perform in human society and, that done, a rendezvous to keep with his God. The charity that fills their own lives and gives surpassing nobility to their vocation will make that easier for them.

With these few words of encouragement, gentlemen, and expressing Our paternal joy in receiving you, We are very happy to impart the Apostolic Blessing.

(viii) *RESPONSIBILITIES OF STUDENTS*
[Excerpts from the address to students and professors of
STUDIUM URBIS, June 15, 1952]

B E conscious of your responsibilities as students, and perfect your understanding of religion. Settlement of the alleged conflict between religion and science presupposes in the first place that the techniques and processes of science are applied only in the domain proper to it, namely, the sense-world; secondly, that the existence of other realities besides those met with in natural science be recognized, more especially metaphysical realities which transcend the senses and depend on the laws common to every kind of being.

It is truly distressing that side by side with wonderful and rapid progress in natural knowledge, we meet with men of science who forget basic truths as fast as they discover new positive laws. Some, but not all. For, in every branch of science we find men who are at once masters of their subject and at the same time deeply religious. Up to the end of his life, the question of a wise Creator was present in the mind of Darwin. He tells us how such a thought " often comes over me with overwhelming force " and he speaks of his belief that the universe is not the work of chance. Today it is noticeable that there is among scientists a return to the idea of creation.

Difficulties about religion should not be considered in isolation, but should be viewed in their bearing on the whole problem of life. Particular questions have had or will have their answer—be sure of that, be confident, have faith, do not be sceptical and fail your rôle and vocation as students. Do not fall into the terrible graves of scepticism or agnosticism.

In modern times one law stands out and makes an impact on the student of history and sociology, namely—this, that life in keeping with the dignity of man is possible only when individuals as well as communities and public authorities recognize a personal God and conform to His order and Commandments. Peoples without God do not in the long run obey aught but terror. This law has always been true. But no generation has had to prove it by its own experience so tragically as ours.

(ix) *NUCLEAR ENERGY IN THE SERVICE OF MAN*
April, 1957.

R ECEIVING in private audience (on April 14) the Japanese Premier's envoy specially charged to protest against further nuclear tests, the Supreme Pontiff urged in a note, the text of which was published ten days later, that leaders everywhere should endeavour to employ nuclear energy in the service of man instead of wasting effort in an " exhausting and costly race towards death ".

His Holiness said:

" Our increasing control over natural forces of a terrifying intensity gives cause for the gravest anxiety. Nuclear arms are no longer restricted by the critical mass which checked the awful enough power of the first atomic bombs. Their power is now without theoretical limit, and this leads to a sinister competition between the opposing camps, each seeking to surpass the other because of the growing and alas! all too real terrors that inspire it.

" When natural catastrophes occur, we cannot but bow before the will of God. But if a catastrophe comes because of the perverse will of man and his unholy desire to dominate his fellows—such an act cannot but be condemned by every right-thinking person.

" Let, then, there be no longer a useless, nay, a criminal, expenditure of scientific activity that can achieve nothing except to prepare the way for a universal cataclysm, with immediate and remote consequences whose magnitude no man can foretell with certainty. Who, for instance, can say what will be the biological results of radio-active fall-out or strontium 90? Who can foresee the precise effects on living species?

" Instead, therefore, of an exhausting and costly race towards death, the leaders of all nations and creeds should pursue the noble aim of taming nuclear energy and harnessing it for the service of man. They must be constantly conscious that they are under a grave moral obligation to do so. Every group or organization, whether it be scientific or economic, industrial or political, should support with all its might each and every effort which studies to develop atomic force to the highest possible degree for the good of mankind."

In his Easter message to the world on April 21, the Holy Father appealed to mankind to give up evil practices as he contrasted the immense powers for good or ill of nuclear force in the new age.

He said:

" The human family resembles a poor sick body covered with sores and with no two parts of it on speaking terms. Individual classes and peoples are out of touch. When they do not ignore each other, they fill up with hate and seek to destroy one another.

" But the dark night in which the world is plunged shows signs of a coming dawn, of a new day made bright by a new and more resplendent sun. Nuclear energy has in fact already given birth to a new age. Homes are lighted by power drawn from fission. The day appears not far distant when cities will be illuminated and machines driven by energy won from the hearts of atoms. By means of electronics, automation is at work revolutionizing the efforts of both capital and labour, and endowing each with a new quality and a new skill. Faster than the daily sun in its journey across the sky a man can encircle the earth and swiftly move from place to place transporting his freights and cargoes. Missiles cleave into the depths of the heavens, and artificial satellites are about to startle space with their arrival.

" With the help of nuclear chemistry, agriculture promises to feed a vastly increased population of the globe. And biological research is all the time making progress in its battles with disease.

" None the less, all is dark night, the dark night of the soul, full of groaning and hope but still dark night, night fraught with 'dread and menace and liable to burst apart with thunderous roar and stab of lightning. For science, technology and organizing skill are now capable of bringing terror to the hearts of men rather than joy. It is seen that physical progress by itself alone cannot renew the world and make it be born again.

" Many begin to realize—and even admit—that the dark night of the world is upon us because Christ has been exiled from the family, from culture, from social life; because the people have risen up against Him; because they have crucified Him.

" There are souls full of courage who know that the death and burial of Christ took place because one of His friends denied and betrayed Him. They are aware that many of His friends fled in confusion before the threats and vituperations of His enemies. These zealous souls know that timely, co-operative action can change the face of the earth and bring back upon its brow a fresh gentle dew. A new renaissance is needed, a new Resurrection of Jesus for the twentieth century, a true resurrection triumphing over the dominion of death and black night. In individuals, the risen Christ must drive away the night of mortal sin with the dawn of grace regained. In families the dark night of indifference and cool-ness must give way to the sunshine of love. In workshops, in factories, among the nations, in lands pitted with suspicion and hatred, the night must grow bright as day so that strife will cease and be replaced by peace.

" Men in every nation and in every continent have been forced to live confused and frightened lives in a topsy-turvy world. Error in countless forms has enslaved the minds of men, for all their great gifts, and immoral behaviour of every kind has reached a stage of precocity, of imprudence and of universality that cannot but cause anguished concern to those who care for the fate of the world."

8. *Modern Tensions*

[*Extracted from the CHRISTMAS MESSAGE to the world, December 24, 1954*]

RIVER OF PEACE? "Behold I will bring upon her, as it were, a river of peace" (Is. 1xvi, 12). A river of peace upon the world! This is the desire which We have most constantly cherished in Our heart, for which We have most fervently prayed and worked, ever since the day when God in His goodness was pleased to entrust to Our humble Person the exalted and awe-inspiring Office of Common Father of all peoples, which is proper to the Vicar of Him to Whom all races are given for His inheritance (Psalm ii, 8). Alas! We had to experience during the first six years of Our Pontificate the indescribable bitterness of seeing nothing around Us but peoples in arms, carried away by the mad fury of mutual destruction.

We had hoped, and many others had hoped with Us, that once the rage of hatred and revenge had ceased, there would have dawned a period of secure peace. Instead, there continued that agonizing state of uneasiness and danger, which public opinion described as the "cold war", because it had little or nothing in common with true peace, and had much of the character of a truce that trembled at the slightest touch. According to many reports, the cold war has slowly been replaced by a period of decreased tension between the opposing parties, as if they were giving each other a breathing-space. Not without irony, this decreased tension has been called the "cold peace". In the political world, what is meant by "cold peace" if not the mere co-existence of peoples, based on fear of each other and on mutual disillusionment? Now it is clear that simple co-existence does not deserve the name of peace, peace to which Christian tradition (formed in the school of the serene minds of Augustine and Thomas Aquinas) applies the definition "tranquillity of order". Cold peace is only a provisional calm, whose duration depends on spasmodic fears and the varying estimates of present strength.

CO-EXISTENCE IN FEAR. It is the common impression that the principal foundation on which the present state of relative calm rests, is fear. Each of the groups, into which the human family is divided, tolerates the existence of the other because it does not want to perish. By thus avoiding the fatal step, the two groups do not live together; they co-exist. It is not a state of war, but neither is it peace. Each of the two groups drags on under fear of the other's military and economic power; in both of them there is grave apprehension of the catastrophic power of the latest weapons. Each follows with anxious attention the technical development of the other's armaments and the productive capacity of its economy, while it entrusts to its own propaganda the task of turning the other's fear to advantage by strengthening and extending its meaning.

The most obvious absurdity of the situation arising from such a wretched state of affairs is this: current political practice, while dreading war as the greatest of catastrophes, at the same time puts all its trust in war, as if it were the only expedient for subsistence and the only means of regulating international relations. In other words, we place our trust in that which we loathe above all other things.

On the other hand, the above-mentioned political practice has led many to revise the entire problem of peace and war, and has induced them to ask themselves if deliverance from war and the ensuring of peace ought not to be sought on higher and more humane levels than on that dominated by terror. So, there has been an increase in the number of those who rebel against the idea of having to be satisfied with mere co-existence and forced to live all the days of their lives in an atmosphere of withering fear. Hence they have come once more to consider the problem of peace and war as a fact involving a higher and Christian responsibility, a responsibility before God and the moral law. Undoubtedly, in this changed manner of approach to the problem there is the element of "fear", as a restraint against war and a stimulus to peace; but here fear is that wholesome fear of God—guarantor and vindicator of the moral law—and, therefore, as the Psalmist teaches (Ps. cx, 10), the beginning of wisdom.

Once the problem is lifted to this higher plane (which alone is worthy of rational creatures), there again appears the absurdity of the doctrine which held sway in the political schools of the last few decades; namely, that war is one of the admissable forms of irreconcilable dispute between two countries; and that war, therefore, is a fact without relation to moral responsibility. It is likewise clear how absurd is the principle—also long accepted—according to which the ruler, who declares war, would only be guilty of having made a political error, should the war be lost; and that he could in no case be accused of moral guilt for not having preserved the peace when he was able to do so.

Now, who can be astonished if peace and war prove to be closely linked with religious truths? Everything that is, is of God: the root of all evil consists precisely in separating things from their beginning and their end.

Hence, a pacifist effort (or propaganda set on foot by those who deny all belief in God)—if not undertaken as an artful expedient to obtain the tactical effect of creating excitement and confusion—is always very dubious and incapable of lessening or of eliminating the poignant sense of fear.

The present co-existence in fear has two alternatives before it. Either it will move higher towards a co-existence in the fear of God, and thence to true peaceful living-together, inspired and protected by the divine moral order; or else it will shrivel more and more into a frozen paralysis of international life, the grave dangers of which are even now foreseeable. In fact, prolonged restraint of the natural expansion of the life of peoples can ultimately lead them to that same desperate outlet that we wish to avoid: war.

Co-EXISTENCE IN ERROR. Although the "cold war" (and the same is true of the "cold peace") keeps the world in a noxious state of division, yet it does not, up to the present, prevent an intense rhythm of life from pulsating within. It is true that it is a life which is developing almost exclusively in the economic sphere. It is, however, undeniable that the science of economics, taking advantage of the swift progress of modern techniques, has, by feverish activity, attained surprising results, of such a nature as to foreshadow a profound transformation in the lives of peoples, even of those heretofore considered rather backward. Admiration, unquestionably, cannot be withheld for what it has done and what it promises to do. Nevertheless, economics, with its apparently unlimited ability to produce goods without number, and with the multiplicity of its relationships, exercises over many of our contemporaries a fascination beyond its capacity, and extends to fields extraneous to economics. The error of placing great trust in modern economics is again shared in common by the two camps into which the world is divided. In one of these, it is thought that, since man has given proof of such power as to create the marvellous technico-economical composite of which he boasts today, he will be able to free human life from all its privations and evils and so bring about a kind of self-redemption. On the other hand, the idea gains ground in the opposing camp that the solution of the problem of peace must be sought in economics, and particularly in a specific form thereof, that of free trade.

We have already had occasion to expose the shallowness of such teachings. About a century ago, the followers of the free commerce system expected wonderful things from it, and assigned it an almost magical power. One of its most ardent converts did not hesitate to compare the principle of free trade, in so far as its effects in the moral world are concerned, with the principle of gravity which rules the physical world. He attributed to it (among its proper effects) the drawing of men closer together; the elimination of antagonism based on race, faith, or language; and the unity of all human beings in unalterable peace (Cp. Richard Cobden, *Speeches on Questions of Public Policy*, London, Macmillan & Co., 1870; Vol. I, pp. 362-363).

The course of events has shown how deceitful is the illusion of entrusting peace to free commerce alone. Nor would the result be otherwise in the future if there were to persist that blind faith which confers on economics an imaginary mystic force. At present, moreover, there are lacking those foundations of fact which could in any way warrant the over-rosy hopes nourished today, as in the past, by the followers of this teaching. As a matter of fact, while, in one of the camps which co-exist in the cold peace, this highly vaunted economic freedom does not in reality yet exist, it is, in the other, completely rejected as an absurd principle. There is, between the two, a diametrical opposition in their ways of conceiving the very fundamentals of life—an opposition which cannot be reconciled by purely economic forces. Nay, more, if there are —as there actually are—relations of cause and effect between the moral world and the economic world, they must be so ordered that the primacy be assigned to the former; that is, it is the moral world, which authoritatively permeates with its spirit the social economy. Once this scale of values has been established and its actual exercise permitted, economics will, in so far as it is able, consolidate the moral world and confirm the spiritual postulates and the forces of peace.

A FALSE IDEA. There is a false idea, concrete and effective, which apparently holds together in cohesion, not without the aid of violence, the half of the world opposed to the traditions of a Christian Europe. This is the idea of an earthly paradise to be attained as soon as a determined form of social organization is realized. Though illusory, this idea has succeeded in creating, at least outwardly, a compact and hardy unity. It is accepted by the uninformed masses. It knows how to inspire its members to action and to make sacrifices willingly. The same idea, within the political framework which expresses it, gives to its directors a strong capacity for seduction, and to the adept the audacity to penetrate as a vanguard even into the ranks of the other side.

Europe (or Western civilization), on the other hand, still awaits the re-awakening of her own consciousness. Meanwhile, in what she stands for as wisdom and organization of associated living and as a cultural influence, she seems to be losing ground in not a few regions of the earth. True, such a retreat concerns the promoters of the nationalistic policy, who are forced to fall back before adversaries who have taken over the same methods and made them their own. Especially among some peoples until now considered colonial, the process of organic ripening towards an autonomous policy, which Europe should have guided with shrewdness and care, has rapidly turned into nationalistic outbreaks, greedy for power. It must be confessed that even these unforeseen outbursts, damaging to the prestige and the interested of Europe, are, at least in part, the fruit of her own bad example.

Does this mean only that Europe has momentarily lost her way? In any case, that which must remain, and without doubt will remain, is the genuine Europe, that is, that gathering together of all the spiritual and civil values which the West has accumulated, drawing from the riches of individual nations to dispense them to the whole world. Europe, following the dispositions of Divine Providence, will again be able to be the nursery and dispenser of those values, if she will know how to resume wisely her proper spiritual character and to repudiate the divinization of power. Just as in the past the well-springs of her strength and of her culture were eminently Christian, so now, too, will she have to impose on herself a return to God and to the Christian ideals, if she is to find again the basis and the bond of her unity and true greatness. And if these well-springs seem to be in part dried up, if this bond is threatened with rupture and the foundation of her unity is crumbling, the historical and present responsibility falls back upon each of the two groups who find themselves now facing each other in anguish and mutual fear.

CO-EXISTENCE IN TRUTH. Although it is a sad thing to note that the present rupture of the human race took place, in the beginning, between men who knew and adored the same Saviour, Jesus Christ, still there appears to Us to be a well-founded hope that, in His name, too, a bridge of peace may yet be built between the opposing shores, and the common bond, so sadly broken, be re-established.

There is, in fact, some hope that today's co-existence may bring mankind closer to peace. In order, however, that this expectation be realised, such co-existence must in some way be a co-existence in truth. Now a bridge cannot be built in truth between these two separate worlds unless it be founded on the human beings living in one and the other of these worlds, and not on their governmental or social systems. This is so because, while one of the two parties still strives in large measure, whether consciously or unconsciously, to preserve the natural law, the system prevailing in the other has completely abandoned this basis. A one-sided supernaturalism might refuse entirely to take such an attitude into consideration, alleging as reason that we live in a redeemed world and are therefore withdrawn from the natural order; or some might say that the collectivist character of that system ought to be recognized as an ' historical truth ', in the sense that it too corresponds to the will of God; but these are errors to which a Catholic can by no means submit.

The right road is quite different. In both camps there are millions in whom the imprint of Christ is preserved in a more or less active degree: they too, no less than faithful and fervent believers, should be called upon to collaborate towards a renewed basis of unity for the human race. It is true that, in one of the two camps, the voice of those who stand resolutely for the truth, for love and for the spirit, is forcibly suffocated by the public authorities, while, in the other, people suffer from excessive timidity in proclaiming aloud their worthy desires. It is, however, the duty of a policy of unification to encourage the former and make heard the sentiments of the latter. Particularly in that camp where it is not a crime to oppose error, statesmen should have greater confidence in themselves; they should give proof to others of firm courage in foiling the manœuvres of the obscure forces which are still trying to establish power-hegemonies. They should also show more active wisdom in preserving and swelling the ranks of men of goodwill, especially of believers in God, who everywhere adhere in great numbers to the cause of peace. It would certainly be an erroneous unification policy—if not actual treachery —to sacrifice in favour of nationalistic interests the racial minorities who are without the strength to defend their supreme possessions: their faith and their Christian culture. Whoever were to do this would not be worthy of confidence, nor would they be acting honourably if later, in cases where their own interests demanded it, they were to invoke religious values and respect for law.

There are many who volunteer to lay the bases of human unity. Since, however, these bases, this bridge, must be of a spiritual nature, those sceptics and cynics are certainly not qualified for the task who, in accordance with the doctrines of a more or less disguised materialism, reduce even the loftiest truths and the highest spiritual values to the level of physical reactions, or consider them to be mere ideologies. Nor are those fitted for the task who do not recognize absolute truths or admit moral obligations in the sphere of social life. These latter have already in the past, often unknowingly by their abuse of freedom and by their destructive and unreasonable criticism, prepared an atmosphere favourable to dictatorship and oppression. Now they push forward to obstruct the work of social and political pacification begun under Christian inspiration. In some places it happens not rarely that they raise their voices against those who, conscientiously, as Christians, take a rightful active interest in political problems and in public life in general. Now and then, likewise, they disparage the assuredness and strength Christians draw from the possession of absolute truth; and, on the contrary, they spread abroad the conviction that it is to modern man's honour (and redounds to the credit of education) that he should have no determined ideas or tendencies, nor be bound to any spiritual world. Meanwhile, they forget that it was precisely from these principles that the present confusion and disorder came, nor will they remember that it was those very Christian forces they now oppose that succeeded in restoring, in many countries, the freedom which they themselves had dissipated. Certainly it is not upon such men that the common spiritual foundation can be laid and the bridge of truth built. Indeed, it may well be expected that, as occasion demands, they will not find it at all unseemly to be partial to the false system of the other side, preparing themselves even to be overcome by it in case it were momentarily to triumph.

In awaiting, therefore (with confidence in the divine mercy) that the spiritual and Christian bridge, already in some way existing between the two shores, take on a greater and more effective consistency, We would exhort primarily the Christians of the nations, where the divine gift of peace is still enjoyed, to do everything possible to hasten the hour of its universal re-establishment. Let these convince themselves, above all, that the possession of truth, if it were to remain closed within themselves, almost as if it were an object of their contemplation for deriving therefrom spiritual pleasure, would not be of service to the cause of peace. The truth must be lived, communicated, and applied to all phases of life. Also truth, and particularly Christian truth, is a talent that God places in the hands of His servants in order that with all that they undertake, it may bear fruit in works for the common good.

9. *Address to the Governing Body of the International Labour Office*

[*Delivered at Castel Gandolfo, November 19, 1954.*]

ALTHOUGH We have frequently had an opportunity this year of meeting representatives of various occupational associations and of informing each of them of Our interest and solicitude, it gives Us particular pleasure to receive the delegates of the INTERNATIONAL LABOUR ORGANIZATION, which truly represents the great mass of workers with their cares, their troubles and, above all, their desire for a better and a nobler world that is attentive to justice.

Over the past 30 years and more you have patiently and untiringly built up an achievement of which you can justly be proud. Not only have you contributed to the progress of social legislation in different countries but, above all, you have united Governments, employers and workers in courageous and successful collaboration. You have led them to cast out passion and bitterness from their demands, and accept with grace inevitable developments. They have learned to listen to each other's arguments calmly, weigh the facts of an extremely complex problem and jointly propose the necessary solutions. You have thus created a kind of international forum, a clearing house where essential information and useful ideas are collected, tested and published. After long preparation and unremitting scrutiny and discussion, the General Conference adopts Conventions which, though they do not possess legal force in the member countries, must be discussed by them and may after ratification become real international treaties.

In order to appreciate the magnitude of the task that has been accomplished, one has only to compare the state of labour legislation today with what it was at the outbreak of the First World War. Even during the last century, the need was felt for a co-ordinating body to unite the workers' efforts in their struggle against inhuman conditions. There was a realization that social safeguards and restrictions would involve economic burdens and weight the scales against those countries that were willing to adopt them.

Our predecessor, Leo XIII, had a clear perception of the great importance of international collaboration in labour questions. As early as 1890, one year before the publication of the Encyclical *Rerum Novarum,* he wrote, in connection with the international conference about to meet in Berlin to seek means of improving the conditions of the working classes, that it responded to one of his "dearest wishes", and he added: "Conformity of views and legislation, at least to the extent permitted by differing conditions in places and countries, will contribute greatly to the advance towards a just solution of the question." A little later, in 1893, he approved the proposal to call a Congress of workers' delegates without distinction of nationality or political opinion.

In 1900 the International Association for Labour Legislation was formed, but the war soon interrupted its work. However, this was only a private venture. More solid achievements could be expected of an institution that was officially recognized by Governments. This unanimous desire finally bore fruit in 1919, and the INTERNATIONAL LABOUR ORGANIZATION has, ever since, increasingly fulfilled the expectations of the workers and of all those who have the establishment of justice at heart.

Both through its central organs—the General Conference, the Governing Body, the International Labour Office—and its more specialized bodies—the Regional Conferences and the Industrial Committees—the INTERNATIONAL LABOUR ORGANIZATION has effectively supported trade unions in their efforts to improve the conditions of the workers. While the International Labour Charter aimed above all at the suppression of abuses and laid down your main objectives at the time of the foundation of the Organization, the Declaration of Philadelphia of 1944 was designed to adapt these objectives to new circumstances. The struggle between the wars had brought a clearer awareness of the need for positive action and had led to the first steps in this direction. The limitation of hours of work, the regulation of the employment of women and young workers, the protection against illness, unemployment and accidents called for measures forming an organic whole, a need which is widely considered to be met by schemes for social security and full employment. Among all the fields in which your efforts are deployed today, particular attention must be drawn to the relationship between employers and workers, which is one of the most delicate points in the evolution of modern society. The INTERNATIONAL LABOUR ORGANIZATION has already concerned itself with collective bargaining, conciliation and arbitration, and collaboration between employers and workers at the level of the undertaking. At the present time, the human factor, whose importance was neglected for too long—though not however by Catholic social doctrine—is attracting the attention of sociologists and We know that you intend to make it one of your foremost concerns.

The effectiveness and authority of your organization largely result from its respect for the lofty ideals which must inspire all those who strive for a civilization that gives full scope to the rightful aspirations of the workers. The INTERNATIONAL LABOUR ORGANIZATION has not tried to represent one social class alone, or to become the vehicle of any single trend. It welcomes whatever is constructive, whatever meets the real needs of a balanced society and that is why Our predecessor, Pius XI, did not hesitate to draw attention to the remarkable resemblance between the principles set forth in the Labour Charter and those of the Encyclical *Rerum Novarum*. The Christian movements for their part have given full support to the INTERNATIONAL LABOUR ORGANIZATION and consider it an honour to take part in its work. They hope thereby that their social objectives will be reached more quickly and more surely. These objectives include, first and foremost, living conditions which safeguard the inalienable rights of man, as contained in natural law or formulated in statute law. But legislation by itself is a soulless standard, a mere barrier against wrongdoing. The essential factor is the spirit that moves its defenders, the urge to improve upon the present, which although it may be better than the past, is still overshadowed in many ways and burdened with the uncertainty of human weakness. If men are to strive with all their might to build a temporal society where private initiative can flourish without fear, where the rights of the individual are fully respected so that the aptitudes and abilities of each can find their full expression and where everyone can adhere with heart and soul to the highest principles of morality and religion, they must put their faith in spiritual values, confident that these will triumph over the forces of dissolution and discord.

What is at stake is not only the interests of the working class and its admission to the full exercise of its responsibilities, but the future of human society as a whole. The labour movement cannot rest satisfied with material success, a fuller system of safeguards and security and a greater measure of influence on the economic system. It cannot visualize the future merely in terms of opposition to other social classes or the excessive subordination of the individual to the State. It must seek its objective on the plane where your Organization has placed it, that is to say, on the plane of universality—as the Encyclical *Quadragesimo Anno* proposed —in a social order where material prosperity is the outcome of the sincere collaboration of all for the common good and serves as a foundation for the higher cultural values and above all for the indissoluble union of hearts and minds.

We wish you success in your work at the 127th Session of your Governing Body. Pursue unflaggingly your study of the problems which face the world of labour and continue to add to the existing fabric in order to complete and consolidate the whole structure. May the Master of all things, who became a divine workman in order to bring to the earth His message of peace and brotherhood, continue to watch over your activities and grant you the courageous perseverance which overcomes all obstacles. As a pledge of His benevolence and as a proof of Our high consideration, We grant to you and to all the collaborators of the INTERNATIONAL LABOUR ORGANIZATION Our Apostolic Blessing.

IV *BIOLOGICAL SCIENCE*

1. *Evolution*

THE publication of the encyclical *Humani Generis,* J. S. Weiner's *The Piltdown Forgery,* Julian Huxley's *Evolution in Action,* P. G. Fothergill's *Historical Aspects of Organic Evolution* and other books in recent years has once again focussed attention on organic evolution. For Catholics, *Humani Generis* is outstanding. In this document, Pope Pius XII begins by pointing out false trends in modern teachings which are dangerous to all, but especially to those outside the Christian fold. He gives as an example evolution applied without reservation to the origin of all things. A striking feature is that for the first time a biological theory is mentioned by name in an authoritative papal document. In his official capacity, the Sovereign Pontiff is not concerned with evolution as a scientific theory. But it is very much his concern if the theory is used, rightly or wrongly, to support a particular ideology or to bolster up an artificial code of morality. This is precisely what has happened with organic evolution, Darwin's great publication on the origin of species appeared nearly a century ago, and since then the study of scientific evolution has progressed by leaps and bounds. But the theory has been employed outside biological science to give colour to a materialistic view of life. Atheistic communists welcome it with open arms.

In the public mind, evolution continues to be linked with Charles Darwin and his book " on the origin of species by means of natural selection and the preservation of favoured races in the struggle for life " (1859). The association reflects a double confusion. Darwin's great book mixed up the evidence for two very different things, namely: 1, the working *hypothesis* or *theory,* that organisms show evolution, that is, there is descent with modifications which produce permanent changes in the race, so that the complex species of to-day can be regarded as descended from originally simpler types; 2, the *mechanism* of evolution: evolution occurs through a process called " natural selection ", which consists in an accumulation of gradual modifications which favour survival, and eventually add up to produce a new species by " survival of the fittest ".

The second confusion arose through confounding the biological theory of evolution with the materialistic philosophy it was used to support. Darwin described the origin of species without reference to God or Genesis, as he was quite entitled to do, since he was working at the natural level in terms of secondary or proximate causes. His explanation did not exclude an account of the same facts in terms of creation or ultimate causes. However, it suited agnostics to pretend it did. Also, an interpretation which omitted final causes appealed to materialists who were science-conscious and eager to use science to discredit theology if they could: they were ready to take a stick from science and use it to beat religion. The theory could be (illegitimately) extrapolated outside biology to support the notion of progress prevailing in the 19th century: this suited the secularists as well as the followers of naturalism and those suffering from scientism. Some of them went so far as to claim that not only the body of man but his soul had evolved, and that neither had been created. One recalls how Haeckel was so violently atheistic that he even faked illustrations in order to push his version of evolution to the utmost extreme. The really pernicious notion was that man's soul had evolved, a notion which had received no vestige of support from Darwin or biological science.

Let us return from history to the cool plane of biology and glance at the kind of evidence on which the theory of organic evolution has been built up. The evidence is of two kinds, being drawn from (*a*) the structure of creatures, and (*b*) the fossil record. The likeness of basic structure in different groups of creatures is very remarkable and suggests something in common, some sort of relationship and descent from simpler forms of life. If we look at different kinds of fish, there seems to be a basic plan for all fish, a fish-plan or model for them all, suggesting consanguinity of some sort. Then the fossil record reveals the appearance, the spread, and sometimes the extinction, of different sorts of animals and plants. Evolution theory connects up the vast assemblage of facts relating to structure and to discoveries of remains in geological strata by *supposing* that plants and animals have actually in the course of ages by a series of gradual changes developed from simple common ancestors into present complex structures with high organization and great differentiation. This theory of organic evolution—referring only to the development of corporeal organisms—is strongly supported, and is generally accepted by biologists as the most satisfying and helpful *interpretation* of otherwise disparate facts in comparative anatomy, geological succession, geographical distribution, embryology and genetics.

THE MECHANISM OF EVOLUTION. The theory about the mechanism of evolution is on a different footing. The evidence for natural selection by the processes imagined by Darwin is nowadays admitted to be weak, certainly not cogent, as will be indicated presently.

While nearly all biologists use evolution theory as a good working hypothesis that links together in simple fashion what could be otherwise a chaos of discrete facts, that does not mean all is plain sailing. Botanists and entomologists in particular will tell you they have difficulties (cp. *Species Revalued* by Desmond Murray). Insect and plant life provide them with numerous examples of great complexity and perfect adaptation to a way of life. They are struck by the complexity of the association between insect and insect, between plant and insect, e.g., as illustrated by the fertilization mechanism of the orchids. Such mechanisms are either perfect and of use to both parties, flower and insect; or, they are nothing at all. It is found hard to conceive how they could be brought into play by the suggested processes of orthodox evolution theory.

As argued by Desmond Murray (*op. cit.*), there seems to be no doubt that many biologists fail to realize the full importance of species, especially the notion of the fixity and stability of species. The truth about species—whether a biological species is stable and fixed like an atom of copper; or, unstable and changeable like an atom of radium or uranium; whether species is a horse indefinitely repeating its kind, or a mule without pride of ancestry or hope of posterity—can only be discovered, perhaps after centuries, by sifting out the evidence very thoroughly and by freeing oneself from preconceived ideas popularized by a school. The true scientist does not fit facts to theories, but the other way round.

The botanists and entomologists one meets are impressed by the fixity of species as a natural unit. True, genetics and recent breeding methods show that considerable variation can be produced within a particular group—instances are the new breeds of wheat or the vast number of domestic dogs. But there is no sign of such fixed groups ever becoming anything else: the variations are all within themselves, and are definitely restricted or " contained ". One is reminded of Belloc's rejoinder to H. G. Wells's advocacy of natural selection. " If natural selection be true ", said Belloc, " then what we call a pig is but a fleeting vision : all the past he has been becoming a pig and all the future he will spend evolving out of pigdom, and pig is but a moment's pause in the eternal flux, while all around us should be quarter-pigs, half-pigs, near-pigs, all-but-pigs, slightly superior pigs, just beginning to be pigs, and so on. But there aren't. They are just pigs ".

Moreover, the fossil record does not show evolution, it only shows change. There is no fossil evidence of slowly changing forms evolving one into another. *We* can *arrange* the fossils in series to indicate there has been evolution. When we do so, there are great gaps or "missing links". These are supplied in the family tree but only because they are provided by the theory itself. This is quite legitimate and a normal practice of science, if we keep in mind the nature of a scientific theory and what is its purpose. The story of the periodic table of the chemical elements is an example from another branch of science of the normal development of a theory. The evolution theory has proved itself to be a powerful working hypothesis, as a correlation of phenomena, but it is far from explaining all the facts.

The geologists tell us they find evidence of life in great variety and complexity in the Cambrian rocks but they discover no fossils in pre-Cambrian strata. While the geologist can think up a good reason for this vacuum, this missing link, it means, however, that there is no positive evidence for supposing an early period of simpler forms. In other words, we are only guessing (but of course we are entitled to guess—that is part of a theory whose function is to interpret) about simpler forms. Again, some of the Cambrian types have survived almost without change to the present day; others have died out. Hence it is clear that the mere passage of time does not bring about change in the sense of " becoming " or evolution. Further, the modern study of genetics has raised up fresh barriers to the methods of evolution that were considered to be feasible in Darwin's day.

As Professor Fothergill points out, there have been three periods in the development of the idea of evolution. In the early speculative period, the idea of evolution was worked up by philosophers and theologians before any evidence was collected in favour of the theory. The mechanical view of living things was made popular by Descartes. Kant dismissed teleology or finality from natural science, and he was the first to suggest the possibility of a genetic relationship between all the different kinds of living creatures, just as he was the first to suggest the nebular theory, the basis or start of inorganic evolution.

The nineteenth century constituted what might be called the formative period, and throughout that time the scientific evidence for evolution was collected and co-ordinated.

In the modern period of synthesis, a new formation is being given to the problem of the mechanism of evolution by (a) the discovery of *mutations,* which are large and sudden variations; (b) Mendel's work on genetics; and (c) discoveries by cytologists of what goes on in the individual cell during growth and reproduction. These have led to a fresh conception of natural selection based on the relatively large changes shown in mutation as compared with the small and gradual variations postulated by Darwin.

All this results in a new idea of natural selection as secondary to the production of mutations on which it can act. Much experimental work is being done on mutations, both natural and artificial. The results indicate that natural selection can account readily enough for new varieties within the species, but it is less plausible as an explanation of differences between species; and still less is it satisfactory as an interpretation of divergences between larger groups. We must conclude that the general question remains unsettled, that evolution by a Darwinian process of "natural selection" is, to say the least of it, unproved.

2. "Humani Generis" and Evolution

Catholic biologists and anthropologists must feel grateful to the Holy Father for rolling away so many of the mists that have enveloped them regarding the subject of evolution. They now know where they stand and they can advance to the front line of research and feel secure and confident that there will be no attack from behind as they proceed against the real enemy, ignorance.

Evolution is mentioned in different parts and contexts of the encyclical *Humani Generis*. In this document, H.H., Pope Pius XII first indicates the benefit of profane learning to priests, then appeals to Catholics engaged in advanced studies to make themselves highly competent in their special fields, and finally gives warning about the pitfalls that accompany some modern teachings. One example of the snares is seen in the way in which evolution is made use of to explain the origin of all things, absolutely, and without drawing the line anywhere. It is extended to embrace all processes including human experience and the human spirit. Wholesale acceptance of evolution in this sense gives rise to monistic and pantheistic speculations. Dialectical materialists find it a happy hunting ground, and from it springs existentialism, the new system of philosophy based on mere personal existence and nothing more.

It is not a belief in the origin of species by evolution that is the pitfall but absolute, and particularly materialist, evolutionism, as against scientific evolution. In this early part of the encyclical, the Sovereign Pontiff also states (par. 5) that evolution is a thing

" which has not yet been proved beyond yea and nay even in the sphere of natural science ". This, accordingly, leaves the subject of scientific evolution open for experiment and discussion. Later on in the document (par. 36) the Pope speaks of the evolution of man's body and declares: " In the present state of scientific and theological opinion this question [of human evolution] may be legitimately canvassed by research and by discussion between experts on both sides ".

In the same paragraph, referring specifically to the evolution of man, the Pope states the position of the Church in the clearest terms. The unique creation of each individual human soul is a doctrine of Catholic Faith, but the evolution of man's body is a matter for reasoned and restrained discussion.

Taken as a whole, these statements about evolution in *Humani Generis* are a warning to men of science and others not to depend entirely on a scientific theory if it has implications which encroach on theology and philosophy.

3. *Excerpts from " Humani Generis"*

(*From the translation by Mgr. Ronald Knox, C.T.S., paragraphs 5, 6, 7, 35, 36, 37.*)

5. PRESENT-DAY FALLACIES. A glance at the world outside the Christian fold will familiarize us, easily enough, with the false directions which the thought of the learned often takes. Some will contend that the theory of evolution, as it is called—a theory which has not yet been proved beyond contradiction even in the sphere of natural science—applies to the origin of all things whatsoever. Accepting it without caution, without reservation, they boldly give rein to monistic or pantheistic speculations which represent the entire universe as left at the mercy of a continual process of evolution. Such speculations are eagerly welcomed by the communists, who find in them a powerful weapon for defending and popularizing their system of dialectical materialism; the whole idea of God is thus to be eradicated from men's minds.

6. EXISTENTIALISM. These false evolutionary notions, with their denial of all that is absolute or fixed or abiding in human experience, have paved the way for a new erroneous philosophy. Idealism, immanentism, pragmatism, have now a rival in what is called " existentialism ". Its method, as the name implies, is to leave the unchanging essences of things out of sight, and concentrate all its attention on particular existences.

7. HISTORICAL METHOD. There is, too, a false use of the historical method, which confines its observations to the actual happenings of human life, and in doing so contrives to undermine all absolute truth, all absolute laws, whether it is dealing with the problems of philosophy or with the doctrines of the Christian religion.

35. CAUTION. It remains to say something about further difficulties concerned with the positive sciences (as they are called), and yet connected in a more or less degree with the truths of the Christian faith. Some thinkers are loud in their demand that the Catholic religion should make these sciences of the greatest possible account. An excellent principle, where it is a question of really ascertained facts; but what of hypotheses, based to some extent on natural science, which yet affect the doctrines enshrined in Scripture and in tradition? Here we must be cautious; where such conjectures are directly or indirectly opposed to the truths God has revealed, the claim is inadmissible.

36. EVOLUTION. Thus, the Teaching of the Church leaves the doctrine of *Evolution* an open question, as long as it confines its speculations to the development from other living matter already in existence, of the human body. (That souls are immediately created by God is a view which the Catholic faith imposes on us.) In the present state of scientific and theological opinion, this question may be legitimately canvassed by research, and by discussion between experts on both sides. At the same time, the reasons for and against either view must be weighed and adjudged with all seriousness, fairness, and restraint; and there must be a readiness on all sides to accept the arbitrament of the Church, as being entrusted by Christ with the task of interpreting the Scriptures aright, and the duty of safeguarding the doctrines of the faith (cf. Address to Pontifical Academy, Nov. 30, 1941). There are some who take rash advantage of this liberty of debate, by treating the subject as if the whole matter were closed—as if the discoveries hitherto made, and the arguments based on them, were sufficiently certain to prove, beyond doubt, the development of the human body from other living matter already in existence. They forget, too, that there are certain references to the subject in the sources of divine revelation, which call for the greatest caution and prudence in discussing it.

37. POLYGENISM. There are other conjectures, about *polygenism* (as it is called), which leave no such freedom of choice. Christians

cannot lend their support to a theory which involves the existence, after Adam's time, of some earthly race of men, truly so
called, who were not descended ultimately from him, or else
supposes that Adam was the name given to some group of our
primordial ancestors. It does not appear how such views can
be reconciled with the doctrine of original sin, as this is guaranteed
to us by Scripture and tradition, and proposed to us by the
Church. Original sin is the result of a sin committed, in actual
historical fact, by an individual man named Adam, and it is a
quality *native* to all of us, precisely because it has been handed
down by descent from him (cf. Rom. v. 12-19; Conc. Trid. sess.
v, can. 1-4).

4. *Genetics and Eugenics*

(Address to First International Congress of Medical Genetics,
September 7, 1953.)

Y OU are most welcome, gentlemen. You have sought to pay Us
a visit on the occasion of the *Primum Symposium Geneticae
Medicae*. We acknowledge your act of courtesy, and We show
Our pleasure by gladly spending some time in your company.

In recent times, many scientific congresses have been held here.
Your subject differs from other branches of biology and medicine
by the tenderness of its years. Yet, young as it is, it is already
known for its rapid growth and ambitious aims, which some may
be tempted to describe as over-ambitious.

Such aims arouse a lively interest in those who study man
as a moral being, and envisage the kind of education needed to
effect in him a mature formation along with awareness of responsibilities—that is to say, character endowed with the qualities
of resoluteness and constancy. In response to your request, We
cannot refuse to say some words about your objects and
endeavours.

Of all the departments of biology, it is perhaps in the field of
genetics that the most vigorous work is being prosecuted at the
present time—genetics, the science which studies how hereditary
characters are transmitted, that is to say, passed on in regular
fashion according to definite laws from one generation to another.
In Our address, We should like to begin with the principles encountered in classical writings on the subject, leaving it to you
to judge the justness of the summary. Having reviewed the fundamentals, We would propose for your consideration a metaphysical

and moral estimate of the principles operating in the theory and practice of genetics and eugenics as we find them today.

PRINCIPLES OF HEREDITY: THE INITIAL CELL. Your science has focussed attention on the initial cell of the new life which comes into existence in the very act of fecundation or fertilization. This unit, you say, is formed by the fusion of two cells, male and female. You tell us that the living being, that begins with the initial cell, is built up by normal cell division and continues to grow under the direction of genes, the carriers of ancestral heritage, continued in the nucleus or core of the cell. Moreover, your branch of knowledge affords a comprehensive and deep understanding of this initial cell in its origin and structure as well as in its power, purpose and material content. In this cell your science sees both a product and an origin; the product of a long previous evolution with transmission of a hereditary patrimony from both parent lines over great periods of time; from the start of the species to the latest member; the origin from which will begin a fresh line of descendants to whom the hereditary patrimony can be and should be passed on so that generations will continue one after another without cease.

Here, genetics is engaged in analysing life and its laws, and at this point one must refer with emotion to the mysteries of atomic processes. Studies of this kind have already yielded fruits, and the fruits include well established facts; but the researches have raised many problems of theory and practice which still await solution.

LAWS OF HEREDITY. Genetics does not limit itself to facts but it tells also about the nature and laws of heredity. Transmission of hereditary patrimony, it says, follows strict laws, some of which are known though many still require further investigation. Mendel's laws (established by the Augustinian priest, Gregor Mendel, in whose honour there is a scientific institute in Rome) tell how the genes, carriers of hereditary characters, are transmitted and distributed to descendants. The group of genes (located in a structure called the chromosome which is found in a sex-cell or gamete) constitutes the material basis of character (as a set of properties or characteristics). Genetical science teaches that inheritance depends on the group of genes in the gametes; it studies the various combinations that can occur when the transmitted genes encounter one another; it deals also with homozygotes and their correlatives the heterozygotes (carriers of variations of the same characteristic); and it notes that certain genes, the *recessives*, may be conquered, so to speak, and supplanted by others—the *dominants*. Neverthe-less, the recessives maintain their full character in heredity, and are so well transmitted that in subsequent generations in the absence of dominant genes they may re-appear with all their former power.

Your work lays stress on one of the features or traits of heredity. For you show that the genes are practically impervious to attack or change. A thousand instances have demonstrated that acquired or lost aptitudes do not modify them, and that acquired charac-teristics are not passed on to posterity. Technically, this constitutes ' classical genetics '. (Of late, Russian specialists had challenged the view by denying the stability and permanence of hereditary factors, but now appear to have revised their view more recently.)

Still, it is generally recognized that factors contributing to heredity can be adapted and can react to external circumstances, especially to climate. The same kind of plant with the same kind of inheritance can in different climates assume appearances so varied that ordinary people will think it belongs under the different conditions to different species. In this context the science of genetics states: Inheritance in itself does not entail any fixed shape or form but rather the power to react to circumstances through form or shape. Inheritance is therefore no more and no less than a norm of reaction.

According to genetical science, such reactions or ' variations ' are not rare, but this does not mean there has been any change in the basic elements of hereditary processes. Living things receive their individual characteristics or ' phenotype ' from inheritance and from the world in which they live and move and have their being. Inheritance is said to be more or less plastic in the sense that it can be fashioned by environment. Every living thing in its definitive state is the result of nature and nurture, but neither inheritance nor environment is in itself a complete determinant.

However, certain changes in hereditary factors are believed to occur. They are known as ' mutations '. They arise in quite a differ-ent way from ' variations '. For instance, those giant molecules, the genes, can undergo structural alterations when subjected to the action of various natural agents such as cosmic rays. The gene molecule, radically altered in its structure, develops new char-acteristics in the growing organism. Nearly all the characteristics of a living being—and they run to thousands—can undergo change in this manner. Such mutations can also be brought about by arti-ficial means, for instance, by irradiating reproductive cells, say, with X-rays; but it is not possible to tell in advance what will be the exact nature of the change effected in this case.

By means of mutations, nature and men may produce an 'élite', that is, beings armed and adapted for life and able to assert themselves over others less well equipped, so that the latter tend to degenerate, in fact may tend to perish and disappear altogether.

The existence of 'variations' and 'mutations' indicates that hereditary factors, of whose constancy We spoke earlier, are in fact liable to some modification.

What biology, and especially genetics, teach about germinal cells and factors of heredity as well as about variations, mutations, and selection goes beyond the individual and the various distinct species, and leads to the question of the origin and evolution of life in general, involving all living things. One asks: Have all existing creatures come from one single being and its prolific seed, descending and evolving in the manner and under the influences We have referred to? The mention of 'all existing creatures' explains why, according to certain geneticists, a theory of heredity must be linked with theories of evolution and descent. One theory, they say, leads to and entails the others.

In recent work on genetics, it is claimed that nothing better explains the bond between all living creatures than the notion of a common genealogical tree. At the same time, it is admitted that this is only a picture, an hypothesis, not a demonstrated fact. It must be added that if a majority of biologists present such an opinion as 'fact', then theirs is a premature conclusion. For it is easy to advance other, equally plausible, hypotheses. Several specialists in biology have actually done so without contending that life has evolved from brute matter, or that certain specimens discovered by anthropologists are necessarily primitive forms of the human body. Moreover, these research workers have pointed out that no precise meaning so far attaches to the terms 'evolution', 'descent' and 'transmission'; further, that no natural process is known by which one being begets another of a different kind; further, that the passage from one species to another is impenetrable and has never been convincingly visualized or explained even though countless intermediary stages be imagined, granted or postulated; further, that no experiment has so far succeeded in producing one species from another; and finally, that we simply do not know at what stage in evolution the *hominoid* [thing like a man] abruptly became a human being. Over and above, there are two prime discoveries of specimens which remain matters of dispute because of doubt about the age of the geological strata in which they were found, and not because there is any doubt about the degree of evolution attained in the specimens themselves. The latest view is this: only the future can decide between current theory and some other hypothesis which may replace it in accord with experiment and observation. Meanwhile, it must be said that research into the origin of man is at a very early and primitive stage. The present state of the question cannot be regarded as final. So much can be fairly said about heredity theory in relation to evolution theory. We are only approaching the fringe of either subject.

PRACTICAL GENETICS. Publications on genetics show that the subject is not only of theoretical value in so far as it enriches our knowledge of nature and her operations, but that it is also of practical importance. First, in the realm of things devoid of reason, it tells us how to make better use of the plant and animal worlds.

In the case of man, too, the laws of heredity may be of great utility. The primitive cell, the source of the living man, is even at its inception amazingly fashioned and unbelievably rich in structure. It is pregnant with purposes under the control of genes; and the genes are the basis of future happiness or the reverse, of vitality or languor, of strength or frailty. This explains why research on heredity always arouses great human interest and ever widens the range of its application. Efforts are made to retain those traits that are valuable with a view to improving them. Worsening of hereditary factors is something to be averted. So, attempts are made to remedy existing defects. Precautions are taken to prevent the deterioration of characteristics—even those of little positive value—that is a consequence of fusion with a homozygotous partner. Rather, we try to select characters at their best and join them with others endowed with a similar healthy heritage.

Such are the tasks confronting the science of genetics and eugenics, with its remarkable branches relating to the genetics of blood groups and of twins.

We have refrained from any expression of Our opinion in this review of your subject, since the evaluation of purely scientific questions is your province. Our aim has been to outline a common basis for developing considerations of moral principle to which We now turn.

SCIENCE AND TRUTH. It is a fundamental proposition that science is built on truth and integrity.

Truth is conformity of the mind with things. It is the conformity of a man's judgment with reality either in being or in action. It is in contrast with the images and fantasies generated by an imagination broken loose from reality and out of touch with it.

A prevalent opinion holds that the message of objective reality enters into the mind as through a filter, being modified both in degree and kind as it enters. This is called dynamic thought because the mind moulds and transforms the object of knowledge. Dynamic thought is in contrast with static thought which merely reflects an object without altering its form. The claim is made that, in principle, dynamic thought constitutes the only actual way of acquiring knowledge [implying that truth is relative to one's time, and not absolute]. Truth would then be only such personal thought as would be in accord with the public or scientific opinion of the day.

Thinkers in every age, in particular Christian thinkers, have taken up their stand on the ground of sound sense and have seen it their duty to defend the idea of truth as an absolute, as the agreement of judgment with the very being of things. There is no need, then, for Us to enter here on a refutation of the opinion referred to above, which, though in the main erroneous, is in part justifiable. We touched on the question in Our encyclical ' Humani Generis ' of August 19, 1950, and stressed there a point which We think well to repeat now, namely, the obligation to keep in mind the great ontological laws, because without them we cannot understand reality. We refer chiefly to the principles of contradiction and sufficient reason in addition to the principles of causality and finality.

From your writings We see that you agree with Our notion of truth. We see, too, that in your investigations you seek for truth: on it you base your inferences and build your theories. You assert that genes exist as a fact and not as mere hypothesis. You admit then the existence of objective facts and that science is both able to understand them and aims to do so, and is not just content to work out fantasies that are entirely subjective.

The distinction between sure facts and their interpretation (or orderly arrangement in a system) is as basic as the idea of truth. A fact is always true because it can contain no ontological contradiction; but the same does not hold for scientific elaborations. Here one runs the risk of committing errors of judgment and coming to premature conclusions.

All this makes it necessary to have respect for facts both singly and collectively, to have prudence in making scientific statements, to be sober in judgment, to be modest with the modesty of the learned who are always conscious that human knowledge has limits. Such an attitude helps to broaden the mind and increase the humility of the true scientist, who is loath to hold on to his own ideas once they are proved not well-founded. Finally, it enables a man to examine the views of others and judge them impartially.

When one is possessed of such a disposition, respect for truth will naturally be accompanied by integrity, that is, conformity between one's private convictions and the scientific stand taken up in one's speech or writings.

The importance of truthfulness and integrity calls for another remark about scientific knowledge. It is rare to find only a single science concerned with a given subject. More often than not, one and the same subject-matter engages the attention of several sciences, each from its own stand-point. If the various studies are carried out by competent workers, there can be no contradiction in the several conclusions or findings. That would suppose a contradiction in ontological reality, and reality cannot contradict itself.

If, in spite of everything, contradictions do arise, they can only be the result, either of faulty observation or of incorrect interpretation of sound observations; or else they derive from the research worker jumping the fences of his special field and advancing on to a terrain in which he is without competence. We feel that this remark is clearly applicable to all scientific disciplines.

If, therefore, a theory of heredity based on what is known of cellular structure (and, more recently, on what is known of the structure of cytoplasm) and on what is known of the immanent laws of descent, can say why a man possesses certain characteristics, that does not mean the theory is in a position to explain the *whole* life of that man. Once there is question regarding the spiritual principle of his life, the existence and origin of the human soul (which is by its nature independent of matter) the theory must enlist the aid of other sciences to achieve completeness. The unity of man's nature cannot be explained by what genetics has to say about the initial cell and the growth of a man's body through normal cell division under the influence of the genes, any more than a man's knowledge and free will can be explained by what the science has to say about variations and mutations, and the balance between inheritance and environment. Genetics, as such, has nothing to say concerning the fact that, in the unity of a human nature, an immaterial soul is joined to an organic substrate which enjoyed a relative autonomy. It is here that philosophy (as psychology or metaphysics) must enter in, not in opposition to genetics, but as a complement which furthers and tends to complete its findings. Equally, philosophy may not neglect genetics if, in its analysis of psychic activities, it wishes to remain in contact with reality.

In so far as the psyche is conditioned by the body, one cannot claim to make the entire psyche dependent on the '*anima rationalis*' [rational soul] as the '*forma corporis*' [form of the body], and say that the amorphous '*materia prima*' [prime matter] receives all its determinations from the immaterial soul directly created by God, and none at all from the genes contained in the sex cells.

There are different sources of knowledge, and this leads us to another fact of crucial importance, namely, the distinction that exists between knowledge personally acquired and the knowledge which one owes to the research—and, therefore, to the testimony or witness—of others. When one is sure that the testimony is worthy of belief, then it constitutes a normal source of knowledge which neither everyday life nor science can ignore. Apart from the necessity we are all under, to depend on the witness of others for much of our knowledge, the mind of the prudent scientist, mentioned earlier, makes him certain that the proved specialist in his field is always in closer contact with reality and objective truth than anybody not versed in the subject.

We cannot refrain from applying to the witness of God what We have just said about human testimony. Revelation (that is, the formal and explicit witness of the Creator) touches natural science at some points; for instance, it has something to say about the descent of man, a question of moment in your own discipline. Now, the Creator exemplifies the attributes of truth and integrity in the most perfect way. Judge, therefore, for yourselves if it is in keeping with scientific objectivity to ignore That Witness Who is the supreme guarantee of reality and its content.

As for the theory of man's descent, the question has really to do with the origin of man's body, not of his soul. Your science is very interested in this matter, of course; but theology, a science which has Revelation as its subject, also discusses the question. On two occasions—in 1941, in addressing Our Academy of Science [see *Acta Apostolicæ Sedis*, 33 (1941) 506], and in 1950, in the encyclical [*Humani Generis*] referred to earlier, We called for further investigations and research in the hope and desire that some day more convincing conclusions may be reached; for, up to the present, nothing decisive has been obtained. We urged that meanwhile the question be treated with the prudence and maturity of judgment its great importance demands. From publications on your special subject. We took a quotation in which, after an outline of all up-to-date discoveries and the opinions of specialists about them, the same sobriety was recommended and final judgment was reserved.

If you reflect on what we have said about research and scientific knowledge, you will see that neither from the side of reason nor from the side of thought oriented in a Christian sense are any barriers raised to investigation, to knowledge, or to affirmation of truth. There are some barriers, but they do not serve to imprison truth. Their purpose is to prevent hypotheses that have not been proved from being taken as established facts, and to keep people from forgetting they should check one source against another and avoid misinterpreting the value and certitude of a given source of knowledge. It is to guard against such causes of error that there are barriers, but there are none for truth.

EUGENICS. Genetics has not merely a theoretical interest, but it is practical as well. It contributes to the welfare of both individuals and the community, chiefly by its investigations in the two fields of physiology and pathology.

Experience shows that the outcome of a man's schooling and training depends very much on his natural dispositions, good and bad. One can say that the human body with its aptitudes and parts is an instrument and the soul is the artist that manipulates it. The artist can make up for defects in the instrument, but he plays best, and more easily, on a good instrument.

His talent will avail him nothing if the instrument is grossly, defective. (One should bear in mind the weak point in the analogy, due to the body and soul, though matter and spirit, forming a substantial unit.)

Yet, keeping to the comparison: through the science of genetics, we can understand the structure and operation of an instrument and so make it play better. By studying a man's lineage, we may to some extent discover his natural qualities and be able to foretell which of them will turn out well and—what is more important still—which will betray hereditary weakness.

Our power to influence heredity may be limited, but practical genetics is by no means reduced to the rôle of a spectator. Everyone knows how certain parents by their behaviour produce very injurious effects as they transmit life, giving rise to intoxications and infections of the body. Genetics shows how and to what extent such undesirable results may be prevented. It affords particularly valuable information about the consequences to be expected from mixed breeding, pointing out what unions of different stock should be encouraged, tolerated or discouraged.

The fundamental object of eugenics is to influence the transmission of hereditary factors so as to promote what is good and eliminate what is injurious. This basic purpose is unassailable from the moral standpoint. But certain methods employed to attain this end, and certain protective measures, are morally questionable; so also is a misplaced regard for the end to which eugenics tends. You will permit Us to cite one of today's leading geneticists. In a letter addressed to Us, he expresses his regret that, in spite of enormous progress made, genetics "from the technical and analytical point of view, has become entangled in manifold doctrinal errors, such as racialism; mutationism applied to phylogenesis in order to explain in modern terms the evolution theory of Darwin; birth control (either by preventive methods or by abortive practices, pre-nuptial certificates, etc.) for all persons who are really or supposedly defective."

In fact, certain measures are adopted in eugenics which good sense and Christian morals must reject both in principle and in practice.

EUGENIC STERILIZATION. Methods contrary to morality include racialism, already mentioned, and *eugenic sterilization.* Our predecessor, Pius XI, and We Ourselves were obliged to declare as contrary to the natural law, not only eugenic sterilization but every direct sterilization of an innocent person (man or woman) whether temporary or permanent in character. Our opposition to sterilization has been and is firm; for, although racialism has come to an end, there are still persons who wish to and try to use sterilization in order to suppress a lineage affected by hereditary disease.

MARRIAGE BAN. Another road leading to the same goal is: *A ban on marriage.*

To make marriage physically impossible by segregating those whose heredity is defective, must also be rejected. The intention is good, but the means to be used violate a person's right to contract and use marriage. When a person with a hereditary taint is unable to behave like a human being, or, in consequence, is unfit to contract marriage; or when, later, he becomes incapable of claiming by an act of free will the right he has acquired through valid marriage, then he can be prevented by lawful means from procreating a new life. Outside these cases, the banning of marriage or of marital intercourse for biological, genetical or eugenical motives, is an injustice, no matter who it is who issues the prohibition, whether a private individual or a public authority.

Without doubt it is right, and often it is a duty, to point out to those whose heredity is certainly tainted, what grave responsibilities they are assuming towards themselves, towards the spouse and to their offspring. The burden may well become unbearable. But to advise against doing something is not to forbid it. There may be other motives, above all of a moral or personal nature, that have such weight as to authorize people to contract and use matrimony even in the circumstances just indicated.

In order to justify direct sterilization in the interests of eugenics, or the alternative of segregation, it is claimed that the right to marriage (and to the marriage act) is not affected by sterilization, even though it be pre-nuptial, total, and certainly definitive. This attempt to justify sterilization must fail. For, if, in the judgment of a prudent person, the fact in question is doubtful, the unsuitableness for marriage is also doubtful. One must then apply the principle that the right to marry persists until such time as the contrary is proved with certainty. Here, too, marriage must be allowed; but the question of its objective validity remains open. If on the contrary, there is no doubt about the fact of sterilization, it is premature to say that the right to marry remains quite unimpaired notwithstanding; and in any case, such a statement leaves room for serious doubt.

As to the other ways of averting hereditary defects, which the text quoted above calls " preventive means and abortive practices ", they do not even come up for consideration in eugenics, because by their very nature they are to be rejected.

That, gentlemen, is what We have to say to you.

The practical aims pursued by genetics are noble and worthy of recognition and encouragement. May your science, in devising means to achieve its ends, be ever conscious of the chasm that separates man from the plant and animal world. In the latter case, the means for bettering species and race are entirely at the disposal of science. Where man is concerned, genetics is always dealing with personal beings who possess inviolable rights, with individuals who are bound by invariable moral law in disposing of their power to raise up a new life. The Creator Himself it is Who has set up certain barriers which no human authority can remove.

When it is a question of normal married life, the life of men free and able to develop according to the laws written by the Creator in the heart of man, and confirmed by Revelation, may your science find a strong support in public morality and in the social order. Perhaps it is in such laws that you will find the most precious aid for your efforts, on which We wish and invoke God's most abundant blessings.

5. *Mendelism*

MENDELISM is a scientific theory concerning the distributive mechanism of inheritance.

Mendel, to explain results which he obtained from the breeding of peas, supposed:

1. There are characters or characteristics which are inherited.

2. Corresponding to these characters, there are *genes* or determiners, that is, hereditary factors in the gametes whose union gives rise to the individual.

3. Every gamete carries a factor for each heritable characteristic that the future individual may exhibit; accordingly, the individual in the union of two gametes, has a double set of factors (each gamete a single set).

Certain structures or functions may have *alternative* (or allelomorphic) characters: e.g., hair may be straight or curly, eyes may be brown or blue.

For unknown reasons, brown eye-colour is *dominant* to blue, which is therefore called *recessive*. That is, the offspring of parents, one of whom is blue-eyed and the other brown, is *always* browneyed. The brown-eyed parent may have received one factor for the brown-eye character by way of one gamete, and one factor for blue-eye by way of the other gamete. He is a *heterozygote*. Or, the brown-eyed parent may have received the brown eye-colour by way of both gametes, each having the factor for brown eye. Such a parent is said to be *homozygotous*.

The homozygotous brown-eyed individual, mating with a blueeyed, will beget none but brown-eyed offspring; while the heterozygotous brown-eyed will produce both browns and blues—in the proportion of 3 to 1 usually.

This distribution of 3 to 1 follows, (a) if in any fertilization there are available equal numbers of ova and sperm, and each of the allelomorphic or alternative characters is equally divided among them; and (b) if fertilization is at random. Then, on the average, 3 out of every 4 offspring will exhibit the dominant character of the parents, while only 1 in 4 will show the recessive quality.

GLOSSARY

ALLELOMORPH, either of any pair of contrasting Mendelian characters. (See *Mendelism*.)

CHROMOSOME, a structure carrying the genes present in the nucleus of a cell which is about to divide.

DOMINANT, a gene which obscures the action of its allelomorph (the recessive) when present with it in the heterozygous state.

GAMETE, a male or female sex cell, a germ-cell.

GENE, one of the hereditary units which control the appearance of definite characteristics; it is located in the structure called the chromosome.

GENETICS, study of heredity and variation.

GENOTYPE, a group of individuals similar in genetic constitution, i.e., having characters which are transmitted through germ-cells or gametes.

HETEROZYGOTE, a Mendelian hybrid with recessive characters; each cell of the organism contains unlike genes likely to beget unlike characters.

HOMOZYGOTE, an organism in which each cell contains genes that bring out like characters (Mendelism).

MUTATION, a variation that abruptly appears and breeds true.

NUCLEUS, central part of cell.

PHENOTYPE, external appearance produced by reaction of an organism with its environment; group of individuals of similar appearance but different genetic constitution.

PHYLOGENESIS, ancestral evolution, ancient development of the race.

RECESSIVE, the gene in an allelomorphic pair whose action is overshadowed by its fellow *dominant* gene.

VARIATION, divergence from type in some characteristics, making an organism appreciably different from its parents.

ZYGOTE, fertilized egg-cell, i.e., cell formed by union of male and female gametes and giving rise to a new individual.

V *MORALITY AND SCIENCE : MEDICAL ETHICS*

1. *Address to Neurologists*

[The First International Congress of Histopathology of the Nervous System was held in Rome in the month of September, 1952. The programme included discussions on the causes and origins of nervous and psychic diseases. Recent discoveries relating to lesions of the brain and other organs, tending to produce nervous and mental ailments, were described, and there was a liberal exchange of views.

On September 14, the members of the Congress were received in audience by the Holy Father. At their own request, he addressed them on the subject of the moral barriers to research and treatment. Having stated the principles, he pointed out that the application to cases must be decided by a doctor himself in his capacity as doctor, because only doctors are entitled or fit to find the medical facts. Without an exact knowledge of the medical data, one cannot always say what moral principle enters into a particular question. The rule is clear: the doctor studies the medical aspect of the case, and the moralist considers the moral norms. After exchange of views between doctor and moralist, certitude can be reached about the lawfulness of a proposed treatment.

To justify new treatments, new techniques, and new methods of research, one must take into account:

1. The interests of medicine;

2. The interests of the patient; and

3. The common good.

The Sovereign Pontiff went on to consider the limitations of medical treatment and research under these three heads. We give the full text of his exposition except for the introduction.]

How far the interests of science justify research and the use of new methods.

As in the case of the other sciences such as physics, chemistry, cosmology and psychology, medical knowledge that is truly scientific has a value in itself apart altogether from its usefulness or the use actually made of it. Knowledge as such, knowledge in all its fulness and as an end in itself, cannot be objected to on moral grounds. In virtue of this principle, research and the constant advancement of learning, involving the acquisition of fresh and deeper truths, are perfectly in keeping with the moral order.

This does not mean, however, that every method—well established though it be in theory or in practice—is morally sound; or
further, that every and any method becomes lawful from the fact
that it adds to or deepens our knowledge. For it may happen that
a method cannot be employed without infringing somebody's
rights, or without violating an absolute norm of morality. Advancement of knowledge can well be the goal aimed at, yet the means
taken to get there may be not at all permissible. Why? Because
science is not the ultimate value to which all others have to be
subordinated. Science itself, along with its aims and achievements,
has a place in the order of things. There exists a well-defined
hierarchy of values which medical science must recognize and
conform to. The right of a patient to life, his right to psychic
and moral integrity, the sacredness of the doctor-patient relationship—these, like others that could be mentioned, are values which
have primacy over scientific interests. Therefore, the following
statement cannot be accepted as it stands, but requires qualification:

> "Given that the intervention be determined by scientific
> interest, and that it observes the code of professional etiquette,
> then there are no further restrictions on the methods that may
> be employed to advance and enrich the sum total of medical
> knowledge."

*How the patient's interests justify new methods of research
and treatment.*

One can likewise see how the true and the false are intermingled
in other formulations which have been put forward, such as: "The
medical treatment of the patient demands this particular measure,
and that very fact justifies its use." Or again: "This new method,
up to now neglected or little used, will give possible, probable or
certain good results. Therefore, ethical considerations go by the
board and may be ignored in this case."

In these instances, the 'interests of the patient' are invoked to
furnish the doctor with a moral cloak. But the point that has to be
considered is: does the principle have an absolute value, and show
that the intervention the doctor has in mind conforms to the moral
law?

We, of course, take it as basic that the doctor has the consent of
the patient for any measure he proposes to try out. The doctor
has only that power over the patient that the latter gives him,

explicitly or implicitly. For his part, the patient cannot impart to another rights which he himself does not possess. The decisive point is the lawfulness of the right which the patient disposes of. It is here that we come up against the moral barrier confronting the doctor who acts with the consent of his patient.

The patient is not absolute master of himself, of his body, or of his soul. He cannot, therefore, freely dispose of himself as he pleases. His motive is not the sole determinant in the case. He is bound by the purposes inherent in his nature. He has the right to use—in accord with nature—the faculties and powers of his humanity. Because he is the beneficiary, and not the proprietor, he does not possess the power to permit wholesale acts of destruction or mutilation, whether of a purely anatomical or functional kind. In virtue of the principle of totality (i.e., his right to enjoy the organism as a whole), he may allow individual parts to be destroyed or mutilated, in so far as it may be necessary for the welfare of his whole being; to ensure its continued existence, or to avoid (and, naturally, to repair) grave and lasting injury which otherwise would ensue.

The patient has not the right to risk his integrity, whether physical or psychic, in medical experiments or research of such a nature that the interventions entail, either then or later, notable destruction, mutilation, wound or other grave consequence.

Furthermore, in exercising the right to dispose of himself, or of his faculties and organs, the patient must observe the scale of values enshrined in the canons of morality. [There must be no undue subordination of essences.] Thus a man may not permit a medical intervention (whether in the somatic or psychic order) calculated to cure a serious defect but at the same time entailing permanent damage of the human personality, say, by a notable lessening of freedom. An operation might degrade a man to the level of a brute beast or an automaton. Such a reversal of values is not countenanced by the moral law, which, accordingly, sets a limit to what may be done in the ' medical interests of the patient '. Another example. In order to rid oneself of repressions, inhibitions or complexes, one may not stir up the sexual appetites on the plea that it is being done for therapeutic purposes. A man may not make these appetites the object of his desires or actions and run the risk of all the upheavals and repercussions that usually accompany such activities. There is a personal obligation of purity and self-respect which forbids every Christian—nay, every individual—to plunge without let or hindrance into a sea of sexual phantasms and lures. The " medical and psycho-therapeutical interests of the patient " encounter here a barrier set up by the moral law. It has not been proved—nay, it is not true—that the pan-sexual method of a certain school of psycho-analysis is an indispensable component in all psycho-therapy worthy of the name. It is not true to say that neglect of this method in the past has been the cause of serious psychic evils affecting the spheres of education, psychotherapy and even pastoral medicine. Nor is it true to say there is a pressing need to make good the deficiency, and to train those engaged with psychic questions in its principles, and even in the manipulation of sexual technique.

We speak of this subject because all too often today it is coolly assumed that the case for pan-sexual treatment has been proved. It would be better in what pertains to the instructive life to give more attention to indirect methods, and to the effect that conscious effort can have on the imagination and affections. Such technique avoids signal aberrations. It tends to enlighten, heal and guide. It influences also the dynamic in sexuality (on which so much stress is laid) which ought to reside—and does in fact reside—in the unconscious or the subconscious.

So far we have spoken rather of the patient and not of the doctor. We have explained at what point the individual right of the patient to dispose of himself, of his mind, of his body, of his faculties, organs and functions comes up against a moral boundary. At the same time, We have found an answer to the question: What limit is set by the moral law to medical research and treatment for the ' good of the patient '? The frontier is the same as it is for the patient: it is fixed by right reason, and has its source in the final end and scale of values imprinted in things. The bounds are the same for the doctor as for the patient, because, as We have already said, the doctor like the private individual, disposes of rights—and those rights only—which are granted by the patient; and because the patient cannot confer more than he himself possesses.

What we have already said applies likewise to the legal representative of any person who is incapable of disposing of himself and his affairs; for instance, children not yet come to the use of reason, feeble-minded persons, and the insane. Legal representatives, whether appointed privately or by public authority, do not possess over the body and life of their clients any other rights than the latter would have if they were capable. They cannot, therefore, give the doctor permission to dispose of patients outside the limits already mentioned.

How far the common good justifies new medical methods and treatments.

A third set of interests is put forward to justify the employment of new processes and experiments in medical science, namely, the interests of the community, the *bonum commune* or 'common good', as philosophers and sociologists call it.

Nobody denies there is such a thing as the common good. And nobody denies that it calls for and justifies fresh researches. The two sets of interests already named, those of science and those of the patient, are bound up with the general interest, the interest of the community.

Hence, for a third time the question arises: Are the medical interests of the community subject to moral checks? Must we give a free hand to every serious experimenter on human beings? Do barriers exist for the good of science, for the good of the individual? To put it in another way: May the public authority, whose business it is to care for the common good, empower the doctor to experiment on the individual (by trying out new methods and processes) for the sake of science and the community, even if the experiments violate the rights of the individual? May the public authorities plead they are acting for the good of the community if they restrict or suppress the rights of an individual over his own body and life?

Let us have no misunderstanding. We are speaking of genuine research, an honest sincere effort to promote scientific theory and practice. We are not dealing with pretences, with shams, with something that masquerades as science in order to conceal its true purpose and realize it with impunity.

As to the questions already posed, many think the answers must be in the affirmative. In support, they argue that the individual is subordinate to the community, that the good of the individual must therefore give way to that of the community; and, if necessary, be sacrificed to it. They add that the individual will in the long run benefit from his sacrifice to serve purposes of scientific investigation.

The great post-war trials produced a terrible heap of documents which revealed how individuals had been sacrificed in ' the medical interests of the community '. The documents are full of evidence showing that, with the assent, and sometimes by formal command of the public authority, certain centres received a regular supply of human "guinea-pigs" from concentration camps for their medical researches. Detailed reports specify how people were delivered up to the experimental stations: so many men, so many women, so many for this experiment, so many for that. There are reports on the various phases and results of the experiments. Observations are recorded on the objective and subjective symptoms of the human material. One cannot read the notes without being seized with a deep compassion for the victims, many of whom met their death in the process. One recoils before such an aberration of the human heart and mind. We can add: those responsible for such atrocities supply the answer to the queries We have put. They show the practical consequence of permitting unlimited research and experiment in the name of the ' common good '.

One must needs be blind to realities if one can see any person in the medical world at the present day holding and defending the views responsible for the deeds referred to. It is enough to read a few of the reports on the medical trials to reach conviction. One's immediate reaction is to wonder: what could possibly have caused this or that doctor to do such a thing? Whence could he imagine he had authority for such action? With calm cold words each experiment is described as it proceeded and came to a head: notes are made on what is established as true and what is not so. But of morality, not a word.

The question remains, however; and passing it over in silence does not dispose of it.

Is it a case of subordinating the individual to the medical interests of the community? Have we here really a transgression (maybe in good faith) of the most basic demands of the natural law, a transgression that cannot be tolerated for any reason of medical research?

In so far as justification for the above medical experiments is claimed because of a mandate from the public authority, such a claim rests on a misunderstanding or a misapplication of the relevant principle concerning the relation between the individual and the community. It must be recalled that man does not exist for society, but society exists for man. Man in the final reckoning is a person, an individual; not an abstraction or a unit in statistical studies.

The community is the great medium ordained by nature and by God to regulate the exchanges by which mutual needs are met, and to help each individual to develop his personality according to his social capacity. The community is not a physical unit subsisting in itself. Its members are not integrating parts of the whole, but integrant parts only. The physical organism of living beings (plants, animals or men), has a unity which subsists in itself, so that each constituent part (for example, the hand, foot, heart, eye) is an integrant part; that is, destined by its whole being to be a part of one complete organism. Outside the organism, it has not of itself, of its own nature, any meaning or purpose: its being is absorbed in the organism to which it contributes and to which it belongs.

A quite different state of affairs exists in the moral community—as in every organism of a purely moral nature. In these cases, the whole has not [a physical or natural unity] a unity which subsists in itself, but only a single unity of purpose and of action. In a community, the individual members are no more than collaborators and instruments for realizing the ends of the combined or composite body.

What do we infer in regard to the physical organism? We infer that the master, the person who uses an organism endowed with a subsisting unity, may dispose directly and immediately of the integrant parts within the framework of their natural purpose. Likewise, he can intervene (when and in so far as the well-being of the whole requires) to paralyse, destroy, mutilate or separate the members. In marked contrast, when the whole does not possess a unity of finality and action, its head—that is to say in the present case, the public authority—retains, of course, direct authority and the right to impose its demands on the activity of the parts; but in no case is it entitled to dispose directly of their physical being. Morever, any direct assault on its own essential being by a public authority is a departure from the sphere of activity which rightly belongs to it [and constitutes anarchy, social suicide].

Now, medical intervention, of the kind we are dealing with, affects immediately and directly the physical being, either of the whole or of the individual organs of the human body. In virtue of the principle already stated by Us, the public authority has no right in this matter; it cannot, therefore, delegate power to research workers and doctors. Furthermore, whenever a doctor, for the good of the community, interferes with the organism of an individual, his authorization must come from the State. Then, he acts not as a private individual, but as a mandatory of the public power. But the latter cannot confer a right which it does not possess itself.

Even when there is question of executing a man condemned to death, the State does not dispose of the individual's right to live. The individual has dispossessed himself of the right to life by his crime, and the public authority has then the right to deprive him of life in expiation of his fault.

In the cases We have been dealing with, the principle of totality is often invoked. The principle states that the part exists for the whole, and, consequently, the good of the part remains subordinate to the good of the whole: the whole determines the part and can dispose of it in its own interest. The principle has its root in the nature of things, and is, therefore, absolute.

Accordingly, the principle is one that must always be followed. But in order to apply it correctly, one must be clear about certain points. First of all, there is the question of fact: do the objects, to which the principle is being applied, really stand in the relation of whole and part? Secondly, what is the precise nature and degree of the relationship? Does it fall into the category of essence, or action, or of both? Does the relation hold of the part under every, or only under a limited aspect? To the extent in which it applies, does the whole absorb the part completely, or does it leave a certain amount of independence?

The reply to these questions can never be deduced from the principle itself—that might look like a vicious circle. The reply must be got from other facts and from other sources of knowledge. The principle of totality affirms no more than this: where the relationship of whole to part is verified, and in the measure in which it is verified, the part is subordinate to the whole, and the latter can in its own interest dispose of the part. Too often, alas, these points are not considered when recourse is made to the principle of totality: this happens not only in speculative studies and in applications of law, sociology, physics, biology and medicine; but even in logic, psychology and metaphysics.

Our purpose has been to draw your attention to certain principles of deontology [science of duty, ethics] which define the bounds and limits of experiment and new methods in their application to human beings.

In the domain of science it goes without saying that one first carries out research on the dead body or a laboratory specimen or 'subject' and one experiments with brute animals before trying out a new technique on a living person. When this is impossible, inadequate or impracticable, it may be lawful (under the conditions We have stated) to work directly on human beings in the interests of science, the patient and the community.

In authorizing new methods in accord with the moral law, one cannot demand the total and certain exclusion of all danger and risk. That would ask too much of human nature, and would often turn to the detriment of the patient, since it would paralyse scientific research. Assessing the degree of danger must be left in such cases to the judgment of an experienced and competent doctor. One must of course keep in mind the limit of risk which Our exposition has shown to be forbidden by the moral law. In doubtful instances, where known methods have failed, it may happen that a new and insufficiently tried method offers appreciable chance of success along with elements of great danger. If the patient gives his consent, the process in question is lawful. But such action cannot be regarded as the line of treatment to be followed in normal cases.

It may be objected that the ideas here developed will constitute a grave obstacle to research and scientific work. The line We have drawn is not really a hindrance to progress. What is true in other fields of research, experiment, and human activity generally holds good for medicine. The mighty laws of morality control the swift torrent of human thought and make it flow like a river in a well defined channel. They contain it for its own greater effectiveness. They dam the flood and keep it from overflowing to work havoc that would not find compensation in the specious good pursued. Moral restrictions appear to be a curb. In reality, they make their own contribution to the fine and noble achievements of man for the good of science, the individual, and the community.

May Almighty God, in the goodness of His Providence, to this end bestow on you His blessing and His Grace.

2. *Discourse to Psychologists*

(*April* 13, 1953)

[In the month of April, 1953, the fifth of a series of Congresses for Catholic Psychiatrists was held in Rome, the central theme being "Psychotherapies and man in his present state". Twelve nations were represented and the discussions were nearly all in French. Many fundamental human problems were broached. The name of Freud was often heard mentioned, generally in terms of approval for his solid contributions to experimental psychology apart from his theories. There were two main fields of discussion: one, wide, on the relation between the spiritual and the psychological, and the difference between sin and neurosis; and another, at a practical level, on techniques and application of principles, with specific reference to various forms of psychotherapy and the use of electro-shock. A visit was paid to *Marinella* to see the

"Boys' Republic" where responsibility is learned through freedom. On the last morning the members of the Congress were received by the Holy Father who delivered his address in the crimson-damasked Hall of Consistories.

Modern psychologists call attention to three states of the mind, the conscious, subconscious and unconscious states, and employ figures like day, twilight and night, or the top, water-line and submerged base of an iceberg, to explain them. Again they find it useful though artificial to divide the mind into three imaginary parts as if it depended on three sets of "switchboards" in the brain. These would be more or less the seats of reason, desire and conscience. Freud called the conscious part of the mind where thought occurs the *ego*. The great unconscious territory of the mind, filled with desires and urges and drives (dynamisms), he called the *id*. Finally he gave the name of *super-ego* to that part of the mind which stores up what he calls the results of racial experience, such as traditions, taboos and moral precepts. Some of our strange behaviour becomes explicable in the terms now used by psychologists to describe our chief faculty. The ego, or conscious mind, would be the seat of thought, reason and visual imagination, and would control the personality when we are awake, but it is constantly driven by the id and restrained by the super-ego. In sleep, the ego loses much of its power, the super-ego is also enfeebled, and the id may become dominant as censorship by ego and super-ego is relaxed. Dreams are then seen to be often messages in code that the id sends up to the small bit of consciousness which remains active during sleep.]

W E greet you, dear sons and daughters, who have come from all parts, and are gathered together in Rome to listen to learned conferences, and discuss questions of psychotherapy and clinical psychology. Your Congress has ended, and, in order to ensure its fruitfulness and the success of your research and future work, you have come to seek the blessing of the Vicar of Christ. Very gladly, We accede to your wish. We avail Ourselves of this occasion to address to you a word of encouragement and to give you some advice.

Science declares that recent observations have brought to light the hidden layers of the psychic structure of man, and tries to understand the meaning of these discoveries, to interpret them and to see how they can be used. People speak of dynamisms, determinisms, and mechanisms hidden in the depths of the soul, endowed with immanent laws, whence are derived certain ways of acting. Undoubtedly these begin to operate within the sub-conscious or the unconscious, but they also find their way into the realms of the conscious and determine it. People claim to have devised methods that have been tried and recognized as being able to sound the mystery of the depths of the soul, to throw light on them, and put them back on the right road when their influence is harmful.

In these questions, which are within the province of scientific psychology, you are competent. The same may be said of the use of new psychic methods. However, theoretical and practical psy-chology, the one as much as the other, should bear in mind that they cannot lose sight of the truths established by reason and by faith, nor of the moral obligations of ethics.

Last year, in the month of September, to meet the wishes of members of the " First International Congress of Histopathology of the Nervous System ", We traced the moral limits governing medical methods of research and treatment. On the basis of that explanation, We would like to-day to add something by way of complement. We would briefly outline the fundamental attitude which must be adopted by the Christian psychologist and psychotherapist.

This basic approach can be summed up in the following formula : Psychotherapy and clinical psychology must always consider man :

1. As a psychic whole;

2. As a single, complete structure;

3. As a social entity;

4. As a transcendent whole, that is to say, as a human being moving naturally toward God.

MAN AS A COMPLETE PSYCHIC WHOLE.

Medicine has learned to look upon the human body as a mechanism of great precision, whose parts fit into each other and are naturally linked together. The parts depend on the whole and it is their function to promote its well being and activities. This principle applies with even greater force to the soul whose mechanisms are much more subtle and delicately jointed. The various psychic faculties and functions are components of the whole spiritual entity whose destiny they serve.

There is no need to develop the point further. But you, psychologists and psychic healers, must bear this fact in mind: the existence of each psychic faculty and function is explained by the purpose of the whole man. What constitutes man is principally the soul, the substantial form of his nature. From it, ultimately, flow all the life, and all the activity of man; in it are rooted all the psychic forces, with their own proper structure and their organic law; it is the soul which nature charges with the government of man's energies, in so far as these have not yet acquired their final determination. Given this ontological and psychological fact, it follows that it would be quite unreal to attempt, in theory or in practice, to entrust the determining rôle of the whole to one particular factor, for example, to one of the elementary psychic drives, and thus install a secondary power at the helm. Those urges may be *in* the soul, *in* man: they are not, however, the soul, nor the man. They are energies of considerable intensity, perhaps, but nature has entrusted their direction to what is at the centre, namely, the immaterial soul endowed with intellect and will, which is normally capable of governing these energies. That these energies may exercise pressure upon one's activity, does not necessarily signify that they compel it. To deprive the soul of its central place would be to deny an ontological and psychic reality.

It is not right, therefore, when studying the relationship of the ego to the urges that drive it, to admit unreservedly in theory the autonomy of man, that is, of his soul, and then go on immediately to state in everyday life this principle appears to be of small account. In real life, it is argued, man retains freedom to give his consent to what he does, but in no way the freedom to do it. The autonomy of free will is replaced by the heteronomy of the force of instinct. That is not the way in which God fashioned man. Original sin did not take away from man the possibility, or the obligation, of directing his own actions himself through his soul. It cannot be alleged that the psychic troubles and disorders which disturb the normal functioning of the psychic being, make known what usually happens. The moral struggle to remain on the right path does not prove that it is impossible to follow that path, nor does it authorize any drawing back.

MAN AS A SINGLE STRUCTURE.

A WRONG APPROACH. Man is an ordered unit, one whole, a microcosm, after the fashion of a State whose charter, determined by the end of the whole, subordinates to this end the activity of the parts in the right order of their value and function. The charter is, in the final reckoning, of an ontological and metaphysical origin, not a psychological and personal one. There are those who have thought it necessary to stress the opposition between the metaphysical and the psychological. What a mistaken approach! The psychic itself belongs to the domain of the ontological and metaphysical.

We have recalled this truth to you in order to base on it a remark about man in the concrete, whose internal structure is being here examined. Indeed, an effort has been made to establish the contradiction between traditional psychology and ethics, and modern psychotherapy and clinical psychology. Traditional psychology and ethics, they say, have for their object man's being in the abstract, homo " *ut sic* ", who, in fact, nowhere exists. The clarity and logical connection of those sciences, they add, calls for admiration, but they suffer from a basic fault: they cannot be applied to the real man as he exists. Clinical psychology, on the contrary, deals with real man—with " *homo ut hic* ". And the conclusion is: between the two conceptions there opens an abyss which cannot be crossed unless psychology and ethics change their stand.

Whoever studies the constitution of real man, ought, in fact, to take as his object " existential " man, as he is, and such as his natural dispositions, the influence of his *milieu,* education, his personal development, his inner experiences and other circumstances have made him. It is only man in the concrete that exists. Yet, the structure of this personal " ego " obeys, in the smallest detail, the ontological and metaphysical laws of human nature of which We have spoken above. They have formed it, and thus should govern and judge it. The reason behind this is that " existential " man is one and the same in his inner structure as " essential " man. The essential structure of man does not disappear when individual qualities are added to it; it is not further transformed into another human nature. Now the charter, of which We spoke just now, rests precisely, in its principal terms, on the essential structure of real man, man in the concrete.

Consequently, it would be erroneous to establish for real life standards which would move away from natural and Christian morality, and which, for want of a better word, could be called " personalist ethics ". The latter would, without doubt, receive a certain " orientation " from the former, but this would not admit of any strict obligation. One does not invent the law of a man's constitution, one applies it.

MAN AS A SOCIAL UNIT.

SOCIAL ASPECT OF THE PSYCHE. What We have said up to now concerns man in his personal life. The psyche has likewise relations with the exterior world, and a praiseworthy task, a field open to your researches, is found in the study of the psychic in its social aspects, in itself and in its roots, with the idea also of making it serviceable for the purposes of clinical psychology and of psychotherapy. However, one should take good care in this matter to make an exact distinction between the facts and their interpretation.

Social psychism touches also morality, and the principles of morality affect, to a large extent, those of clinical psychology and psychotherapy. Now there are some points where the application of social psychism sins by excess or by defect; and it is on this that We would briefly dwell.

INHIBITION OF THE EGO. *Error by defect*: There is a psychological and moral disturbance—that of the inhibition of the "ego" —with which your science concerns itself, in order to discover the causes. When this inhibition encroaches on the moral domain, as for instance, when there is question of dynamic tendencies, such as the instinct of domination, of superiority, and the sexual instinct, psychotherapy would not be capable, without further considerations, of treating this inhibition of the "ego" as a kind of fatality, as a tyranny of the affective impulse streaming forth from the subconscious, and escaping completely from the control of the conscience and of the soul. One should be slow to lower man, in the concrete, along with his personal character, to the level of the brute.

Despite the good intentions of the therapeutists, sensitive natures bitterly resent this degradation to the level of mere instinctive and sensitive life. Furthermore, the observations We have made above on the hierarchy of values among the functions, and the rôle of their central direction, should not be disregarded.

SEX EDUCATION. A word also on the method sometimes employed by the psychologist to set the "ego" free from its inhibition, in the case of aberration in the sexual domain. We refer to complete sexual initiation, which would not pass over anything in silence, leave nothing obscure. Is there not here a harmful exaggeration of the value of knowledge in these matters?

There is, however, an effective sexual education which, quite safely, teaches calmly and objectively what the young person should know, for his own personal conduct and his relationship with those with whom he is brought into contact. For the rest, special stress will be laid, in sexual education, as indeed, in all education, upon self-mastery and religious training. The Holy See published certain norms in this connection shortly after the Encyclical of Pius XI on Christian Marriage (Holy Office, 21st March. 1931—*Acta Apostolicae Sedis*, a. XXIII, 1 1931, p. 118). These norms have not been rescinded, either expressly or "*via facti*".

PSYCHOANALYSIS. What has just been said of ill-considered initiation, for therapeutic purposes, is true also of certain forms of *psychoanalysis*. One should not come to regard them as the only means of relieving or of curing psychical sexual troubles. The trite principle that sexual trouble of the unconscious, like all other inhibitions of the same origin, can be suppressed only by its being brought to the level of consciousness, is not valid if it is stated baldly and without qualification. Indirect treatment is also effective, and often is quite enough. As to the use of the psychoanalytic method in the sexual domain, Our allocution of 13th September, already quoted, has already pointed out its moral limits. Truth to tell, one cannot consider as lawful, without further explanation, the bringing to the level of consciousness of all the images, emotions and sexual experiences which lie dormant in the memory and the unconscious, and which are thus psychically experienced. If protests arising from a sense of human and Christian dignity are heeded, who would dare to claim that this manner of treatment does not imply both present and future moral danger, since, even though the therapeutic necessity of unlimited exploration be asserted, its necessity has not been established.

ERROR BY EXCESS: SURRENDER OF THE EGO. *Error by Excess* consists in emphasizing the need to make total surrender of the "ego", and of its personal assertiveness. With regard to this, We would consider two points: a general principle, and a point of therapeutic practice.

Beginning with certain psychological explanations, the thesis is formulated that the unconditioned extroversion of the ego is the fundamental law of congenital altruism and of its dynamic tendencies. This is a logical, psychological, and ethical error. There exists in fact a defence, an esteem, a love and a service of one's personal self, which is not only justified but demanded by psychology and morality. Nature makes this plain, and it is also a lesson of the Christian faith (cf. St. Thomas, *Summa Theol.*, 2a, 2ae p., q. 26, art. 4, in c.). Our Lord taught: " Thou shalt love thy neighbour as thyself " (Mark xii, 31). Christ, then, proposes as the rule of love of neighbour, charity towards oneself, not the inverse. Applied psychology would undervalue this reality if it were to describe all consideration of the ego as psychic inhibition or a return to a former state of development, under the pretext that it is contrary to the natural altruism of the psychic being.

SAFEGUARDING SECRETS. The point about psychotherapeutic practice that We mentioned, has to do with an essential interest of the community, namely: the *safeguarding* of *secrets* which the use of psychoanalysis places in jeopardy. It is not at all denied that a fact or knowledge which is secret, and repressed in the subconscious, may provoke serious psychic conflicts. If psycho-analysis discloses the cause of this trouble, it will want, following its principle, to draw out this unconscious element completely, and make it conscious, in order to remove the obstacle. Now there are secrets which must on no account be disclosed, even to a doctor. even in spite of grave personal inconvenience. The secret of Confession may never be revealed. It is equally forbidden to make known the professional secret to another, even to a doctor. The same is true of other secrets. One may invoke the principle: " for a proportionately grave reason it is lawful to reveal a secret to a prudent man and one capable of keeping a secret ". This principle is correct, within narrow limits, for certain kinds of secret. It is not right to make use of it indiscriminately in psychoanalytic practice.

From the moral standpoint, and first and foremost for the common good, the principle of discretion in the use of psycho-analysis cannot be sufficiently stressed. Obviously, it is not prim-arily a question of the discretion of the psychoanalyst, but that of the patient, who frequently has no right whatever to give away his secrets.

MAN AS A TRANSCENDENT UNIT TENDING TOWARDS GOD

A MYSTERIOUS DYNAMISM. This latter aspect of man raises three questions which We would not wish to overlook.

First of all, scientific research is drawing attention to a dynamism which, rooted in the depths of the psychic being, would push man towards the infinite that lies beyond him, not by making him know it, but because of an upward gravitation that comes directly from the very depths of his being. This dynamism is regarded as an independent force, and, in fact, the most fundamental and the most elementary force of the soul, an affective impulse carrying man immediately to the divine; just as when a flower unfolds to light and sunshine without knowing it, or as when a child breathes unconsciously as soon as it is born,

Of this assertion We would say, forthwith, that if it be stated that a dynamism is at the root of all religion, and manifests the element common to all, We know, on the contrary, that religion, the natural and supernatural knowledge of God and worship of Him, do not proceed from the unconscious or the subconscious, nor from an impulse of the affections, but from the clear and certain knowledge of God by means of His natural and positive revelation. This is the teaching and the belief of the Church, beginning with the Word of God in the Book of Wisdom, and the Epistle to the Romans, down to the Encyclical " *Pascendi Dominici Gregis* " [on modernism] of Our Predecessor, Blessed Pius X.

Having laid down this principle, the question of the mysterious dynamism still remains. On this subject one might make the following remarks. We should certainly not find fault with depth psychology, if it deals with the psychic aspects of religious phenomena, and endeavours to analyse and reduce them to a scientific system, even if this research is new and if its terminology was not in use in times past. We mention this point, because misunderstandings can easily arise, when psychology attributes new meanings to terms already accepted. Prudence and reserve are needed on both sides in order to avoid false interpretations, and to make it possible to reach a mutual understanding.

It belongs to the technique of your science to clarify the questions of the existence, the structure, and the mode of action of this dynamism. If the outcome proves to be positive, it should not be declared irreconcilable with reason or faith. This would only show that, even in its deepest roots, " *esse ab alio* " also implies an " *esse ad alium* ",[1] and that St. Augustine's words : " Thou hast made us for thyself, O Lord, and our heart shall not rest until it rests in thee " (*Confessions,* Book I, Chapter 1, N.1), find a new confirmation in the very depths of man's psychic being. Even if there were questions of a dynamism involving all men, peoples, epochs, and cultures, what a help, and what an invaluable help, this would be for the search after God and the affirmation of His existence !

_____

[1] i.e., being " from another " implies being " for another ", or moving " towards another ".

SENSE OF GUILT. To the transcendent relations of the psychic being, there belongs also the *sense of guilt*, the awareness of having violated a higher law, by which, nevertheless, one recognizes oneself as being bound, an awareness which can find expression in suffering and in psychic disorder.

Psychotherapy, here, approaches a phenomenon which is not within its own exclusive field of competence, for this phenomenon is also, if not principally, of a religious nature. No one will deny that there can exist—and not infrequently—an irrational and even morbid sense of guilt. Yet a person may also be aware of a real fault which has not been wiped away. Neither psychology nor ethics possesses an infallible criterion for cases of this kind, since the workings of conscience which beget the sense of guilt have too personal and subtle a structure. In any case, it is certain that no purely psychological treatment will cure a genuine sense of guilt. Even if psychotherapists, perhaps even in good faith, question its existence, it still abides. Even if the sense of guilt be eliminated by medical intervention, auto-suggestion, or outside persuasion, the fault remains, and psychotherapy would deceive both itself and others if, in order to do away with the sense of guilt, it pretended that the fault no longer existed.

The means of eliminating the fault does not belong to the purely psychological order. As every Christian knows, it consists in contrition and sacramental absolution by the priest. Here, it is the root of the evil, it is the fault itself, which is extirpated, even though remorse may continue to make itself felt. Nowadays, in certain pathological cases, it is not rare for the priest to send his penitent to a doctor. In the present case, the doctor should rather direct his patient towards God, and to those who have the power to remit the fault itself in the name of God.

MATERIAL SIN. A final remark on the transcendent leaning of the psychic being towards God. Respect for God and His holiness must always be reflected in man's conscious acts. When, even without subjective fault on the part of the person involved, these acts are in contrast to the divine model, they still run counter to the ultimate purpose of his being. That is why what is called "*material sin*" is something which should not exist, and which constitutes in the moral order a reality not to be discounted.

From this, a conclusion follows for psychotherapy. In the presence of material sin it cannot remain neutral. It can, for the moment, tolerate what remains inevitable. Yet it must know that God cannot justify such an action. With still less reason, can psychotherapy counsel a patient to commit material sin, on the ground that it will be without subjective guilt. Such counsel would also be wrong if this action were regarded as necessary for the psychic easing of the patient, and thus as being part of the treatment. One may never counsel a conscious action which would be a deformation, and not an image, of the divine perfection.

So much We feel obliged to say to you. Furthermore, be assured that the Church follows your research and your medical practice with warm interest and best wishes. You work on a terrain that is very difficult. Your activity, however, is capable of achieving precious results for medicine, for the knowledge of the soul in general, for the religious dispositions of man and for their development. May Providence and divine grace light your path! In pledge thereof We impart to you with fatherly goodwill Our Apostolic Blessing.

3. *Medical Ethics and Medical Law*

[Discourse to Delegates attending the XVIth Session of the International Congress of Military Medicine, October 19, 1953.]

Having completed the work of the Sixteenth Session of the International Office of Military Medical Documentation, you have come, gentlemen, to give Us the pleasure of your visit. We thank you, and bid you welcome.

A full series of medical congresses and medical associations has visited Us during the past and the preceding years, and indeed in such large numbers, that We have experienced how much the relationship between the Pope and doctors is a relationship of confidence. Nor are there wanting profound reasons for this. The doctor, as well as the priest and the Church, must be a friend and helper of human kind; he must heal men stricken by disease, by wounds and by sufferings; and these three things, sickness, wounds and suffering are found always and everywhere, in times of peace, as even more so, in times of war.

You have answered in advance Our confidence in you, and you have asked Us to take a stand upon fundamental points, or, more exactly, upon the moral aspect of various questions which concern you as army doctors. We are very glad to meet your wishes. The words which We address to you, therefore, concern the military doctor as such, the doctor in time of war. Taking this for granted, We would like to speak of ethics and of the medical law for doctors.

MEDICAL ETHICS.

A first question on the ethics of military medicine presents itself from the scientific standpoint. The extraordinary number of cases which war puts into the hands of the doctor, helps to widen and deepen his theoretical and practical science. As We have explained before, science, in itself, has always a positive value, in medicine as in other departments. Otherwise, omniscience could not be a divine attribute. This holds good for the biological and medical phenomena, both the good and the bad, which war reveals to the doctor. But if, in itself, the growth of science is beneficial, it does not follow that all means of acquiring it are legitimate. Moreover, generally speaking, not every science is suitable for every man, nor for every group of men. Science is certainly not a benefit when one has the perverse intention of using it in order to harm others or to injure them unjustly.

Let Us apply this. The research for, the discovery of, and the knowledge of, new methods of mass-annihilation by biological and chemical warfare, of new processes for suppressing political, national or racial enemies, of new types of euthanasia for the wounded, for those who are mutilated or incurable, could—as a pure development of science—be of positive value; but they are not so in the hands of every doctor, every commander-in-chief, or even of every nation. Thus one answers (only in part, be it understood) the question: should such discoveries, such new experiments, be published indiscriminately by their inventors and made known, if not to the whole world, at least when higher authority insists on such communication?

Although, in certain cases, there may be no need for reserve or secrecy regarding the results in themselves, there may perhaps be all the more need for reserve regarding the means of achieving the results. If it is impossible to arrive at the knowledge of a principle or to be certain of the possibility of its practical application without dangerous and perhaps fatal experiments upon living men, the end pursued does not thereby justify the means. Neither in peace nor in war—and much less so in war—are the wounded, prisoners of war, victims of forced labour, displaced persons in concentration camps, subjects for medical experimentation, subjects of whom one may dispose freely, or with the approval of authority. The last decades have made it clear to all that the violation of this norm, sad to say, could actually happen.

This first point of medical ethics has to do with the acquisition of theoretical knowledge by the doctor in war time; but the principal preoccupation of a doctor must be his professional activity.

In the reports of your sessions, in the project for world-wide codification of medical ethics, in the project for an International Medical Law, and in the proposed formula for a world-wide Doctor's Oath which would be valid everywhere, one idea keeps recurring, namely, that the principle underlying professional and moral conduct, of conscience and of medical practice, is to aid and to heal, not to injure, destroy or kill. These reflections have led you to demand of the doctor, in times of peace and more so during war, respect for human life from its inception until death, its care and well-being, the healing of its wounds and maladies, the relief of its suffering and infirmities, the preservation from, and the fight against, dangers, the abandonment of whatever opposes these duties. You have underlined the principle that this should apply to all men, friend or foe, regardless of sex, age, race, nation or culture.

Apply the guiding principle of the medical conscience to wartime, when the pitiless fury of modern arms destroys so many lives, inflicts so many wounds, so much mutilation, so much suffering and pain, causes so much dereliction and abandonment, on the battlefield as well as in the bombed city. The realization of this essential law of conscience and of medical practice will meet with the approval of all righteous men throughout the world. It is the response to the yearning of every human heart and to the hope of every sane person.

We have no need to explain that the medical conscience, as you yourselves have pointed out, can be the collective conscience of all the doctors of the world. For human nature, biological and medical laws, suffering and misery, and also gratitude to those who bring health and help, are the same everywhere.

Here, at once, one touches another fundamental truth, namely, that this medical conscience is not purely subjective; it is formed rather by contact with fact, and it steers its course in accordance with reality and with the ontological laws which govern all thought and all judgment.

These ontological laws should be considered along with what We have said concerning the scientific point of view as such. The latter, too, is subordinate to these norms. The doctor who would be unwilling to realize this would forfeit his title as doctor in the full and noble sense of the word. In your reports, it has been proposed that a distinction be made between two classes of doctors: the research worker and the practitioner. This distinction permits the supposition that the "research doctor" is considered as entirely at the service of the "practitioner". In any event, if the former does not accept the imperative prohibition to do evil, to destroy and to kill, he would then be rejecting at the same time the medical conscience and medical ethics by which he is likewise bound.

But the activity of the conscientious doctor, for whom the basic principle " to aid and heal, not to destroy and kill " is taken for granted, could also be faced with limits against the transgression of which there is a veto, a ' no ' demanded by interests that, in the scale of values, prevail over the health of the body and over life. A year ago (13th September, 1952) We spoke at some length to the First Congress of Histopathology of the Nervous System, on the moral limits of research and of medical treatment. It will suffice today to refer to what We said on that occasion concerning points which have a special bearing on the questions which interest you.

As your reports show, the problem of moral limits became clear in your own discussions, and various opinions were then expressed. We said last year that the doctor justifies his decisions by the interests of science, of the patient, and of the common good. The interest of science has already been discussed. As for the interests of the patient, the doctor has no more right to intervene than the patient gives him. The patient, on his part, the individual himself, has no right to dispose of his own existence, of the integrity of his body and soul, of his particular organs and of their functions, except in the measure demanded by the good of the whole organism.

This provides the key for the answer to the question which interests you. May the doctor apply a dangerous remedy, undertake intervention which will probably or certainly be fatal, solely because the patient wishes it and consents? Likewise to the question, in itself understandable by the doctor working just behind the front lines or at a military hospital: could he, in a case of insupportable or incurable suffering, or horrible wounds, administer, at the express demand of the patient, injections which are equivalent to euthanasia?

Now with regard to the interest of the community, public authority has, in general, no direct right to dispose of the existence and the integrity of the organs of its innocent subjects. (As to the question of corporal punishment and the death penalty, We do not discuss it here, since We are speaking of the doctor, not of the executioner.) Since the State does not possess this direct right of disposal, it cannot communicate authority to the doctor for any motive or end whatsoever. The political community is not a physical being like an organic body, but an assembly which possesses only a unity of purpose and action. Man does not exist for the State, but the State for man. When there is a question of irrational beings, plants or animals, man is free to dispose of their existence and their life (not forgetting the obligation which he has before God and his own dignity to avoid unjustified brutality and cruelty), but not of other men or of subordinates.

The military doctor derives from this a sure directive, which, without taking away from him the responsibility of his decision, is capable of saving him from errors of judgment, by furnishing him with a clear, objective standard.

The fundamental principle of medical ethics demands not only the directive " to aid and heal, not to harm or kill ", but also to prevent and to preserve.

This point is decisive for the position of the doctor as regards war in general and modern war in particular. The doctor is an adversary of war and promoter of peace. As he is ready to heal the wounds of war already inflicted, so also does he devote himself to preventing them as far as possible.

Mutual goodwill always seeks to avoid war as an ultimate means of overcoming disputes between States. A few days ago We again expressed the desire that every war should be punished on the international plane (unless it be demanded by the absolute necessity of self-defence against a very grave injustice which affects the whole community and cannot be prevented by other means, but yet must be prevented) lest in international relations free rein be given to brute force and lack of all conscience. It is not enough, then, to have to defend oneself against any injustice whatever in order to use violent methods of war. If the damage resulting from the latter is not comparable with that of the " injustice tolerated ", one may be obliged to " submit to the injustice ".

What We have just said holds above all for A.B.C. warfare— atomic, biological, and chemical. It is enough that We refer here to the question: what conditions must be satisfied to justify one in *defending oneself* against an A.B.C. war. The answer can be deduced from the same principles which are decisive today for permitting war in general. In any case, another question at once presents itself: is it not possible to proscribe and effectively ward off A.B.C. warfare by international agreement?

After the horrors of two world conflicts, We have no need to recall that all apotheosis of war is to be condemned as an aberration of the mind and heart. Certainly, strength of soul and bravery, even to the giving up of life when duty demands it, are great virtues; but to wish to provoke war because it is the school of great virtues and an occasion for practising them, must be considered as crime and folly.

What We have said shows the direction in which to find the answer to this other question: can the doctor place his science and his energies at the service of A.B.C. warfare? He can never countenance injustice, even in the service of his own country; and when this type of war constitutes an injustice, the doctor cannot collaborate with it.

THE MEDICAL CONSCIENCE. A word remains to be said about the control and the sanctions of the medical conscience.

The final and highest control is the Creator Himself, God. We would not do justice to the fundamental principles of your programme and to the consequences derived therefrom, were We to describe them merely as requirements of mankind, as humanitarian ends or aims. They are that also, but they are more. The ultimate source whence they derive their force and dignity, is the Creator of human nature. If it were simply a matter of principles elaborated by the will of men only, then their obligation would have no more binding force than men have; they could be applicable today and be passed over tomorrow; one country could accept them and another refuse them. The case is just the opposite if the authority of the Creator intervenes. Now the basic principles of medical ethics are a part of the Divine Law. This, then, is the motive which authorizes the doctor to place unconditional confidence in these basic principles of medical ethics.

But the medical conscience feels, in addition, the need for a visible control and sanction. It will find one, first of all, in public opinion; this sides with you, gentlemen, since you recognize these principles. One counts thousands and tens of thousands of soldiers once wounded and sick, in whose minds and hearts so many doctors—some at the cost of their lives—have won an imperishable esteem and gratitude.

More important still, and more efficacious, is the check exercised by each doctor on his colleagues. The combined judgment takes on a particular importance in safeguarding medical ethics, when doctors are united in a professional community, even if it does not possess the character of public law. It could give its verdict with regard to a doctor devoid of conscience, and strike him off the Register.

If, in addition, one were to succeed in forming, as you are striving to do, a world-wide league of doctors who recognize the above-mentioned principles of medical ethics, and fulfil, at least in part, the rôle of overseers of the activity of the doctors, above all in time of war, the medical conscience would find in it an even more efficacious security. A similar world-wide league could found an international Order of Doctors whose judgment would be decisive as to the lawfulness of certain practices, and would have power to stigmatize the unlawful measures taken by individuals and even perhaps by States and by groups of States.

You rightly hold the opinion that the essential tenets of medical ethics should first of all become the common conviction of the whole medical profession, and eventually of a more numerous public; and, further, that, in the training of medical students, it is necessary to incorporate, as an obligatory branch, a systematic exposition of medical ethics. In your reports, finally, you demand a Medical Professional Oath, identical in different countries and nations. Before a doctor could obtain permission to exercise his profession, he would be obliged to take this oath before the delegates of the international medical profession. The oath would be a personal profession of the principles of medical ethics, and, at the same time, a support and an encouragement to observe them. Give, therefore, to this oath, or rather, leave to it, what belongs to it of its very nature: the religious significance of a promise made in the presence of the supreme authority of the Creator, from Whom your claims ultimately receive their binding force and their highest consecration.

Your efforts show—and for good motives—that you aim also at the creation of medical institutes of public and international law, supported by agreements between States. We shall broach this subject when treating of medical law.

MEDICAL LAW

There are certainly serious reasons for the creation of an International Medical Law for doctors, sanctioned by the community of peoples. First, because morality and law, by their very nature, are not always co-terminous, and when they do coincide, they remain, nevertheless, different in form. We can refer here to what We said in this regard to the members of the Congress of International Penal Law.

With regard to ethics, the law fulfils different functions: thus, for example, those of selection and of concentration. Both amount to this: that law does not promulgate again the demands of ethics, except in the measure requisite for the common good. It remains always fundamental, under this aspect, that positive law, as distinguished from the simple ethical postulate, proposes a norm of conduct, formulated by the competent authority of a community of peoples or States, and binding on the members of that community, keeping in mind the realization of the common good. To this positive law belong juridical obligation, juridical control, and the power of coercion.

LEGAL CONTROL. The drawing up of a legal code for doctors is not within the competency of the profession, nor of its governing bodies; it is reserved to the legislative power. Moreover, one can easily see the importance and the necessity of a medical law, by reason of the doctor's profound influence both on the individual and on society. The legislation of various States, also, contains regulations, sometimes scattered, sometimes grouped, often very detailed, on the training of doctors and the exercise of their profession. These legal dispositions give guidance to the doctor in his work, and provide others with a guarantee that he will act rightly. Moreover, they are a barrier for his conscience against malpractice and abuse of his power; they give peace to the community and assurance that it has entrusted its sick members to men of sound knowledge and proved skill, who are, moreover, subject to legal control. Naturally, it is always presupposed that this medical law is just, that is to say, in accord with truth and morality, and that it has not its origin in a system of violence without conscience.

If the urgency of a medical law is stressed in normal circumstances, it is all the more so in time of war. At no time is the observance of justice more important; at no time is there more threatening danger, not only of error, but also of unjust treatment. At no time are the consequences more serious for the soldier as well as for the doctor—perhaps it should even be added: at no time are the one and the other more unprotected than in war-time.

The fortunes of war may deliver the doctor into the power of the enemy, or confide to him their sick and wounded. He may find himself on the side of victors or the vanquished, in his own country or in enemy territory. What law, then, governs his person and the exercise of his profession? Even if he himself is a non-combatant, he is attached to groups of combatants; but then, to which category will he be recognized as belonging? May he exercise his profession, and upon whom? Upon his friends and enemies, military and civilian personnel? Wherever his assistance is required and necessary? And how can he exercise it? According to the principles of medical ethics and as conscience bids?

All these matters remain to be determined by international agreements. Many questions have already been settled in this way, but others await decision. Besides, the number of States which take part in these agreements is not very large, and still less is the number of those which have ratified them. The medical services could get in touch with legislative assemblies through movements and proposals, with a view to becoming part of the proposed international law regarding the points determined in those treaties which have already found agreement. Another possibility would be to annex to the existing agreements, with equal juridical value, the code of medical law already in force.

Such a task will not be undertaken with the Utopian hope of attaining the objective from one day to the next, but with calmness, with inflexibility, and with that tenacious perseverance without which important enterprises nearly always come to nought.

What has just been said concerns the *necessity* of creating an international medical law, and the means of its realization.

As for the *content* of this law and the juridical formulæ to be drafted, the project already prepared gives sufficiently clear ideas. From the technical point of view, We have no intention of intervening. We are treating of medical ethics.

Under this aspect, codified medical law should have as its foundation your basic principles. It should, then, be a point of law that the doctor can exercise his profession always and everywhere, when it is practically possible, even for the wounded enemy, for soldiers as well as civilians, prisoners and internees, as, in general, for all those who are afflicted by illness, misfortune, and suffering. The greatest needs always have priority, as also does that aid which cannot be deferred. It should not be possible to bring legal action against any doctor on the sole ground that he has cared for those in need, or that he has refused to harm life or the human body, to mutilate or even to kill.

OBLIGATIONS. It is not enough for medical law to lay down what a doctor *may* do; it is necessary to say also what he *must* do. In other words, whenever a permission is granted, a duty must also become evident. This should concern the doctor on the one side as much as the doctor on the enemy side, and one also who, coming from a neutral country, has been engaged in the service of one of the belligerent powers. This first directive applicable to doctors presupposes a second, applicable to Governments and their military leaders, on the one hand forbidding them to hinder the doctor in his work, and on the other obliging them to support him, as far as possible, by giving him the space he needs, and by putting at his disposal the necessary material. These requirements cannot become binding norms of an international law, unless the doctor himself refrains from all political and military activity for the duration of the conflict, and is not induced thereto by either of the two parties.

Another point should become part of the international medical law: the professional secret. The doctor should have the possibility and the obligation, by virtue of a formal law, of keeping secret, even in wartime, that which was confided to him in the exercise of his profession. It would be a faulty interpretation to see in this secret only a " *bonum privatum* ", a measure designed for the benefit of the individual; it is demanded just as much by the " *bonum commune* "—the common good. In case of conflict between two aspects of the same common good, calm consideration will show which prevails. We do not have to explain now what motives may, *by way of exception,* release from the medical secret, even against the will of the patient. It is the law's rôle to decide on the normal case, and for that case, silence is the rule.

If one were to succeed—and partial success has already been obtained—in inserting the aforesaid moral demands into international treaties having the force of law, the result obtained would be anything but negligible. It must always be realized that in such matters the doctor is the " weak party." For the juridical prescriptions which concern him serve little purpose in case of conflict, if the authorities of the State are not induced to submit to such obligations and to sacrifice a portion of their sovereignty, a sacrifice which is always required in one way or another by international agreements of this nature.

SANCTIONS. There remains the question—difficult also in other international treaties—of the *authority* and the *sanctions* of an international medical law. One must, indeed, admit that such agreements do not produce their wholesome effects unless this problem is solved satisfactorily. The question which was posed to the United Nations during the discussion on human rights, and to which you have called Our attention, gives point to the present difficulty: " Is the General Assembly merely an academy convened to formulate agreements which will never be put into practice?" (*Vers un Statut Mondial de la Médecine,* p. 52, annex 1, *in fine*). The well-known and important Geneva Agreement of 1949 considered the question of authority and sanction, but there the matter rested.

You, then, offer concrete proposals: you call attention to the International Court of Justice, already in existence, and you propose to add to it a section concerning world medical laws, whose task it would be to supervise, to receive complaints, to supply information, and, in certain cases, to pronounce judgment and condemnation. Execution of the sentence, when it concerns isolated individuals, is entrusted to the State to which they belong, or to that in whose territory they are, or to that to which they must be extradited. As for the question so often decisive in case of war, that of sanctions, when judgment affects a sovereign State or group of States, in particular when the guilty State emerges victorious from the conflict, this question still awaits regulation by a codified law.

We would not end Our address with thoughts that do not satisfy. We wish, therefore, in conclusion, to draw your attention to something on a higher plane. We have just said that the ultimate sanction of the medical conscience is God. God is also your most powerful inner strength when your profession demands the strength of the love of Jesus Christ, God-made-man. You know very well yourselves what imposing works Christian charity, inspired by this love, has accomplished in every domain for the welfare of suffering mankind. This strength and this love, We wish you with all Our heart.

4. *Medical Problems*

[This Address was delivered to members of the World Medical Association, September 30, 1954. Following the example of other groups in recent years, the President of the World Medical Association, in presenting his request for an audience, added " an earnest petition to be permitted to hear from the lips of the Holy Father his views on the ethical problems connected with medicine, with special regard to the attitude to be adopted by doctors towards atomic and bacteriological warfare and the carrying out of experiments on human beings ". Acceding to this entreaty, His Holiness spoke to the assembly and dealt with the points suggested, making reference to his preceding discourses on these problems.]

W E are happy to be once again with the medical men, as We have been so often in recent years, and to speak a few words to them.

You have informed Us of the aims of the World Medical Association and of the results obtained in the seven years of its existence. It is with great interest that We have noted this information and heard of the great number of tasks to which you have devoted your attention and efforts: the establishment of contacts between national medical associations and their organization into groups; the exchange of individual experiences; investigation of the actual problems of different countries; formal discussions with a number of kindred organizations; the creation of a general secretariat in New York; the founding of a special review, the *World Medical Journal*. Side by side with these accomplishments of a more administrative type, there are the definition and valuation of certain points concerning the medical profession and its status: the defence of the reputation and honour of the guild of doctors; the drawing up of an international code of medical ethics, which has already been accepted by 42 nations; agreement to a revision of the Hippocratic oath (the Geneva oath); the official condemnation of euthanasia. Moreover, among many other questions, there are those concerned with the modification and development of university teaching for the training of young doctors and the prosecution of medical research. We have mentioned only a few points. To the agenda of the present VIIIth Congress you have also added, for example: the duty of a doctor in time of war, especially of bacteriological war; the attitude of doctors towards chemical and atomic warfare, and towards carrying out experiments on human beings.

The medical as well as the technical and administrative aspects of these questions is your province. As regards the moral and juridical aspects, We would draw your attention to certain points. A series of problems that occupy your attention have occupied Ours also and been made the themes of special addresses. Thus, on the 14th of September, 1952, We spoke to the members of the 1st International Congress of Histopathology of the Nervous System (at their request) on the moral limitations imposed on modern methods of research and treatment. We based Our explanations on the investigation of the three principles from which medicine derives its justification for these methods of research and treatment: the scientific interests of medicine, the interests of the patient, the interests of the community, or, as it is called, the common good (*Discorsi e Radiomessaggi*, XIV, 318-30). In an address to the members of the XVIth International Congress of Military Medicine We expounded the essential principles of medical ethics and law, their origin, their content and their application (Oct. 19, 1953, *ibid.* XV, 417-28). The XXVIth Congress of the Italian Association of Urology put to Us the much discussed question: is it lawful to destroy a healthy organ to prevent the spread of a disease that threatens life? We gave Our answer delivered on 8th October, last year (*ibid.* XV, 373-75). Finally, We touched upon the questions that are engaging your attention during the present Congress, that is, questions regarding the moral verdict to be pronounced on modern warfare and its methods in a discourse on 3rd October, 1953, to the members of the VIth International Congress of Penal Law (*ibid.* XV, 337-53).

If, on this occasion, We make only brief mention of some of these points, despite their importance and wide range of application, We hope that the explanations given on former occasions will serve to fill up what is wanting.

WAR AND PEACE. It is clear that, in time of war, the doctor has a part to play, and, moreover, a privileged part. At no other time is there so much to be done in the way of treatment and healing among soldiers and civilians, friends and enemies. The doctor must be granted, unrestrictedly, the natural right to offer his services when they are required and, furthermore, that right must be guaranteed by international agreements. It would be a crime against both judgment and heart to seek to deny medical assistance to the enemy and to leave him to perish.

Has the doctor also a part to play in developing, perfecting and increasing the means of modern warfare, especially the means of A. B. C. warfare? This question cannot be answered before a solution is first found to this other question: Is modern " total warfare ", especially A. B. C. warfare, permissible in principle? There can be no doubt, mainly by reason of the horrors and unlimited sufferings caused by modern warfare, that to unloose such warfare without a just motive (that is to say, without its being necessitated by a clear and extremely grave injustice that cannot otherwise be repelled), constitutes a crime deserving of the severest national and international sanctions. In principle it is wrong even to raise the question of the lawfulness of atomic, chemical and bacteriological warfare, except in the case when such warfare can be deemed indispensable for defence in the aforesaid conditions. Even then, however, all means must be taken to avoid it through international agreements or to determine for its use limits sufficiently well-defined and narrow so that its effects can be contained within the strict needs of defence. If, despite all this, the loosing of the dogs of war produces such widely spread evil effects that they get completely beyond human control, even a defensive war must be rejected as immoral. It would then no longer be a case of " defence " against injustice and of the necessary " protection " of lawful possessions, but of the pure and simple annihilation of all human life within the radius of the destructive action. That is not permissible on any account.

Now let us turn again to the doctor. If at any time within the compass of the limits laid down, a modern (A. B. C.) war can be justified, and is in fact justified, then the question of the lawful moral co-operation of the doctor can arise. But you will agree with Us in this: it is preferable that the doctor should not be engaged in a task of this kind. It is too much in contrast with his primary duty, which is to give help and cure, and not to injure or kill.

EXPERIMENTS ON HUMAN BEINGS. According to the information you have given Us, you have added to the initial agenda of your present Congress the question of carrying out experiments on living human beings. The lengths to which such experiments can go and the abuses to which they can lead have been shown by the trials of doctors in the post-war period.

That medical research and practice cannot entirely dispense with experiments on living human beings is understood without difficulty. But the point is to know what are the necessary prerequisites for such experiments, what the limiting factors, the obstacles in their way, the determining basic principles. In desperate cases, when the patient is lost if nothing is done and when there is a medicine, a means, an operation that, although not being wholly without danger, nevertheless offers a certain possibility of success, then a right-thinking person admits at once that the doctor can, with the explicit or tacit permission of the patient, proceed to give the treatment indicated. But research, life and practice are not restricted to cases as these. They outstrip and go far beyond them. Even among serious and conscientious doctors the idea is sometimes expressed that, if new paths are not ventured upon, if new methods are not tried, a brake is put upon progress, if indeed it is not completely paralysed. In the sphere of surgical operations especially, it is stressed that many an operation that does not nowadays involve any special danger has behind it a long history and a long period of experience—the time necessary for the doctor to develop the requisite knowledge and skill—and that a more or less large number of fatal cases mark the early history of these operations.

It is within your professional competence to answer questions concerning medical prerequisites and conditions for carrying out experiments on living human beings. However, the difficulty of a moral and juridical judgment seems to demand some guiding remarks.

In Our allocution to military doctors We briefly formulated the essential directives on this subject (Discourse to XVIth International Congress of Military Medicine—*Discorsi e Radiomessaggi*, XV, 420-21).

For the consideration and solution of these problems, use is made, as can be seen in the text quoted, of a set of moral principles of the most fundamental importance: the question of the relations between the individual and the community, that of the compass and limits of the right of using the property of others, the question of the prerequisites and the range of the principle of totality, that of the relations between the individual and social ends of man, and other similar questions. Although these questions are not specifically within the competence of medicine, it must, nevertheless, like any other human activity whatsoever, take account of them.

What holds for the doctor in regard to his patient holds also for the doctor in regard to himself. He is subject to the same great moral and juridical principles. He too cannot make himself the subject of scientific experiments or procedures which entail serious injury or threat to his health; still less is he entitled to attempt any investigation which, according to authoritative opinion, could result in mutilation or suicide. Furthermore, the same must be said for nurses and for all who are ready to devote themselves to research in therapeutics. They cannot submit themselves to experiments of the kind now under discussion. This denial of moral justification does not apply to the personal motives of those who offer themselves, sacrifice themselves and renounce themselves on behalf of the sick, nor to the desire to co-operate in the furthering of a serious science that seeks to give help and service to mankind. If their justification were in question, the reply would, of course, be in the affirmative. In every profession, and especially in that of the doctor and the nurse, there is no lack of people who are ready to devote themselves wholly to others and to the common good. These motives and personal commitments are not in question. When all is said and done, the question here is of the disposal of a good that is not one's own, over which one has no unlimited right. Man is only the steward and not the independent possessor and owner of his body, of his life and of all that the Creator has given him for his use, and that only in conformity with the ends of nature. The fundamental principle:

> " Only he who has the right of disposal of anything is entitled to use it, and then only within the limits that have been fixed for him ",

is one of the most important and most universal norms of action, to which the spontaneous and sound judgment of reason firmly subscribes and without which all juridical order and that of the common life of men in society is impossible.

As regards the removal of parts of the body of a deceased human being for medical purposes, the doctor cannot be allowed to treat the corpse as he likes. It falls to the public authority to lay down suitable rules. But not even the public authority can proceed arbitrarily. There are certain legal pronouncements against which serious objections can be raised. A provision, like that which allows the doctor in a sanatorium to remove parts of the body for medical purposes, though all motives of gain are excluded, is not admissible because it may be too freely interpreted. Account must also be taken of the rights and duties of those who are responsible for the body of the deceased. Finally, the demands of natural ethics must be respected, and they make it unlawful that the body of a human being should be considered or treated simply as a mere thing or as the body of an animal.

5. *Address on Painless Childbirth*

January 8, 1956

W E have received information about a new technique in the field of gynaecology, and We have been asked to pass judgment on it from the moral and religious point of view. The new method concerns natural, painless childbirth, in which no artificial means are employed, but recourse is had to the mother's natural powers alone.

PREVIOUS DECLARATIONS RECALLED. In Our Address to the members of the Fourth International Congress of Catholic Doctors, on 29th September, 1949 (*Discorsi e Radiomessaggi*, XI, 221-34), We said that the doctor proposes to mitigate, at least, the evils and sufferings that afflict men. We then called to mind the surgeon, who strives in the course of an operation to avoid causing pain as much as possible. We spoke of the gynaecologist, who tries to lessen the pangs of childbirth without endangering mother or child, and without weakening the bonds of motherly affection which—it is affirmed—usually have their origin at that moment. Our last observation referred to a procedure then employed in the maternity hospital of a great modern city. In order to avoid pain for the mother, she was plunged into deep hypnosis, but it was noted that the result was an emotional indifference towards the child. Others, however, believe that this fact can be otherwise explained.

In the light of this experience, care was taken to waken the mother on several occasions during labour for a few moments each time; in this way, the effect feared was successfully avoided. Corresponding treatment was made use of during a prolonged narcosis.

The new method of which We now desire to speak does not entail this danger. It leaves the mother at childbirth in full consciousness from beginning to end, and with the full use of her psychic forces (intellect, will, emotions); it suppresses or, as some would say, it simply lessens pain.

What attitude must be taken in regard to it from the moral and religious standpoint?

OUTLINE OF THE NEW METHOD

PAST EXPERIENCE. We remark first of all, that painless childbirth in general is in contrast with common human experience today, as well as in the past, however far back one goes.

Most recent research indicates that some mothers give birth without feeling any pain, even though no analgesic or anaesthetic has been employed. It also shows that the degree of intensity of pain is less among primitive peoples than among civilized peoples; that if, in many cases, this intensity is moderate on the average, yet it is high for the majority of mothers, and not rarely it even proves to be insupportable. Such are the observations currently noted.

The same must be said of past ages, in so far as we can know from history. The pains of women in childbirth were proverbial. They were mentioned as an example of the most lively and anguished suffering, and literature, both profane and religious, affords proof of the fact. Indeed, this way of speaking is general and is found in the Old and New Testaments, especially in the writings of the prophets. We shall cite a few examples. Isaias compares his people with the woman who is in pain and cries out when she draws near the time of her delivery (cp. Is. xxvi, 17); Jeremias, viewing the approaching judgment of God, says:

> " I have heard the voice as of a woman in travail, anguish as of a woman in labour of a child " (Jer. iv. 31).

The evening before His death, Our Lord compared the situation of His Apostles with that of a mother awaiting the moment of childbirth:

> " A woman about to give birth has sorrow, because her hour has come. But when she has brought forth the child, she no longer remembers the anguish for her joy that a man is born into the world " (John xvi, 21).

All this allows it to be stated, as a fact accepted among men in the past and now, that mothers give birth in pain. The new method would make this assertion unwarranted.

GENERAL PRELIMINARY CONSIDERATIONS. Two general considerations, presented by those who favour the method, guide and set the direction for all who outline its principal elements. The first concerns the difference between painless and painful activity of organs and members; the second concerns the origin of pain and its connection with organic function.

The functions of the organism, it is said, when normal and duly completed, are not accompanied by any painful sensations. These latter tell of the presence of a complication; otherwise, nature would contradict herself, since she associates pain with such processes in order to provoke a defence reaction or protection against what would prove harmful. Normal childbirth is a natural function, and consequently should take place without pain. What then, is the source of such pain?

The sensation of pain, it is replied, is set in motion and controlled by the cerebral cortex, where stimuli and signals are received from the whole organism. The central organ reacts to such stimuli in very different ways; some of these reactions (or reflexes) have by nature a precise character, and are associated by nature with determined processes (absolute reflexes); others, on the contrary, have neither their character nor their connections fixed by nature, but are determined by other factors (conditioned reflexes).

Sensations of pain are among those reflexes (absolute or conditioned) which arise from the cerebral cortex. Experience has proved that it is possible, by means of arbitrarily established associations, to provoke sensations of pain, even when the stimulus which arouses them is by itself totally incapable of doing so.

In human relationship, these conditioned reflexes have an agent, a most efficacious and frequent one, namely, language, the spoken or written word or, if you will, the opinion prevailing in a given group, which everyone shares, and expresses in language.

ELEMENTS OF THE NEW METHOD. Consequently, the origin of the lively sensations of pain experienced at childbirth is understandable. Such sensations are considered by certain authors to be due to contrary conditioned reflexes set in motion by erroneous ideological and emotional reflexes.

The followers of the Russian experimenter, Pavlov (in the field of physiology, psychology and gynæcology), availing themselves of their master's research into conditioned reflexes, present the question substantially as follows:

(a) *Its basis*: Childbirth was not always painful; it became so in the course of time because of "conditioned reflexes". These may have had their origin at a first painful childbirth; perhaps heredity also plays a part, but such factor would be only secondary. The principal elements are language and the opinion of the group manifested by language. Childbirth, it is said, is "the mother's difficult hour", it is a torture imposed by nature, which hands the defenceless mother over to unbearable suffering. This association created by environment provokes fear of childbirth and fear of the terrible pains which accompany it. Thus, when the muscular contractions of the womb are felt at the beginning of labour, the defence reaction against pain sets in. This pain provokes a muscular cramp which, in its turn, causes increased suffering. Labour pains are therefore real pains, but their cause is wrongly interpreted. It is a fact that in childbirth there are normal contractions of the womb and organic sensations accompanying them, but these sensations are not interpreted by the central organs for what they really are: namely, simple natural functions. Because of conditioned reflexes, and particularly because of extreme "fear", they are deviated into the region of painful sensations.

(b) *Its purpose*: Consequently, it is clear what the aim and task of painless obstetrics will be. By applying scientifically acquired knowledge, it must first dissociate the associations already existing between the normal sensations of contractions of the womb, and the pain reactions of the cerebral cortex. In this way, negative conditioned reflexes are suppressed. At the same time, new, positive reflexes must be created to replace the negative set.

(c) *Its practical application*: Consider now the practical application. It consists in giving mothers (long before the period of childbirth) intensive instruction—adapted to their intellectual capacities—concerning the natural processes which take place during pregnancy and, in particular, during childbirth. They already knew about these processes to a certain extent, but most frequently without perceiving clearly their interconnection. Many things still remained wrapped up in deep obscurity, and were even susceptible of wrong interpretations. The characteristic conditioned reflexes also acquired a considerable force, while anxiety and fear were constantly nourished and fed. All these negative elements would be eliminated by the aforesaid education.

At the same time, repeated appeal is made to the mother's will and emotions not to allow feelings of fear to arise which are, and which have been proved to her to be, without foundation. The impression of pain must also be rejected which might perhaps tend to manifest itself, but which, in any case, is not justified, being based only, as has been taught her, on a wrong interpretation of natural organic sensations in the contracting womb. Mothers are especially induced to consider the natural grandeur and dignity of what they accomplish at the moment of childbirth. Detailed technical explanations are given them concerning what they must do to ensure normal labour and delivery. They are taught, for example, how precisely to exert their muscles, how to breathe properly. This teaching takes on the form of practical exercises, so that the technique may be familiar to them at the time of delivery. It is then a question of guiding mothers and preparing them not to go through childbirth in a purely passive manner, as an inevitable process, but to adopt an active attitude and influence it through mind, will and emotions, so as to bring childbirth to term in the manner intended by nature and with her aid.

During labour, the mother is not left to her own resources. She profits by the assistance and the constant supervision of a staff trained in the new techniques, who remind her of what she has learned; and point out, at the proper moment, what she should do or avoid. They quickly right her mistakes as occasion arises and aid her to correct the anomalies which may happen.

This is, in essence, according to the Russian researchers, the theory and the practice of painless childbirth. The English scientist, Grantly Dick Reid, has perfected a theory and technique which are analogous in several points. In his philosophical and metaphysical postulates, however, he differs substantially, because his are not based, like theirs, on a materialistic outlook.

(d) *Extension and success*: As for the extension and the success of this new method (called the psycho-prophylactic method), it is asserted that in Russia and China it has already been used in hundreds of thousands of cases. It has also taken root in various countries of the West. Many municipal hospitals are said to have provided special wards. Such maternity hospitals, organized according to these exclusive principles, seem to be, at present, far from numerous in the West. France, among other nations, has one such (Communist) in Paris. In France also, two Catholic institutions, at Jallieu and Cambrai, have completely absorbed this method among their services, without sacrificing what had previously proved successful.

The method is alleged to be highly successful, and it is claimed that 85% to 90% of the births taking place in this manner are really painless.

EVALUATION OF THE METHOD

SCIENTIFIC EVALUATION. After having given an outline of the method, We may now consider its worth. In the documentation that has been supplied to Us, We find this characteristic statement:

> "For the personnel, the primary and indispensable requirement is that of having unreserved faith in the method."

Can an absolute faith of this kind be required on the basis of the scientific results attained?

The method, unquestionably, has elements that must be considered as scientifically established, others that have only a high probability, and still others which remain as yet (at least for the present) of a problematic nature. It is scientifically established that, in a general sense, conditioned reflexes do exist; that some determined representations or emotional states can be associated with certain events, and that this can also be verified in regard to the sensation of pain. But at the present moment it is not clearly established that the pains of childbirth are due exclusively to such a cause. There are also responsible thinkers who maintain reserve concerning the axiom asserted as almost *a priori*:

> "All normal physiological acts, and thus also normal birth, ought to take place without pain; otherwise nature contradicts herself."

They do not admit that the above can be applied universally and without exception, nor that nature would contradict herself if she made childbirth an intensely painful act. They affirm, in effect, that it would be perfectly comprehensible (physiologically and psychologically) if nature, in her care and provision for the mother who gives birth and for the infant who is born, had chosen such means to produce unmistakable awareness of the importance of the act, and had wished to ensure that necessary measures be taken to safeguard mother and infant.

The scientific verification of these two axioms, which some claim to be certain and others to be debatable, We leave to the competent specialists; but it is necessary, in order to discern the true from the false, to keep to the decisive objective criterion:

> "The scientific character and the value of a discovery should be measured exclusively according to its agreement with objective reality."

It is important not to neglect here the distinction between "truth" and "affirmation" ("interpretation", "subsumption", "systematization") of the truth. If nature rendered childbirth painless in fact, if it became painful subsequently by reason of conditioned reflexes, if it can become painless again, if all this is not only asserted, interpreted, systematically construed, but really demonstrated, it follows that the scientific results are true. If this is not so, or at least if it is not yet possible to have full certitude in the matter, one should abstain from all absolute assertion, and consider the conclusions arrived at as scientific "hypotheses".

But, refraining for the moment from forming a definite judgment on the degree of scientific certitude attained in the psychoprophylactic method, We pass on to examine it from the moral standpoint.

THE ETHICAL QUESTION. Is the method morally irreproachable?

The answer, which must take into account the object, end, and motive of the method, may be given briefly:

" Considered in itself, it contains nothing that can be criticized from the moral point of view."

The instruction given in regard to nature's travail in childbirth; the correction of wrong interpretations of organic sensations and the invitation to correct them; the influence exercised to avoid groundless anxiety and fear; the timely assistance afforded the mother in childbirth so that she may collaborate with nature, and remain tranquil under self-control; an increased consciousness of the greatness of motherhood in general, and particularly of the hour when the mother brings forth her child—all these are positive values to which no objection can be made; they are benefits for the mother in childbirth, and fully conform to the will of the Creator. Viewed and understood in such a way, the method has a natural uplifting influence, protecting the mother from superficiality and levity. It influences her personality in a positive manner, so that at the very important moment of childbirth she may manifest the firmness and solidity of her character. Under other aspects, too, the method can lead to positive moral achievement. If pain and fear are successfully eliminated from childbirth, that very fact frequently lessens an inducement to commit immoral acts in the use of marriage rights.

With regard to the motives and the purposes of the aid given to the mother in childbirth, the material action, as such, does not imply any moral justification, either positive or negative; that is the concern of the one who renders aid. It can and should be done for motives and for purposes which are irreproachable, such as the interest presented by a purely scientific fact; the natural and noble sentiment which creates esteem and love for the human person in the mother, which desires to do her good and help her; a deep religious and Christian feeling, which is inspired by the ideals of living Christianity. It can happen, however, that the assistant seeks an end and yields to motives which are immoral. In this case, it is the personal action of the one who assists which is to be judged wrong; the immoral motive does not change the assistance, which is good, into something that is bad, at least so far as its objective character is concerned, and, conversely, an assistance which is good in itself cannot justify a bad motive or furnish the proofs of its goodness.

THEOLOGICAL ASPECT. There remains to be said a word about the theological and religious aspect, in so far as this is distinguished from the moral issue in the strict sense. The new method is often presented in the context of a materialistic philosophy and culture, and in opposition to Sacred Scripture and Christian teaching.

The ideology of a researcher and of a scholar is not in itself a proof of the truth and the value of what he has discovered and expounded. The theorem of Pythagoras or (to remain in the field of medicine) the observations of Hippocrates which have been recognized as correct, the discoveries of Pasteur, the heredity laws of Mendel, do not owe their truth to the moral and religious ideas of their authors. They are not either " pagan " because Pythagoras and Hippocrates were pagans, or Christian because Pasteur and Mendel were Christians. These scientific tenets are true because, and in so far as, they correspond with objective reality.

Even a materialist in his research can make a real and valid scientific discovery; but this contribution does not in any way constitute an argument in favour of his materialistic ideas.

The same reasoning holds good for the culture to which a scholar belongs. His discoveries are not true or false according as he is the heir of this or that culture, from which he has received inspiration and which has left its mark deeply impressed upon him.

The laws, the theory, and the technique of natural childbirth without pain, are undoubtedly valid, but they have been elaborated by scholars who, to a great extent, profess an ideology belonging to a materialistic culture. Such ideology and culture would not be true simply because the scientific results mentioned above are true. It is even much less accurate to say that the scientific results are true and demonstrated as such, because their authors and the cultures from which they derive have a materialistic slant. The criteria of truth are elsewhere.

The convinced Christian finds nothing in his philosophical ideas and his culture that prevents him from studying seriously, in theory and in practice, the psycho-prophylactic method. He knows that, as a general rule, reality and truth are not identical with their interpretation, subsumption or orderly arrangement, and that, consequently, it is possible at the same time to accept the one completely and reject the other altogether.

THE NEW METHOD AND SACRED SCRIPTURE. A criticism of the new method from the theological point of view should in particular take account of Sacred Scripture, because materialistic propaganda claims to find a glaring contradiction between the truth of science and that of Scripture. In Genesis (Gen. iii, 16), we read:

> "*In dolore paries filios.*" ("In pain shall you bring forth children.")

To understand the saying correctly, it is necessary to consider in the whole of its context the sentence passed by God. In inflicting punishment on our first parents and their descendants, God did not wish to forbid, and did not forbid, men to seek after, and make use of, all the riches of creation; to make progress step by step in culture; to make life in this world more bearable and better; to lighten the burden of work and fatigue, pain, sickness and death —in a word, to subdue the earth (Gen. i, 28).

Likewise, in punishing Eve, God did not wish to forbid—nor did He forbid—mothers to make use of means which render childbirth easier and less painful. One must not seek subterfuges for the words of Sacred Scripture: they remain true in the sense intended and expressed by the Creator, namely: motherhood will give the mother much suffering to bear. In what precise manner did God conceive this chastisement and how will He carry it out? Sacred Scripture does not say. There are some who allege that originally childbirth was entirely painless, and that it became painful only at a later date (perhaps due to an erroneous interpretation of the judgment of God) as a result of auto-suggestion and hetero-suggestion, arbitrary associations, conditioned reflexes, and because of faulty behaviour of mothers in labour. So far, however, these assertions on the whole have not been proven. On the other hand, it could be true that an incorrect behaviour, psychic or physical, on the part of those in labour, is capable of increasing considerably the difficulties of delivery, and has in reality increased them.

Science and technique can, therefore, use the conclusions of experimental psychology, of physiology and of gynæcology (as in the psycho-prophylactic method) in order to eliminate the sources of error and painful conditioned reflexes, and to render childbirth as painless as possible. Sacred Scripture does not forbid it, that much is certain.

FINAL CONSIDERATIONS OF CHRISTIAN OBSTETRICS

By way of conclusion, We would add some remarks on Christian obstetrics.

Christian charity has always taken an interest in mothers at the time of their confinement. It has tried and still tries today to render them effective assistance, psychic and physical, in accordance with the advance of science and technique. This could be applicable at the present time to the discoveries of the psycho-prophylactic method, in the measure in which they meet the approval of serious scholars. Christian obstetrics can here incorporate into its principles and its methods all that is correct and justified.

Nevertheless, it must not be content with them in the case of patients who are capable of receiving more, nor must it abandon anything of the religious values which it has been turning to good account up to the present. In Our address to the Congress of the Italian Association of Catholic Midwives on 29th October, 1951 (*Discorsi e Radiomessaggi,* XIII, 333-53), We spoke in detail of the apostolate which Catholic midwives have in their power to exercise and which they are called upon to practise in their profession. Amongst other things, We mentioned the personal apostolate, namely, that which they exercise by means of their science and their art and by the solidity of their Christian faith (1.c. 334 ss.); and then the apostolate of motherhood, by endeavouring to remind mothers of its dignity, its seriousness, and its nobleness. One can apply here what We have said today, for they assist the mother in the hour of her delivery. From her faith and from her life of grace the Christian mother gets the light and strength to have full confidence in God, to feel that she is under the protection of Providence, and also to accept willingly the suffering God gives her to bear; it would be a pity, therefore, if the Christian obstetrician were to confine himself to rendering her assistance of a purely natural order, namely, psycho-prophylactic services.

There are two points which deserve to be emphasized here: Christianity does not interpret suffering and the Cross in a merely negative fashion. If the new technique spares her the sufferings of childbirth, the mother can accept it without any scruple of conscience; but she is not obliged to do so. In the case of partial success or failure, she knows that suffering can be a source of good, if she bears it with God and in obedience to His will. The life and sufferings of Our Saviour, the pains which so many great men have borne and even sought, and through which they have matured and risen to the summits of Christian heroism, the daily examples we see of acceptance of the cross with resignation: all this reveals the meaning of suffering, of the patient acceptance of pain in the present plan of salvation, for the duration of our earthly life.

One word more: Christian thought and life, and therefore

Christian obstetrics, do not attribute an absolute value to the progress of science and the perfection of technique. Such an attitude, on the contrary, is regarded as natural by materialist thought and by the concept of life which materialism inspires. For them it serves as a religion, or as a substitute for religion. Although the Christian applauds new scientific discoveries and makes use of them, he rejects materialism's exaggerated glorifications of science and culture. He knows that they occupy a place on the scale of objective values, but that, while they are not the lowest, neither are they the highest. In their regard, too, he repeats today as ever and always:

" Seek ye first the kingdom of God and His justice " (Matt. vi, 33).

The highest, the ultimate value for man is to be found, not in science or its technical capabilities, but in the love of God and devotion to His service. For these reasons, when faced with a scientific discovery of painless childbirth, the Christian is careful not to admire it unreservedly and not to use it with exaggerated haste. He judges it in a positive manner and with reflection, in the light of sane natural reason, and in the brighter light of the faith and love which streams from God and from the Cross of Christ.

6. *Use of Anæsthetics*

[In an address to some 500 doctors from many lands on February 23, 1957, the Holy Father dealt with the moral aspects of preventing pain. Having outlined the history of the origin and development of anæsthetics, he answered questions that had been put earlier by a national Congress of Italian anæsthetists. He said that in order to avoid, prevent or suppress pain, one was perfectly entitled to make use of anæsthetics, hypnosis or other methods of killing pain as long as the methods were not wrong in themselves. We give the complete discourse apart from a few abridgements of references.]

T HE Ninth National Congress of the Italian Society of the Science of Anæsthetics, held at Rome on October 15-17, 1956, submitted three questions to Us, through its President. The questions deal with the religious and moral implications of pain prevention in the light of the natural law, and according to Christian doctrine as contained in the Gospel and taught by the Church.

The questions are of undeniable interest and they evoke intellectual and emotional reactions in men today. Among Christians especially, there is evidence of very diverse trends. Some approve unreservedly of the practice of analgesia [suppressing pain]. Others would be inclined to reject it outright as contrary to the ideal of Christian heroism. Still others, without the least sacrifice of that ideal, are ready to adopt a middle position. That is why We are asked to voice Our thoughts on the three following points:

1. Is there a universal obligation to refuse analgesia and to accept physical pain in a spirit of faith?

2. Is it in accord with the spirit of the Gospels to deprive a person of consciousness and the use of the higher faculties, by means of drugs?

3. Is it lawful for the dying or those in danger of death, to employ them, if there are medical reasons for availing of them? May one use drugs even if the lessening of pain is likely to result in a shortening of life?

HISTORY OF ANÆSTHETICS. Modern surgical progress is due to two decisive steps, the introduction of antisepsis by Lister (after Pasteur had demonstrated the part played by germs in promoting infection), and the discovery of an effective method of anæsthesia. Before Horace Wells had thought of employing nitrogen protoxide to induce sleep in the patient, surgeons were forced to work quickly, for short periods only, on an individual writhing in dread anticipation of terrible pain.

The introduction of anæsthetics was to revolutionize such a state of affairs and to allow operations, both long and delicate, and sometimes of great daring.

Indeed, anæsthesia assured to surgeons and patient alike, the basic conditions of calm repose and ' muscular silence ' indispensable for a skilful and safe operation.

At the same time, it means there has to be a careful watch on the physiological activities of the body. The anæsthetic, indeed, penetrates the cells and lowers their metabolism. It weakens the defence reflexes and lowers the vitality, already more or less seriously endangered by sickness and the wound inflicted by the healer's knife. Moreover, the surgeon, though engrossed in his work, has to note at each instant the general condition of the patient—a heavy responsibility, especially in grave cases.

Consequently, recent years have witnessed the development of a new branch of medicine, that of the anæsthetist, who is called upon with increasing frequency to play a part in modern hospital organization.

ROLE OF ANAESTHETICS. The rôle of the anæsthetist is so much hidden that it is almost unknown to the public. He is less in the limelight than the surgeon, but he is equally essential for success. Into his hands, indeed, the patient's life is entrusted, so that he may help the sick person to pass as safely as possible through the painful period of the operation.

The anæsthetist must first of all prepare the patient medically and psychologically. To forestall difficulties which might result from the weakness of a particular organ, he carefully learns the peculiarities of each case. He imparts confidence to the patient, seeks his co-operation, and gives medicine to calm and prepare the organism. According to the nature and duration of the operation, he selects the most suitable anæsthetic and decides on the method of administering it.

Above all, it is his duty, during the operation, to watch closely the patient's condition.

He is alert, so to speak, to the slightest symptoms, and knows just how far the anæsthetic has been effective. He follows the nerve-reactions, the breathing-rhythm and blood pressure, in order to forestall possible complications such as contraction of the larynx, convulsions and heart or respiratory difficulties.

When the operation is over, the most delicate part of his task begins. He assists the patient to regain consciousness, prevents accidents such as an obstruction of the windpipe and feelings of shock, and he administers natural fluids. The anæsthetist, therefore, unites the important qualities of sympathy, understanding and devotion, to a perfect knowledge of the technique of his art, not only with a view to promoting all the psychological dispositions which help towards the good estate of his patient, but also in a spirit of true and deep charity, befitting a man and a Christian.

WIDE RANGE OF PRODUCTS. To fulfil his task today, the anæsthetist has at his disposal a wide range of products. Some have been known for a long time and have been proved by experience. Others are the fruit of recent research and offer their special contribution to the solution of the difficult problem; namely, how to suppress pain without causing harm to the organism.

Nitrogen protoxide, for which Horace Wells was unable to win recognition at the time of his experiment at Boston Hospital in 1845, continues to have an honourable rank among the agents in current use as a general anæsthetic. In that same hospital, but with happier results than Wells achieved, Thomas Morton, in 1846, experimented with ether, which had already been turned to account by Crawford Long in 1842. Two years later, the Scots surgeon, James Simpson, proved the effectiveness of chloroform, though John Snow, of London, contributed more to popularize its use.

After a period of early enthusiasm had passed, the defects of these first three anæsthetics were clearly shown; but one had to wait till the end of the century for the appearance of a new product, ethyl chloride, which is, however, inadequate when a prolonged state of unconsciousness is desired.

In 1942, Luckhardt and Carter discovered ethylene, the first anæsthetic gas resulting from systematic laboratory research. Five years later, cyclopropane, the fruit of the labours of Henderson, Lucas and Brown, came into use. Its rapid and intense action supposes in the user a perfect knowledge of the closed-circuit system.

Though anæsthesia by inhalation has a well-established supremacy, for a quarter of a century it has been meeting growing competition from intravenous narcosis.

Frequent experiments made in the past with chloral hydrate, morphine, ether, ethyl alchohol, gave results only slightly encouraging, and indeed, sometimes disastrous. From 1925 on, barbiturate compounds have been entering the experimental field in medicine, and have been establishing themselves ever since evipan has shown the undoubted advantage of this type of anæsthetic.

With the barbiturates, the drawbacks of the method by inhalation are avoided: the disagreeable impression of suffocation, the dangers accompanying the administration of the anæsthetic, sickness upon return to consciousness, and injury to the organs.

Sodium pentothal (introduced in 1934 by Lundy) assured the success and popularity of a new type of anæsthetic, so that henceforth barbiturates will be used, either for brief operations, or for ' combined anæsthesia ', with ether and cyclopropane. They cut short the infusion period of the gases, and permit the dosage to be diminished. Sometimes they are used as the main anæsthetic, and their pharmacological defects are then counterbalanced by the use of nitrogen protoxide and oxygen.

HEART SURGERY. Heart surgery, which has had spectacular success in recent years, presents problems of special difficulty to the anæsthetist. It supposes, as a general condition, the possibility of interrupting the circulation of the blood for a more or less lengthy period. Moreover, since it concerns an extremely sensitive organ, the functional completeness of which is often seriously endangered, the anæsthetist must avoid anything that might increase the labour of the heart.

In mitral stenosis [narrowing of a heart valve] for example, he will administer a premedication to allay the nervous anxieties of the patient. He will avoid tachycardia [too rapid heart-action] by means of a quick-acting deep anæsthetic and a mild parasympathetic block; at the moment of the commissurotomy [cutting the join] he will lessen the dangers of anoxæmia [poisoning for want of oxygen] by a generous supply of oxygen, and will carefully watch the pulse and the records of the heart action.

But for other types of operation to succeed, the surgeon must be able to work on a heart emptied of blood, and to interrupt the circulation for more than three minutes, a procedure which normally causes damage to the brain and heart tissues.

To remedy one of the most common of congenital heart diseases, the " foramen ovale ", the surgical technique of a blind intra-auricullar digital was in use as early as 1948; but this was prone to the obvious risks of every blind manipulation.

At present two new methods, hypothermy and the use of an artificial heart, permit direct-vision operation, and thus open up wonderful prospects. Indeed, it has been proved that hypothermy lowers the basic metabolic rate in proportion to the drop in body temperature. In practice, temperature is not lowered below 25° C. (77° F.), in order to leave unimpaired the heart muscle's power of contracting, and especially so as not to increase the excitability of the heart muscle and the danger of causing a ventricular fibrillation [subdivision of fibre] which is virtually irreversible.

Hpyothermy permits a check in the circulation lasting from eight to ten minutes without any destruction of the nervous tissue of the brain. The period of time may be increased by use of a heart-lung apparatus, which first draws off blood from the veins, purifies it, supplies it with oxygen, and sends it back into the organ. The handling of such apparatus demands careful training of the operator, and is accompanied by a variety of minute controls.

The anæsthetist is then carrying out a weightier and more complex task, the success of which is entirely dependent on perfect performance. But results already obtained justify the hope that in the future these new methods will be widely used.

It is not surprising that, in the face of such varied resources offered by modern medicine for the avoidance of pain, and of the very natural desire to draw all possible benefits from them, problems of conscience should arise. You have already submitted to Us some of them which you find of particular importance. Before dealing with them, We wished briefly to draw your attention to other moral problems which claim the anæsthetist's attention: in particular, that of his responsibility for the life and health of his patient, which sometimes depend on him as much as on the surgeon.

With regard to this point, We have already remarked on several occasions—and notably in the address of September 30, 1954, to the English Assembly of the World Medical Association—that man cannot be just an item in a doctor's experiments, a thing on which new medical methods and techniques may be tried out (cp. *Discorsi e Radiomessaggi*, XVI, 170 ss.).

We now pass on to an examination of the questions you have submitted.

I. MORAL ASPECTS OF KILLING PAIN. In the first place, then, you ask whether there is a general obligation to endure pain. In order to give a more precise answer to your question, We shall treat of various aspects of the matter. And first, it is evident that in certain cases the acceptance of physical suffering is a matter of serious obligation. Thus a man is bound in conscience to accept the suffering every time that he is faced with the inescapable alternative of enduring pain or of acting contrary to a moral obligation (either by positive action or by omission).

The Martyrs could not have avoided torture or death without denying their faith or without evading the grave obligation of bearing witness to it when the occasion arose. But it is not necessary to go back to the Martyrs. At the present time there are found magnificent examples of Christians who, for weeks, months, and even for years, endure pain and physical violence in order to remain faithful to God and to conscience.

Your question, however, does not refer to such cases; it has in mind rather the free acceptance and the desire of suffering in itself and for itself. To recall at once a definite example of this, We refer to the address We gave on January 8, 1956, with reference to new methods of painless childbirth (*Discorsi e Radiomessaggi*, XVII, 465 ss.). There it was asked whether, by virtue of the text in Scripture, ' In sorrow shalt thou bring forth children ' (Gen. 3-16), the mother was obliged to accept all the suffering and refuse relief from pain by either natural or artificial means.

We answered that there was no obligation of the kind. Man,

even after the Fall, retains the right of control over the forces of nature, of employing them for his own use, and consequently of deriving benefit from all the resources which it offers him either to suppress or to avoid physical pain.

But We added that, for the Christian, suffering is not something negative, but on the contrary it is linked with high religious and moral values, and hence can be desired and sought even if no moral obligation to do so exists in a particular case.

And We went on: ' The life and sufferings of Our Lord, the pains which so many great men have endured and even welcomed, and by reason of which they grew to maturity and rose to the highest point of Christian heroism, the daily examples which We have before Our eyes of accepting crosses with resignation—all this reveals the meaning of suffering, of patient acceptance of pain in the present working out of salvation during the period of our earthly life ' (*ibid*. 478).

Moreover, the Christian is bound to mortify his flesh and strive after interior purification; for it is impossible, in the long run, to avoid sin and to carry out all one's duties faithfully, if the effort at mortification and purification is neglected. Physical suffering becomes a necessity and must be accepted to the extent that, without its aid, mastery over self and disorderly tendencies is unattainable. In so far as it is not required for this purpose, one cannot assert that there is a strict obligation in the matter. The Christian, then, is never obliged to desire suffering for its own sake. He considers it, according to circumstances, as a means more or less suited to the end he is pursuing.

HIGHER STATE OF PERFECTION. One can consider what is of strict obligation; but it is also possible to look at the demands of the Christian Faith, the invitation to a higher state of perfection, acceptance of which is not imposed under pain of sin. Is the Christian bound to accept physical pain so as not to set himself in opposition to the ideal which his Faith proposes to him? Does not a refusal in this matter imply a lack of the spirit of faith?

That the Christian experiences the desire to accept and even to seek physical pain in order the better to share in the Passion of Christ, to renounce the world and the pleasures of the senses, and to mortify his own flesh, is beyond dispute. At the same time, it is important to give a correct interpretation of the tendency.

Those who manifest it exteriorly do not necessarily possess genuine Christian heroism. It would also be erroneous to declare that those who do not manifest it are quite devoid of it. This heroism can, in fact, reveal itself in many other ways.

Take, for example, a Christian who carries out, day after day, from morning till night, all the duties of his state or profession, the laws of God and of men. He prays with recollection, he does his work wholeheartedly, he resists evil passions, and shows his neighbour the charity and service that are his due. He endures bravely, without murmuring, whatever God sends him. Such a man is living within the shadow of Christ's Cross whether physical suffering is present or not, whether he endures pain or avoids it by means that are lawful.

Even if one considers only obligations binding a man under pain of sin, he cannot live or carry out his daily work as a Christian without being ever ready for sacrifice and, so to speak, without constantly sacrificing himself. Acceptance of suffering is only one way, among others, of indicating what is the real essential: the will to love God and to serve Him in all things. It is in the perfection of this voluntary disposition that the quality of the Christian life and its heroism consist.

In specific cases, what are the motives which permit us to avoid physical pain and yet do not involve any conflict with a serious obligation or with the ideal of the Christian life?

One could list quite a number in spite of their diversity; they can be summed up in this statement: in the long run, the pain if endured will tend to prevent some good or advantage of a higher order. It is possible that suffering may be preferable for a particular person in a particular setting; but, in general, the resulting evil or harm forces men to protect themselves against it.

Beyond doubt, suffering will never be completely banished from among men, but its harmful effects can be restricted. And so, just as one masters a natural force to draw advantage from it, the Christian makes use of suffering as a spur to his effort to mount higher and purify himself in the spiritual life, in order to carry out his duties better and answer the call to a higher degree of perfection.

In keeping with the abilities or dispositions above mentioned, it is for each one to adopt solutions suited to his own case without at the same time hindering other advantages and other goods of higher worth. The value of each solution will be measured according as it is a means of progress in the interior life, of more perfect mortification, of more faithful accomplishment of the individual's duty, of greater readiness to follow the promptings of grace. In order to be sure that such is really the case, a man will have recourse to the rules of Christian prudence and the advice of an experienced spiritual director.

From these replies, you will easily draw useful directives for practical application.

A—The fundamental principles of the technique of anaesthesia, a science as well as an art, and the end pursued, give rise to no difficulties. It combats those forces which, in a great many respects, produce harmful effects and hinder a greater good.

B—The doctor who accepts it, enters into contradiction neither with the natural law nor with the Christian ideal. In accord with the Creator's ordinance, he seeks to bring suffering under control. To do so, he makes use of the conquests of science and the progress of technical skill in keeping with the principles We have set forth and which will guide his decisions in particular cases.

C—The patient desirous of avoiding or of soothing his pain may, without disquiet of conscience, make use of the means discovered by science and which, in themselves, are not immoral. Particular circumstances can impose another line of conduct, but the Christian's duty of renunciation and of interior purification is not an obstacle to the use of anaesthetics because it is possible to fulfil that duty in another manner. The same rule applies to the demands of the Christian ideal which go beyond the call of duty.

II. THE GOSPEL SPIRIT AND THE USE OF DRUGS. The second question concerned the state of insensibility and the total or partial deprivation of consciousness in the light of Christian morals.

You expressed it thus: "The complete abolition of sense-perception in all its forms (general anaesthesia), or the diminution to a greater or less extent of the feeling of pain (partial anaesthesia and analgesia), is always accompanied in the one case by disappearance, in the other by the lessening, of consciousness and of the higher intellectual faculties (memory, association, critical faculties, etc.). Are these phenomena, which enter into the normal framework of insensibility during surgical operations, and of the pre- and post-operational analgesic practice, compatible with the spirit of the Gospels?"

The Gospel tells us that, immediately before the Crucifixion, Our Lord was offered some wine mixed with gall, doubtless to mitigate his sufferings. After having tasted it, He would not drink it, because He wished to suffer with full consciousness, thus fulfilling what He had said to Peter at the time of the arrest: ' The chalice which My Father has given Me, shall I not drink it?' So bitter was this chalice that Jesus had pleaded in the agony of His soul: 'Father, let this chalice pass from Me! But not as I will but as Thou wilt!'

Does the attitude of Christ towards His Passion, as revealed in this and other passages of the Gospel, permit the Christian to accept the total or partial state of insensibility?

Since you are considering the question under two aspects, We shall examine successively the suppression of the pain, and the lessening (or the total suppression) of consciousness and of the use of the higher faculties.

The disappearance of pain depends, as you say, either on the suppression of general sense-perception (general anaesthesia), or on the lowering, more or less noticeable, of the capacity for suffering (partial anaesthesia and analgesia). We have already stated the essential point in the moral aspect of suppressing pain. It is of little consequence, from the ethical point of view, whether suppression is caused by a state of insensibility or by other means. Within the limits declared, it gives rise to no objection and remains compatible with the spirit of the Gospel.

However, one must neither deny nor underestimate the fact that the acceptance of physical suffering (whether obligatory or not), even on the occasions of surgical operations, can reveal a lofty heroism and frequently gives genuine testimony to a heroic imitation of the Passion of Christ. Nevertheless, that does not mean that it is an indispensable part of it; in major operations especially, it is not unusual for anaesthetics to be essential for other reasons, and the surgeon or the patient could not omit them without a lack of Christian prudence. The same holds good for analgesic practice before and after the operation.

SUPPRESSING HIGHER FACULTIES. You next speak of the diminution or suppression of consciousness, of the use of the higher faculties, as of phenomena which accompany the loss of sense-perception. Ordinarily, what you wish to obtain is precisely this loss of sense-perception; but often it is impossible to produce it without bringing about at the same time total or partial loss of consciousness.

Outside the sphere of surgery, this process is often reversed, not only in medicine but also in psychology and in criminal investigations. Here it is claimed that a lowering of consciousness is brought about, and, through it, of the higher faculties, in such a way as to paralyse the psychic control mechanisms which a man constantly makes use of for self-mastery and self-direction; he then gives himself over without any resistance to the play of associated ideas, and of feelings and volitionary impulses. The dangers of such a situation are evident; he can even reach the point where he sets loose instinctive urges that are immoral.

These manifestations at the second level of the unconscious state are well known, and in practice one tries to avert them by means of drugs previously administered. Stopping the control mechanism is declared to be particularly dangerous when it evokes the revelation of secrets of private or social life, affecting the person or the family.

It is not enough that the surgeon and his assistants are severally bound by natural as well as professional secrecy with respect to all that takes place in the operating theatre.

There are, besides, secrets which ought not to be revealed to anyone, not even, as the technical formula says, ' *uno viro prudenti et silentio tenaci* '—' to a prudent and tenaciously silent man '. We have already underlined this in Our address of April 15, 1953, on clinical psychology and psychoanalysis (*Discorsi e Radiomessaggi*, XV, 73). Hence one can approve only of drugs which by application before an operation prevent revelations.

Let Us note first of all that in sleep, nature itself interrupts more or less completely intellectual activity. If, during light sleep, the use of reason (' usus rationis ') is not entirely abolished and the individual is still able to enjoy the use of his higher faculties— as St. Thomas observed—sleep nevertheless excludes the ' dominium rationis ', that power in virtue of which reason freely commands human activity.

It does not follow that if a man gives way to sleep, he is acting contrary to the moral order in depriving himself of consciousness and mastery over himself through the use of his higher faculties. But it is also certain that there may be cases (and it often happens), in which a man cannot permit himself sleep, but must remain in possession of his higher faculties in order to perform a moral duty which is pressing.

Sometimes, without being bound by a strict duty, a man deprives himself of sleep so as to render services of his free choice, or to impose some self-denial for the sake of higher ethical interests.

The suppression of consciousness, then, by natural sleep does not, of itself, raise any difficulty; but it is not lawful to accept it when it impedes the execution of a moral duty. Giving up natural sleep can also, in the moral order, be an expression and a realisation of a voluntary striving towards perfection.

HYPNOSIS.   Consciousness can also be reduced by artificial means. It makes no difference from the moral standpoint whether the result is obtained by the administration of drugs or by artificially produced sleep (hypnosis)—which can be called a form of psychic pain prevention. But hypnosis, even considered exclusively in itself, is subject to certain rules. In this connection, We recall a brief reference We made to the medical use of hypnosis, at the beginning of the address of January 8, 1956, on painless childbirth. (cp. *Discorsi e Radiomessaggi,* XVII, 467).

In the matter which engages Us at present, it is a question of hypnosis as practised by a doctor to serve a clinical purpose, while he observes the precautions which science and medical ethics demand from him as much as from the patient who submits to treatment. The moral judgment which We are going to state on the suppression of consciousness applies to this specific use of hypnosis.

We do not wish what We say of hypnosis in the service of medicine to be extended to hypnosis in general without further qualification.

Hypnosis, in so far as it is an object of scientific research, cannot be studied by any casual individual, but only by a sincere student, and within the moral limits valid for all scientific activity. It is not the affair of a group of laymen or ecclesiastics, who might dabble in it as in some interesting topic for the sake of mere experience, or even as a simple hobby.

To appreciate the lawfulness of suppressing or lessening consciousness, one must consider that reasonable and freely controlled activity is the mark of a human being. The individual will be unable to carry out, for example, his daily work if he remains habitually plunged in a twilight state. Moreover, he has an obligation to regulate all his actions according to the demands of the moral order.

Since the natural energies and the blind instincts, left to themselves, are incapable of assuring a regulated activity, it follows that the use of reason and the higher faculties is indispensable both for seeing clearly the precise terms of the obligation and for applying them to particular cases. Hence originates the obligation of not depriving oneself of consciousness without a sound reason.

It follows that one may not confuse consciousness, or suppress it, with the sole aim of gaining pleasurable sensations, for instance, by indulging in drunkenness and imbibing poisons intended to promote such a state, even if one is seeking only a pleasant state of well-being.

Beyond a certain dose, the poisons cause a disturbance, more or less pronounced, of consciousness and even its complete darkening. Facts show that the abuse of drugs leads to a complete neglect of the most fundamental demands of personal and family life. It is therefore entirely reasonable for the public authorities to intervene and regulate the sale and the use of drugs, so as to remove from society the risk of grave physical and moral harm.

SENSE PERCEPTION. Is there an obligation on surgeons to produce a state of insensibility (narcosis) and thereby lessen or completely suppress consciousness and pain? It is your province to deal with the technical aspects of the question. As to the moral issue, the principles previously stated in answer to your first question apply substantially to the production of insensibility as much as to the suppression of pain. In fact, what interests the surgeon primarily is not the suppression of consciousness but rather the elimination of painful feelings.

When one is conscious, violent and painful sensations readily arouse reflexes and reactions which may be involuntary, but bring undesirable complications in their train so as even to end in a fatal collapse of the heart. To preserve the psychic and organic balance, to prevent its being violently disturbed, is important for both doctor and patient; and nothing short of a state of insensibility allows it to be realised.

It is hardly necessary to remark that, if one fears there will be unlawful interference while the sick person is unconscious, the state of induced insensibility will give rise to serious difficulties necessitating the provision of adequate safeguards.

On the rules of natural morality, do the Gospels impose further requirements? If Our Lord on Calvary refused the wine mixed with gall because He wished to drink to the dregs in full consciousness the chalice which His Father offered Him, it follows that man ought to accept and drink the chalice of suffering whenever God wills it. But one need not believe that every time pain presents itself, God wishes it to be endured no matter the conditions and the circumstances. The words of the Gospel and the attitude of Our Lord do not indicate that such is God's will for all men and at every moment. The Church has not given any interpretation of this kind. But the actions and suggestions of Our Lord hold a deep meaning for everybody.

In this world countless people are weighed down by suffering of all sorts (sickness, accidents, wars, natural disasters) to the bitterness of which they can bring no solace. The example of

Christ on Calvary, His refusal to give relief to His pain, are for them a source of consolation and strength.

Besides, Our Saviour has warned His followers that the chalice awaits everyone. The Apostles, and after them the Martyrs in their thousands, have borne witness to it, and continue to do so gloriously to the present day. Often, however, there is no obligation to accept unrelieved suffering. Embracing pain is not a rule of perfection. Cases occur quite regularly when there are grave reasons for rejecting pain. It is then possible to take steps to avoid pain without going against the Gospel teaching.

The conclusion, then, of Our exposition of the matter up to this point can be stated thus: within the limits laid down, and provided one observes the required conditions, a state of insensibility involving either a lessening or a suppression of consciousness is permitted by natural morality and is in keeping with the spirit of the Gospels.

III. NARCOTICS FOR THE DYING. We now have to examine the question: 'Is it permitted in general, and during the postoperational period in particular, to use analgesic treatments (the employment of which invariably dulls consciousness), even in the case of the dying and of patients in danger of death, there being a medical reason for such a course? Is this permissible even in cases (e.g., inoperable cancer and incurable disease) where unbearable pain is mitigated but only at the cost of the duration of life, which is thereby shortened?' The third question is at bottom no more than an application of the two preceding ones to the special case of the dying, and to the particular effect of shortening life.

To declare that the dying have a greater moral obligation than others—whether by the natural law or from Christian teaching—to accept suffering or to refuse its alleviation, is in keeping neither with the nature of things nor with the sources of Revelation. But, just as, in accord with the spirit of the Gospels, suffering helps towards the expiation of personal sins and the gaining of richer merit, those whose life is in danger have certainly a special motive for accepting it, for, with death quite near, the possibility of gaining new merit is likely to disappear presently.

The motive directly concerns the sick person, not the doctor who is engaged in relieving pain—for We are supposing that the sick person is assenting to relief or has even expressly asked for it. It would clearly be unlawful to employ anaesthetics against the expressed will of the dying person.

A little clarification would seem to be called for at this stage, for it is not uncommon to see explanations presented in a misleading manner. Attempts are sometimes made to prove that the sick and the dying are obliged to endure physical suffering in order to acquire more merit. The reason adduced is either the invitation to perfection which Our Lord addressed to everybody: ' Be ye perfect as your heavenly Father is perfect ': or the words of the Apostle: ' This is the will of God, your sanctification '.

Sometimes arguments based on reason are put forward. It is asserted that one cannot be indifferent about attaining one's final end, nor can one be indifferent about any of the stages leading to that consummation. Or again, it is said that the precept of well ordered self-love entails that a person should seek eternal returns in the same degree as the chance of them is presented by the circumstances of everyday life. Finally, even the first and greatest commandment, to love God above all things, is interpreted as allowing no choice but to seize on the particular occasions offered by Providence and profit by them.

Now, growth in the love of God and in abandonment to His will does not come from suffering in itself however stoically accepted, but from the intention in the will, supported by grace.

This intention, in many of the dying, can be intensified if suffering is eased, for suffering increases the state of weakness and in the physical exhaustion, checks the ardour of soul and saps the moral powers instead of sustaining them. Also, suppression of pain removes tension of body and mind, facilitates prayer and makes possible a more generous gift of self.

If you come across dying persons who accept their suffering as a means of expiation and a source of merit in order to advance in the love of God and in abandonment to His will, do not force anaesthetics on them. They should rather be helped to go their own way. When you meet an entirely different situation, it is not advisable to suggest to a dying person the ascetical considerations set out above. Rather keep in mind that instead of assisting towards expiation and merit, suffering can furnish occasion for new faults.

SUPPRESSION OF CONSCIOUSNESS. Let Us add a few words on the suppression of consciousness in the dying in the circumstance where it is not suggested by pain. Since Our Lord willed to submit to death with a fully conscious mind, the Christian wishes to imitate Him here also. In addition, the Church gives to priests and to the faithful, an " Ordo Commendationis Animae ", a collection of prayers designed to assist the dying as they leave this world and enter into eternity. But if the prayers have their value and meaning when they are spoken beside a sick person who is unconscious, they will normally bring light, consolation and strength to one who is actually able to take part in them. And so the Church lets it be understood that a sick person should not be deprived of consciousness without grave reason.

When this state is produced by natural causes, men must accept it; but it is not for them to bring it about unless they have solid grounds for so doing. In addition, the wishes of the persons concerned must be consulted. When they have the faith, they are anxious to have their near ones, a friend, or a priest, present to help them to die well. They long to preserve the possibility of making final arrangements, of saying a last prayer, a last word to those around them. To disappoint them in this is contrary to Christian, and even to ordinary human sentiment.

The use of anaesthetics at the approach of death with the sole purpose of depriving the sick person of consciousness at the end, would not then be a notable gain in the art of healing but rather a practice to be regretted.

Your question was proposed rather on the supposition that a grave medical reason existed (e.g., violent pains, pathological states of depression and of agony). The dying person cannot allow (still less ask) the doctor to make him unconscious if he thereby renders himself incapable of fulfilling a grave duty, for example, the settling of important business, the making of a will, or going to confession.

We have already said that the intention of gaining greater merit is not in itself sufficient to make the use of drugs unlawful. The question must also be asked whether the state of insensibility will be relatively short (during the night or for a few hours) or prolonged (with or without interruption). One must likewise consider whether the higher faculties will revive—for a few minutes or for hours—and enable the dying person to discharge his obligations (e.g., make his peace with God).

In addition, a conscientious doctor, even if he is not a Christian, will resist the urgings of those who, contrary to the will of the dying person, would wish to remove his clarity of mind in order to prevent his making certain decisions.

When, in spite of unfulfilled duties, the dying man with a show of reason asks to be made insensible, a conscientious doctor will not countenance it, especially if he is a Christian, without having invited the patient (either personally or, better still, through others) to discharge his obligations beforehand.

If the sick man refuses obstinately, and persists in asking to be made unconscious, the doctor can consent to it without rendering himself guilty of formal co-operation in the sin committed. That sin does not really depend on the fact of unconsciousness but on the immoral will of the patient; whether or not he obtains relief from pain, his behaviour will be the same; he will not carry out his obligation. Granted that the possibility of repentance is not excluded, there is yet no serious probability of it; and who knows even that he will not be hardened in evil?

But if the dying man has fulfilled all his duties and received the last Sacraments, if medical reasons clearly suggest the use of anæsthetics, if, in determining the dose, the permitted amount is not exceeded; if the intensity and duration of the treatment is carefully reckoned and the patient consents to it, then there is no objection: the use of anæsthetics is morally permissible.

SHORTENING LIFE. Would it be necessary to give up the treatment if the actual effect of the drug was to shorten the span of life? First, We note that all forms of direct euthanasia (i.e., the administration of a drug in order to produce or hasten death) are unlawful, because, then, a claim is being made to dispose directly of life.

It is one of the fundamental principles of natural and Christian morality that man is not the master and owner, but has only the use, of his body and life. A person is really claiming the right of direct control every time he wills the shortening of life as an end or as a means. In the hypothesis which you are considering, there is question only of ridding the patient of unbearable pain, for instance, in a case of inoperable cancer or of incurable disease.

If there exists no direct causal link (moral or physical, either through the will of interested parties or by the nature of things)

between the induced unconsciousness and the shortening of life
—as would be the case if the suppression of the pain could be
achieved only by cutting the life short; and if, on the other hand,
the actual administration of drugs brings about two distinct
effects, the one the relief of pain, the other the shortening of life,
the action may be lawful.

It is necessary, however, to have a reasonable proportion
between these two effects and see that the advantages of the one
compensate for the disadvantages of the other.

It is important, too, to ask oneself if the present state of science
may not allow the same result to be obtained by other means.
Finally, in using a drug, one should not employ more than is
actually necessary.

To sum up, you ask Us: 'Is the removal of pain and consciousness by means of drugs (when medical reasons suggest it)
permitted by religion and morality to both doctor and patient
(even at the approach of death and if one foresees that the use of
drugs will shorten life)?' One must answer 'Yes—provided no
other means exist, and provided, in the given circumstances, such
action does not prevent the carrying out of other moral and
religious duties'.

As We have already explained, the ideal of Christian heroism
does not require, except in a general way, the refusal of a state
of insensibility, when it is justified on other grounds, not even at
the approach of death. All depends on the particular circumstances. The most perfect and most heroic decision can be present
as fully in acceptance as in refusal.

We venture to hope that these considerations relating to pain
prevention, regarded from an ethical standpoint, will help you to
discharge your professional duties with an even keener sense of
your responsibilities.

You desire to remain faithful to the demands of your Christian
Faith and to abide by it in all your activities. Far from thinking
of these demands as shackles on your liberty and initiative, look
on them rather as an invitation to a life immeasurably higher and
more excellent, which can be achieved only by effort and renunciation. The fulness and joy of that life are already a matter
of experience for anyone who knows how to enter into com-
munion with the Person of Christ living in His Church. He

animates it with His spirit and diffuses through all His members His love as the Redeemer Who alone will finally triumph over suffering and death.

To the end that Our Lord may impart to you His gifts in full measure We earnestly pray to Him for you, for your families and fellow workers, and with all Our heart, We grant to you Our fatherly Apostolic Blessing.

PART THREE

I APPENDIX

THE CHURCH'S ATTITUDE TO MIRACLES

[This article by his Excellency Mgr. Alfredo Ottaviani, assessor of the Holy Office, appeared in *L'Osservatore Romano,* February 14, 1951. While essentially a warning against the false miracle and popular credulity, it is at the same time an up-to-date statement of the Church's position with regard to miracles.

According to Catholic teaching, God still works miracles in the modern world. But the attitude of the Church is cautious. Phenomena officially certified as miraculous are relatively few, usually in conjunction with the canonization of saints after extremely rigorous investigation and examination. At Lourdes, site of the world's best known healing shrine, a medical committee staffed by doctors of many faiths and of no faith meticulously studies every cure. Of twelve hundred recorded since the shrine was built ninety-eight years ago, for which the committee has been unable to find any natural explanation, only fifty-one have been pronounced miraculous.]

No Catholic questions the possibility of miracles or doubts that they happen. Christ's mission and His divine Nature were proved by the many great miracles He performed here on earth. The early Church overcame initial difficulties and persecutions because the Holy Ghost gave her special help that expressed itself visibly in the gifts the Apostles enjoyed and in the large number of the elect among the first generations of Christians. Once the Church was consolidated these special gifts of the Holy Ghost, as we can well understand, grew less; but they have not ceased. The help of the Holy Ghost and the presence of Christ in His Church will last until the end of time. The former shows itself by supernatural signs, and by miracles.

By way of example, it is enough to call attention to the miracles that are examined during the process of the beatification of the servants of God or the canonization of the Blessed. Such miracles are rigorously tested both from the scientific and theological standpoints. One might add that the rigour with which the miraculous cures at Lourdes are examined is common knowledge.

Let no one call us enemies of the supernatural, therefore, if we set ourselves now to the task of warning the faithful against unchecked and wild statements concerning certain supposed supernatural happenings, statements which are fairly widespread at the present time, and which might jeopardize the recognition of a true miracle and bring it into discredit.

Our Lord Himself has put us on our guard against "false prophets" who "will show great signs and wonders, so as to lead astray if possible, even the elect" (Matt. xxiv, 24). Such wonders have occurred from the earliest days of the Church (Acts viii, 9). For this reason the Church has the right and duty to judge the truth and the nature of facts and revelations said to have come about by a special intervention of God. And it is the duty of all good children of the Church to submit to this judgment.

So-CALLED MIRACLES. As a mother, the Church has to bear the burden of a mother's heavy and sorrowful duties, and, like all mothers, she sometimes has the duty not only to take action, but to suffer, to keep silent, and to wait. Fifty years ago who would have thought that the Church would now be in the position of having to warn her children, even her priests to be on their guard against so-called miracles, against all those happenings acclaimed as preternatural, which are arousing the interest of the masses, now here, now there, in almost every continent and country? Fifty years ago, when the positivist attitude was rife, people would have laughed at anyone who paid attention to and believed in what was called superstition of the dark ages. Fifty years ago people reviled the Church because she alone persisted in upholding the existence of miracles, their spiritual worth, negative or positive, and their beauty or ugliness. One of the commonest and most solemn of subjects in the field of apologetics at that time was the miraculous. Now the Church has to warn her children through the lips of bishops, repeating the words of the Divine Master (Matt. xxiv, 24) not to allow themselves to be easily led astray by such happenings and not to believe in them save with eyes wide open and only when the authorities, after the proper inquiries, have given their reports.

For some years past we have witnessed an increase of popular hankering after the marvellous, even in the sphere of religion. The faithful repair in vast crowds to places where visions and wonders are supposed to have taken place, whilst, at the same time, they abandon the Church, the Sacraments, preaching and instruction.

People who are ignorant of the first words of the Creed set themselves up as ardent apostles of religious belief and practice. Some of them do not hesitate to speak of the Pope, the bishops and the clergy in severe terms of blame, and then are very annoyed when the latter do not take part with the crowd, in all the enthusiasm and outbursts of certain popular movements.

Although this is not pleasant, it causes no surprise. Man's feelings are natural, even his religious feelings. Just as a man is a rational animal, so he is a political and a religious animal. By bringing disorder and confusion into the nature and feelings of man, original sin has, one may say, also attacked religious sentiment. This is the explanation of the aberrations and errors and twistings of truth in the history of humankind. Yet it is a fact that such errors are much more troublesome when religion is involved. In coming to redeem man from his darkness and shortcomings, revelation and grace restored him to his true nature especially in matters of religion. Having healed man's wounded and stricken nature, grace gives it an overflow of strength to be used in the service and love of God. The Church, the custodian and interpreter of the true religion, was born of the word and of the blood of Our Lord.

To believe oneself religious, in whatever way that may be, is not necessary. What is needed is to be truly religious. As in the case of other feelings, there can be, and in point of fact there are, lapses from true religious feeling. Religious feeling must be guided by reason, nourished by grace, and governed, as is our whole life, by the Church, and even more strictly governed. There are such things as religious instructions, religious education and religious training. Those who have set themselves against the authority of the Church and religious sentiment so light-heartedly, find themselves, today, faced with imposing outbursts of an instinctive religious feeling that completely lacks the light of reason and the consciousness of grace—a religious feeling that is undisciplined.

There follow deplorable acts of disobedience to the ecclesiastical authorities when they intervene to apply the needed brake. This happened in Italy after the so-called visions of Voltago; in France over the Espis and Bouxierres incidents which were akin to those in Hampsur-Sambre (Belgium); then in Germany at Heroldsback, and in the United States of America in the case of the manifestations at Necedah. One could quote other examples in other countries far and near.

At the present time the Church stands between the two extremes of open debased irreligion, and unrestrained blind religious fervour. Persecuted by the supporters of the first and compromised by those who uphold the second, the Church simply repeats a motherly warning. But the warning is unheard amid denial on the one hand and exaltation on the other.

It is certain that the Church does not wish to cast a shadow over the wonders worked by God. What is desired is simply to keep the faithful watchful concerning what comes from God and what does not come from God, but could, instead, come from His and from our adversary. The Church is the enemy of the *false* miracle.

A good Catholic knows from his catechism that the true religion rests on the true Faith, on that Revelation which ended with the death of the last Apostle, and has been entrusted to the Church, its interpreter and custodian. Nothing else necessary for our salvation can be revealed to us. There is nothing more for which we need look. We have everything, if we wish to make use of it. Even the most accredited visions can indeed furnish us with new motives for fervour but not with new elements of life or doctrine. True religion consists essentially (apart from its place in conscience) in the love of God and in what follows from it, namely, love of our neighbour. And the love of God consists in doing the will of God, and obeying His Commandments rather than in acts of worship and ritual. This is true religion.

A good Catholic knows that in the saints themselves holiness lies not in the preternatural gifts of vision, prophecy, and wonder-working but in the heroic exercise of virtue. That God should in some way endorse holiness by miracles is one thing, but that holiness consists in performing miracles is another. We must not confound holiness with what can be, and is generally, simply an unmistakable sign of holiness, yet not always so clear as not to need the supervision of religious authority.

THE CHURCH'S TEACHING. On this point the teaching of the Church has never been equivocal. The man who turns to events of doubtful interpretation rather than accept the word of God, loves the world more than God. Even when the Church authoritatively canonizes a saint, this does not guarantee the preternatural character of all the extraordinary facts connected with his life. Still less does the Church approve all his personal opinions. There is even less guarantee of all that is written, often with unpardonable levity, by biographers whose imagination outstrips their judgment.

We repeat that to be religious, it is necessary to be so with propriety and as a matter of duty. If we would be good and devout Catholics we must act with the same attention as we employ in the most serious affairs of life. Being incredulous is just as harmful to the sincere believer as being ready to believe. True, not everyone can form his own opinion on every point. Yet we may ask, why should there be bishops? Why the Pope?

Strange it is that no untrained person would dare to build a house by himself, be his own tailor, make himself a pair of shoes or cure himself of a sickness. Yet when it is question of religious life, people set aside authority, refuse to place any trust in it, and even distrust and disobey it lightly.

During the past 200 years, especially the last half century, the Catholic priesthood has been so much the object of attack, insult and defamation at the hands of both politicians and writers that one can well understand how it is that the faithful have the greatest difficulty in approaching a priest and becoming friendly with him. But now when, undoubtedly, there is a return to God, as we see, the faithful must overcome their bias and once again begin to share their feelings, their thoughts, and their faith with the priest.

For the last ten years, while the religious authorities have shown restraint, the people have hastily busied themselves with marvels which, to say the least, have not been verified.

To be honest we must admit that such events may be simply the expression of natural religious enthusiasm. They are not Christian events, and they give a dangerous pretext to those who are ready to discover at all costs the mingling and survival of paganism and superstition in Christian belief and life and especially in Catholicism. Just as wrong-doing may find its way into our daily lives, so may error. We must know it for what it is. Just as the Church has the power to forgive sins, so has it also been commanded by God to keep us from error.

Catholics should give ear to the word of God which the Church, and the Church alone, preserves and repeats whole and untarnished. They should not run like sheep without a shepherd, and listen to other voices seeking to drown the voice of the Church. We have the Sacred Scripture; we have tradition; we have the chief Shepherd and a hundred other shepherds next door to our own homes. Why should we present a spectacle of foolishness or unhealthy excitement to those who oppose and despise us? " Christians, be more prudent," wrote Dante in his day. " Do not be like feathers that are the sport of every wind." The great poet gave the very same reasons that we give today:

> " You have the Old and the New Testament, and the Shepherd of the Church to guide you."

Dante's conclusion too, is the same as ours:

> " This is sufficient for your salvation " (Canto 5, VV, 73-77).

II SOURCES

ACTS OF PIUS XII

relating to

SCIENCE AND TECHNOLOGY

Key to Source Abbreviations:

AAS *Acta Apostolicae Sedis,* Rome.

CD *Catholic Documents,* Salesian Press, London.

CM The *Catholic Mind,* America Press, New York.

CTS *Catholic Truth Society* Publications, London.

DC *Documentation Catholique,* Bonne Presse, Paris.

F The *Furrow,* Maynooth.

IER The *Irish Ecclesiastical Record,* Maynooth.

OR *L'Osservatore Romano,* Rome.

T The *Tablet,* London.

UA The *Unwearied Advocate,* St. Cloud, Minn.

Original versions in AAS and OR; English versions only in CD, CM, CTS, T, UA; and French versions only in DC.

American readers will find English versions also in *The Pope Speaks,* American Quarterly for Papal documents, (3622—12th St., N.E., Washington 17, D.C.).

1 9 3 9

October 20 Encyclical "*Summi Pontificatus*" describes the problems of our tormented age. AAS (1939) 415; CM (Nov. 1939); CTS S151; IER (Jan 1940) 80.

December 3 Address to the Pontifical Academy of Science.

1 9 4 1

November 30 Address in Italian to the Pontifical Academy of Science on modern astronomy and moral reflections provoked by it. "*Richiamo di gioia*". AAS (1941) 504.

December 16 Apostolic Letter in Latin proclaiming St. Albert the Great patron of natural science. AAS (1942) 89, 99; IER (Oct. 1943) 283 (Latin).

1 9 4 2

October 2 — Address to the Italian Society for Natural Science on scientists and a new world order.

November 12 — Address in Italian to an International Congress on higher mathematics as a social bond. " *Al vostro desiderio* ". AAS (1942) 370; IER (Nov. 1943) 356 (Italian).

1 9 4 3

February 21 — Address in Italian to the Pontifical Academy calling attention to the threat and dangers of a nuclear explosion. " *In questa solenne adunanza* ". AAS (1943) 69, and particularly 74.

1 9 4 4

September 1 — Fifth anniversary of the outbreak of war. Address on technical progress and the general good, the longing for a new world, and the contradictory aspects of historical evolution. CM (Oct. 1944); UA I 202.

1 9 4 5

August 30 — Address in private audience to representatives of the six major U.S. newsreel companies on the subject: " The camera cannot lie ". UA II 41.

October 21 — Address in Italian on women's duties in the new age. " *Questa grande* ". AAS (1945) 284; CTS S199; IER (Dec. 1946) (Italian).

1 9 4 6

November 15 — Address on the Life of the Farmer. UA II 117.

1 9 4 7

November 27 — Address in Italian to the Beekeepers of Italy. " *La vostra prezenza* ". CD I; *Social Justice Review,* (Jan. 1954) 310.

1 9 4 8

February 8 — Address in Italian to the Pontifical Academy on natural law and the divine government of the world. " *Nel ritrovarCi* ". AAS (1948) 75; CD I; New York *Times,* Feb. 9, 1948.

March 7 — Address to Congress of International Exchange on Christian principles of international trade and the degradation of man.

| May 20 | Address to the Sixth International Congress of Surgeons on the surgeon's noble vocation. CM (Aug. 1948). |
| October 31 | Message in Italian to the Fiat workers of Turin. CD I. |

1 9 4 9

April 16	Address in French to the French University Mission. CD II; DC (1949).
April 17	Message in French televised to France relating to television. DC (1949); DC II.
September 4	Address on education of youth and how to form men of science and technology. CM (Sept. 1950).
September 29	Address in French to doctors on artificial fecundation. AAS (1949) 557.

1 9 5 0

January 23	Address in English to the American Press. CD III.
February 18	Address in French to the Intermediate Convention of Catholic Pressmen on the " Press and Public Opinion". " *L'Importance de la presse*". AAS (1950) 251; CD II; DC (1950); T (Feb. 26, 1950) 147.
August 5	Address in French to the International Congress of Administrative Sciences. CD III; T (Aug. 26, 1950) 177.
August 12	Encyclical in Latin " *Humani Generis*". AAS (1950) 561; CD III; CTS Do 265; IER (Nov. 1950) 454 (Latin), (Apr. 1951) 303 (English); T (Sep. 2, 1950) 187.

1 9 5 1

January 12	Apostolic Brief declaring the Archangel St. Gabriel patron of telecommunications. " *Quoniam omne datum* ". CM (Dec. 1951); DC (1951) 453; IER (Mar. 1952) 228; OR (2-3.4.51).
February 14	Article on miracles " Signs and Wonders—a warning " by Mgr. Ottaviani in *L'Osservatore Romano*. CD V; T (Feb. 24, 1951) 144.
March 11	Broadcast in Spanish to Spanish workers. CD V.
October 29	Address in Italian to Midwives. " *Vegliare con sollecitudine* ". Insists on the high duties of their apostolate and advises special precautions to safeguard conjugal life and offset the hedonistic wave submerging the world. CD VI; DC (1951) 1473; IER (Dec. 1951) 515; OR (29-30.10.51).

November 22 Address in Italian to the Pontifical Academy on modern science and the existence of God. "*Un' ora di serena letizia*". AAS (1925) 31; CD VI; DC (1951) 1537; IER (Jan. 1952) 60; OR (23.11.51); UA III 174.

December 24 Discourse in Italian on modern arms, and the Church and peace. "*Gia par la decimaterza*". AAS (1952) 5; CD VII; DC (L852) 1; T (Jan. 5 and 12, 1952) 16, 34.

1 9 5 2

January 31 Discourse in Italian on industry. "*Di tutto cuore*". DC (1952) 197; CM (Sep. 1952) 569.

February 27 Address in English to U.S. children. "*The little children*". AAS (1952) 229; IER (Dec. 1952) 464.

March 23 Discourse in Italian on the Christian Conscience. "*La Famiglia*". AAS (1952) 413; CD VIII; IER (Aug. 1952) 137 (Italian) (Apr. 1954) 300 (English).

March 24 Speech in English to U.S. editors of radio and television. CD VIII; T (Mar. 29, 1952) 256 (extract).

April 18 Discourse in French to Young Women's World Federation on the new morality and its dangers. "*Soyez les bienvenues*". AAS (1952) 270; CD VIII; *Clergy Review* (Oct. 1952) 619 (French); DC (1952) 589; IER (Aug. 1952) 137 (English); OR (19.4.52); T (Apr. 26, 1952) 336 (extracts).

April 26 Discourse in French to Third European Congress of Gastro-enterology. "*Vous avez désiré*". DC (1952) 771; OR (27.4.52).

May 30 Discourse in French to the Ninth International Congress of Agricultural Industries. "*C'est avec grand intérêt*". OR (30.5.52).

June 15 Address in Italian to university students and professors of Rome on Faith and natural science. "*Di vivo gradimento*". AAS (1952) 581; DC (1952) 833; OR (16-17.6.52).

July 17 Address in German on rôle of women in the evolution of the world. "*Der Katolische Deutsche*". DC (1952) 1287.

August 12 Letter in French to XXII World Congress of Pax Romana at Montreal on the function of a university, and on the uses of specialization and synthesis. "*Quel motif de joie*". CM (July 1953); DC (1952) 1545; OR (27.9.52).

September 7   Discourse in French on astronomy to 650 members attending the Eighth General Assembly of the International Astronomical Union. "*La présence*".

AAS (1952) 732; CM (Dec. 1952) 742; DC (1952) 1217; OR (8-9.9.52); T (Sept. 13, 1952) 216 (extracts).

See also commentary by "F.A." in OR (12.9.52) with French version in DC (1952) 1223.

September 14   Discourse in French to neurologists on the moral limits of research and treatment. "*Le premier Congrès*".

AAS (1952) 779; CD X; CM (May 1953) 305; DC (1952) 1225; IER (Mar. 1954) 222; OR (17.9.52); T (Sept. 27, 1952) 257, and (May 2, 1953) 376.

For additional note on psycho-analysis, see OR (21.9.52) and French version in DC (1952) 234.

September 23   Discourse in French on civil aviation. "*Nous apprécions*". CD X; DC (1952) 1285; OR (25.9.52).

October 23   Address in Italian to doctor-dentists attending the XXVII Congress of Stomatology. "*Le manifestazioni*". DC (1925) 1541; OR 25.10.52).

December 24   Christmas Broadcast in Italian pointing out what must be done to re-make the world. "*Levate capita vestra*". AAS (1953) 33; CD X; CM (Feb. 1953) 111; IER (Dec. 1953) 437 (extracts and summary); OR (25.12.52).

1 9 5 3

March 19   Address in Italian on adult education. "*Siamo ben felici*". AAS (1953) 230; CD XI; IER (May 1954) 384.

April 11   Discourse on Spanish radio. AAS (1953) 293: CD XI.

April 13   Address in French to Fifth International Congress of psycho-therapy and clinical psychology. "*Nous vous souhaitons*". AAS (1953) 278; CD XII; DC (1953) 513; CM (July 1953) 428; OR (16.4.53).

June 12   Address in French on ophthalmology. "*Répondant au vif désir*". AAS (1953) 418; DC (1953) 947.

September 7   Address in French to First International Congress of Medical Genetics. "*Soyez les bienvenus*". AAS (1953) 596; CD XIV; DC (1953) 1217; IER (Sep. 1954) 1^1 (English): OR (9.9.53).

September 10   Address in French to the members of the International Institute of Statistics on the uses of statistics and their applications in religious and other fields. " *Vous n'ignorez pas* ". CM (Jan. 1954) 58; DC (1953) 1231; OR (12.9.53).

September 13   Discourse in French to biologists on micro-biology. " *En ce mois* ". AAS (1953) 666; DC (1953); OR (14.9.53).

October 1   Address in Italian to attendants in mental hospitals. " *Col sentimento* ".
    AAS (1953) 725; DC (1953) 1361; OR (2.10.53).

October 4   Address in Italian to doctors on medical science. " *All' inizio* ". DC (1953) 1419.

October 8   Discourse in French to the XXVI Congress of the Italian Society of Urology. " *Nous vous saluons* ".
    AAS (1953) 673; *Clergy Review* (1954) 111 (excerpts in French); DC (1953) 1365.

October 9   Address in French to the International Federation of Technicians. CD XVI.

October 10   Address in French to European Union of Accountants. " *Lorsque Nous avons connu* ". DC (1953) 1409.

October 19   Address in French on medical ethics and the rights of doctors. " *Arrivés au terme* ".
    AAS (1953) 744; CM (Jan. 1954) 46; DC (1953) 1409; OR (21.10.53).

December 24   Discourse in Italian on progress, the technological spirit, and peace among peoples. " *Il popolo* ".
    AAS (1954) 5; CM (Mar. 1954) 174; IER (Apr. 1955) 297; OR (25.12.53); T (Jan. 2, 1954) 10 (excerpts and summary).

1 9 5 4

January 1   Address in Italian on television. " *I rapidi progressi* ".
    AAS (1954) 18; CD XV; CM (Oct. 1954) 632; IER (Nov. 1954) 362; OR (3.1.54); T. (Jan. 16, 1954) 58.

April 5   Address in French on the history and importance of medical radiology. " *Nous sommes heureux* ".
    AAS (1954) 214; DC (1954) 449; OR (5-6.4.54).
    The address was intended for 1500 radiologists but was not delivered.

April 18	Easter message in Italian on ABC warfare, and the threat of vast destruction and of pathogenic mutations through reckless use of atomic energy. "*Non altrimenti*".
	AAS (1954) 212; CM (June 1954) 438; OR (19-20.4.54).
June 6	Message to tele-spectators of European television. "*Non è forse*".
	AAS (1954) 369; CM (Oct. 1954) 629; IER (Oct. 1954 and Jan. 1955); DC (1954) 897; OR (7-8.6.54).
	In the course of an inter-European exchange of telecasts for the Feast of Pentecost, the Sovereign Pontiff spoke successively in Italian, French, German, English, Dutch to the tele-spectators of Italy, France, Germany, Belgium, Holland, Denmark and Great Britain.
June 10	Discourse in French on the cinema. "*En confiant*". DC (1954) 905.
September 11	Address in French on poliomyelitis. "*Pour apprécier*".
	AAS (1954) 533; DC (1954) 1223.
September 11	Address in Latin on the history of pharmacy. "*Quinquagesimus*". AAS (1954) 536.
September 17	Discourse in French on the history of medicine. "*Parmi les nombreux*". AAS (1954) 557; DC (1954) 1221.
September 24	Address in French on geodesy and geophysics to the tenth congress of the I.U.G.G. "*En accueillant*". AAS (1954) 580; DC (1954); OR (25.9.54).
September 29	Address in French to foundry technicians. "*Le Congrès*". AAS (1954) 584.
September 30	Address in French to Congress of World Medicine. "*Nous sommes heureux*". AAS (1954) 587; CD XXI; DC (1954) 1281; OR (2.10.54).
November 19	Address in French to the members of the International Labour Organisation. "*Si nous avons eu.*" AAS (1954) 714.
	Discourses in Italian on tensions in the modern world. "*Questa medesima promessa*". AAS (1955) 15; *American Ecclesiastical Review* (Feb. 1955) 123; CM (Mar. 1955); IER (Feb. 1955); T (Jan. 8, 1955).

1 9 5 5

March 19	Address to the United States Press. CD XVIII.
April 3	Discourse in French on industrial accidents. "*En vous accueillant ici*". AAS (1955) 272.

April 7   Address in French to the Latin Medical Union. "*Les statutes de l'union médicale*". AAS (1955) 275; DC (1955).

April 10   Easter Message in Italian on scientific research. "*Surrexit, è risorto*". AAS (1955) 282.

April 24   Address in French to the Pontifical Academy. "*Au moment où nous vous addressons*". AAS (1955) 394; IER (Aug. 1956) 121; F (May 1956); T (June 11, 1955).

May 18   Address in Italian to farmers. "*Eccoli convenuti a Roma*". AAS (1955) 497.

June 10   Discourse on the petroleum industry. DC (1955) 1141.

June 21   Address in Italian on the cinema. "*Ci torna*". AAS (1955) 501; IER (July 1956) 62; F (Nov., Dec. 1955).

June 22   Letter in English on the cinema to the International Study Conference. CD XX.

June 26   Address in Italian to railwaymen. "*E ancora vivo*". AAS (1955) 512.

July 2   Address in English to members of the Canadian Women's Press. CD XIX.

September 7   Address in French to the Tenth International Congress on historical sciences. "*Vous avez voulu*". AAS (1955) 672; DC (1955).

September 14   Address in French on Thomism and recent scientific discoveries. "*Nous vous souhaitons*". DC (1955) 1227.

September 25   Discourse in French on diet and infant diabetes. "*Nous avons*". DC (1955) 1443.

October 11   Discourse in Italian on Communications. "*Con la piu viva soddistazione*". DC (1955) 1432.

October 21   Address in French on broadcasting. "*En vous souhaitant*". AAS (1955) 755; DC (1955) 1421.

October 28   Address in Italian on the cinema. "*Nel dare, una seconda volta*". AAS (1955) 816.

December 24   Christmas Message broadcast in Italian and referring to modern technology, armaments, and atomic disarmament CD XX.

1 9 5 6

January 8   Address in French on painless childbirth. "*Nous avons reçu des informations*". AAS (1956) 82; CD XXII; F (Mar. 1956).

January 20	Discourse in Italian on private industry. DC (1956) 133.
February 4	Discourse in French on human relations in industry. DC (1956) 197.
March 9	Discourse in French on the Church and Culture to the International Union of Archæological Institutes. *"C'est bien volontiers"*. AAS (1956) 210; OR (10.3.56).
April 1	Easter Message in Italian to the whole world on faith, peace and the atom. *"Come desti"*. AAS (1956) 184; OR (2-3.4.56); *THE POPE SPEAKS* (Autumn 1956) 151.
April 11	Address in Italian to farmers. *"Vi siamo"*. AAS (1956) 277; F (Sep. 1956) 561; OR (13.4.56).
April 12	Address to the Automobile Club of Rome. *"Con vivo piacere"*. Italian text OR (14.4.56).
May 8	Discourse in French on coronary diseases to an international convention on cardiology. *"Les circontances"*. AAS (1956) 454; OR (10.5.56); *THE POPE SPEAKS* (Autumn 1956) 185.
May 14	Address in French on transplantation of cornea to eye specialists and donors of the cornea. *"Vous Nous avez demandez"*. AAS (1956) 459; OR (14-15.5.56); *THE POPE SPEAKS* (Autumn 1956) 198.
May 19	Address in French on sterility and fecundity. *"Vous Nous avez exprimé"*. AAS (1956) 467; OR (20.5.56); *THE POPE SPEAKS* (Autumn 1956) 191.
May 24	Address in English to U.S. surgeons. "Care of the sick". CD XXII; OR (27.5.56).
August 19	Address in French to surgeons on cancer. *"Nous saluons avec"*. DC (1956) 1093; OR (20-1.8.56).
September	Address in French to the Astronautical Federation; OR Sept. 1956.

ACTS OF PIUS XII RELATING TO ATOMIC ENERGY
PRIMARILY OR INCIDENTALLY

(DR=*Discorsi e Radiomessaggi*)

1. November 30, 1941. (DR III 276)

2. February 21, 1943. (DR IV 388)

3. February 2, 1948. (DR IX 439)

4. September 12, 1948. (DR X 208)

    Address to Italian Youth on how Max Planck was led by atomic studies to recognise the existence of the personal God.

5. Christmas message, 1951. (DR XIII 396)

6. Easter message, April 10, 1955. (DR XVII 35)

7. Address to Pontifical Academy, April 24, 1955.

8. Christmas message, 1955. (DR XVII 445)

9. Note to Japanese envoy, April 14, 1957. (OR 24.4.57)

10. Easter message in Italian to the world, April 21, 1957.
    "*Ancora una volta*". (OR 22-23.4.57)

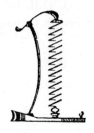

III BIBLIOGRAPHY

(Dates where given refer to the edition used by the author. Books marked with an asterisk are advanced or technical).

BERTIN, Leonard, *Atom Harvest.* (Secker & Warburgh, London, 1955.) Popular account of atomic energy stressing British contributions to its development.

BLÜH and ELDER, *Principles and Applications of Physics.* (Oliver & Boyd, Edinburgh, 1955.) A textbook with sections on the history and philosophy of science.

BONDI, H., *Cosmology.* (Cambridge University Press, 1952.)

BORN, M., *Experiment and Theory in Physics.* (Cambridge University Press, 1943); *Natural Philosophy of Cause and Chance.* (Oxford University Press, 1949.)

BRAITHWAITE, R. B., *Scientific Explanation.* (Cambridge University Press, 1953.) A study of the function of theory, probability and law in science. Partly technical.

BRIDGMAN, P. W., *The Logic of Modern Physics.* (Macmillan, New York, 1927.) Describes "operationalism". Solid, but difficult reading; *The Nature of some of our Physical Concepts.* (Philosophical Library, New York, 1952); *Reflections of a Physicist.* (Philosophical Library, New York, 1950.)

BRÜCK, H. A., "Astronomical Cosmology" in *Studies* [Dublin], 42 (1953) 361; 43 (1954) 31.

BURTT, E. A., *Metaphysical Foundations of Modern Physical Science.* (Keegan Paul, London, 1932.)

BUSH, Vannevar, *Modern Arms and Free Men.* (Heinemann, London, 1950.) Thorough, but no longer sure of anything.

BUTTERFIELD, H., *The Origins of Modern Science : 1300-1800.* (Bell, London, 1949.) An historian's view of the greatest force since Christianity.

CALDIN, E. F., *The Power and Limits of Science.* (Chapman & Hall, London, 1949.) A clear exposition of the theory of science. *Science and Christian Apologetics.* (Blackfriars, London, 1951.)

CARLEN, Sister M. Claudia, I.H.M., *Guide to the Documents of Pius XII* (1939-49). (Newman Press, Westminster, Md., 1951.)

Catholic Documents. (Salesian Press, Surrey Lane, Battersea, London, S.W.11.)

CHADWICK, J., *Radioactivity and Radioactive Substances.* (Pitman, London, 1953.)

CHASE, C. T., *The Evolution of Modern Physics.* (Van Nostrand, New York, 1947.)

COFFEE, P., *Ontology*, 1 vol.; *Epistemology*, 2 vols. (London, Longmans.)

COLLINGWOOD, R. G., *The Idea of Nature*. (Oxford University Press, 1945.)

COMPTON, Arthur H., *Atomic Quest*. (Oxford University Press, 1956.) Destined to be a classic. A political atom-scientist's *Apologia pro vita sua*.

COPLESTON, F., *History of Philosophy*. (Burns & Oates, London, 1953.) 3 volumes have appeared, all very readable.

CROMBIE, A. C., *Augustine to Galileo*. (Falcon Press, London, 1952.)

DAMPIER, Sir W. C. D., *A History of Science and its Relations with Philosophy and Religion*. (Cambridge University Press, 1942.)

DEAN, Gordon, *Report on the Atom*. (Eyre & Spottiswoode, London, 1954.) Semi-popular.

DE BROGLIE, L., *The Revolution in Physics*. (Routledge, London, 1954.)

DINGLE, H., *The Scientific Adventure*. (Pitman, London, 1952); *The Sources of Eddington's Philosophy*. (Cambridge University Press, 1954.)

Discorsi e Radiomessaggi. (Vatican Press) annually.

Documentation Catholique, La. (Mason de la Bonne Press, 5 rue Bayard, Paris 8e.)

DRAPER, J. W., *The Conflict between Religion and Science*. (H. S. King, London, 1874.)

DUHEM, P., *Essai sur la Notion de Théorie Physique de Platon à Galilée*. (Hermann, Paris, 1908); *Le Système du Monde*. 5 vols. (Hermann, Paris, 1913-17); *Le mixte*. (C. Naud, Paris, 1902); *La théorie physique*. (Chevalier & Rivière, Paris, 1906.) Duhem distinguishes two tendencies, atomism with its concrete pictures, and Aristotelianism characterized by exact, minute, logical analysis of perceptions of the external world.

EDDINGTON, Sir A., **Fundamental Theory*. (Cambridge University Press, 1946.) Advanced. *The Expanding Universe*. (Penguin Books, London, 1940.) Popular. *The Nature of the Physical World*. (Cambridge University Press, 1928.) Fanciful and popular. *The Philosophy of Physical Science*. (Cambridge University Press, 1949.) Stimulating subjective idealism.

EINSTEIN, A. and INFELD, L., *The Evolution of Physics*. (Cambridge University Press, 1938.)

ESSLINGER, William, *Politics and Science*. (Philosophical Library, New York, 1955.) Stresses the need for a science of politics in our atomic age in order to achieve peace.

GAMOW, G., *The Creation of the Universe*. (Macmillan, New York, 1952.)

GILL, H. V., *Fact and Fiction in Modern Science*. (M. H. Gill, Dublin, 1943.)

GLASSTONE, S., *Source Book of Atomic Energy*. (Macmillan, London, 1950.)

HALL, A. R., *The Scientific Revolution*, 1500-1800. (Longmans, London, 1954.)

HEITLER, W., *Elementary Wave Mechanics*. (Clarendon Press, Oxford, 1950.)

HOLMES, Arthur, *Principles of Physical Geology*. (Nelson, London, 1954.)

HOYLE, F., *Frontiers of Astronomy*. (Heinemann, London, 1955.) Stimulating and fanciful. *The Nature of the Universe*. (Blackwell, Oxford, 1950). Mixes personal and scientific opinion.

HUBBLE, E. P., *The Realm of the Nebulae*. (Clarendon Press, Oxford, 1936); *The Observational Approach to Cosmology*. (Clarendon Press, Oxford, 1937.)

JANOSSY, L., *Cosmic Rays and Nuclear Physics*. (Pilot Press, London, 1948.)

JEANS, Sir J., *The Growth of Physical Science*. (Cambridge University Press, 1947.) Like all Jeans's popular books, fascinating and illogical.

JONES, G. O., ROTBLAT, J., and WHITROW, G. J., *Atoms and the Universe*. (Eyre & Spottiswoode, London, 1956.) A solid book, but lacks flesh.

KANE, W. H., *"Nature and Extent of the Philosophy of Nature"* in *The Thomist*, 7 (1944) 204.

LINDSAY, J., *The History of Science : Origins and Results of the Scientific Revolution*. (Cohen & West, London, 1951.)

LINDSAY, R. B. and MARGENAU, H., *Foundations of Physics*. (Chapman & Hall, London, 1949.)

LYTTLETON, Raymund A., *The Modern Universe*. (Hodder & Stoughton, London, 1956.) A good introduction to modern astronomy for the general reader apart from an unconvincing opening and ending.

McCREA, W. H., *Physics of the Sun and Stars*. (Hutchinson, London, 1950.)

MACH, Ernest, *The Science of Mechanics*. (Chicago, 1902.) Translated by Thomas J. McCormack.

McLAUGHLIN, P. J., *Modern Science and God*. (Clonmore & Reynolds, Dublin, 1952.)

MARGENAU, H., *The Nature of Physical Reality*. (McGraw-Hill, New York, 1950.)

MASCALL, E. L., *Christian Theology and Natural Science*. (Longmans, London, 1956.) A scholarly work not in agreement with *Humani Generis* at all points.

MEYERSON, Émile, *Identité et realité*. (Paris, 1908.); *De l'explication dans les sciences*. (Paris, 1921.)

MILNE, E. A., *Modern Cosmology and the Christian Idea of God.* (Oxford University Press, 1952.)

MOCH, Jules, *Human Folly: to disarm or perish.* (Gollancz, London, 1955.) Minute and sometimes technical examination of modern warfare and its threat to civilization.

O'NEILL, John, *Cosmology,* Vol. 1. (London, Longmans, 1923.) Outstanding treatise in English on the older cosmology.

O'RAHILLY, Alfred, **Electromagnetics.* (Longmans, London, 1938.) A discussion of fundamentals. [See *Dimensional Methods,* by C. M. Focken; and *Physical Similarity and Dimensional Analysis,* by W. J. Duncan: both Arnold, London, 1953; and 1954, for developments of O'Rahilly's theory of physical dimensions.]

PAYNE-GAPOSCHKIN, C., *Stars in the Making.* (Eyre & Spottiswoode, London, 1953.)

PEIERLS, R. E., *The Laws of Nature.* (Allen & Unwin, London, 1955.) A mathematician's rather abstract idea of a popular exposition.

PLANCK, Max, *The Universe in Modern Physics.* (Allen & Unwin, London, 1937.); *A Scientific Autobiography.* (Williams & Norgate, London, 1950.)

PLEDGE, H. T., *Science Since 1500.* (Philosophical Library, New York, 1946.)

POINCARÉ, Henri, *Science et hypothèse.* (Paris, 1902.); *La valeur de la science.* (Paris, 1905.); *Science et méthode.* (Paris, 1909.);*Dernières pensées.* (Paris, 1913.)

POLLOCK, Robert C., ed., *The Mind of Pius XII.* (Fireside Press, London, 1955.) Excerpts from Papal addresses.

PRICE, H. H., *Some Aspects of the Conflict between Science and Religion.* (Cambridge University Press, 1953.)

RABBITTE, Edwin, O.F.M., *Cosmology for all.* (Cork, the Mercer Press, 1956.) Short and clear account of rational cosmology.

REICHENBACH, H., **Philosophic Foundations of Quantum Mechanics.* (University of California Press, Berkeley, 1946.)

RENOIRTE, Fernand, *Éléments de critique des sciences et de cosmologie.* (Louvain, 1947.) Done into English by J. F. Coffey: *Cosmology,* etc. (New York, 1950.) Gives the philosophical approach but identifies physical science with theoretical physics.

RITCHIE, A. D., *Civilization, Science and Religion.* (Penguin Books, London, 1945.); *Reflections on the Philosophy of Sir Arthur Eddington.* (Cambridge University Press, 1948.) Shrewd criticism.

ROTBLAT, J., *Atomic Energy: A Survey.* (Taylor & Francis, London, 1954.)

SCHRÖDINGER, E., **What is Life?* The Physical Aspect of the Living Cell. (Cambridge University Press, 1944.) As usual with Schrödinger, a fresh and ingenious approach, but unfortunately the body is spoiled in this case by the appendix.

SHAPLEY, H., *Galaxies*. (Churchill, London, 1947.)

SHERRINGTON, Sir C., *Man on His Nature*. (Cambridge University Press, 1951.)

SIMPSON, J. Y., *Landmarks in the Struggle between Science and Religion*. (Hodder & Stoughton, London, 1925.)

SMART, W. M., *The Origin of the Earth*. (Cambridge University Press, 1951.) More scientific than the usual run of books on this theme.

SMITH, V. E., *Philosophical Physics*. (Harper, New York, 1950.)

STEBBING, S., *Philosophy and the Physicists*. (Methuen, London, 1937.) Severe on physicists who are not really physicists or philosophers. *A Modern Introduction to Logic*. (Methuen, London, 1945.)

STEWART and TAIT, *The Unseen World*. (Macmillan, London, 1901.) Physical speculations on a future state by two eminent Victorian scientists. First edition 1875. This book had tremendous popularity. To-day it is hard to read, and practically unknown among scientists for whom it was written.

STOKES, Sir G. G., *Natural Theology*. (A. & C. Black, London, 1891.)

STRANATHAN, J. D., *The Particles of Modern Physics*. (Blakiston, Philadelphia, 1943.)

SULLIVAN, J. W. N., *The Bases of Modern Science*. (Penguin Books, London, 1939.)

TAYLOR, F. Sherwood, *The Attitude of St. Thomas to Natural Science*. (Blackfriars, Oxford, 1944.); *The Fourfold Vision*. (Chapman & Hall, London, 1945.)

THOMPSON, W. R., *Science and Common Sense*. (Longmans, London, 1937).

THOMSON, Sir George, *The Foreseeable Future*. (Cambridge University Press, 1955.)

THORNDIKE, Lynn, *University Records and Life in the Middle Ages*. (Columbia University Press, New York, 1944.); *A History of Magic and Experimental Science*. 5 vols. to 1940. (Columbia University Press, New York, 1944.)

TOULMIN, S., *The Philosophy of Science*. (Hutchinson, London, 1953.)

VANDERVELDT, James H., O.F.M., & ODENWALD, Robert P., M.D., *Psychiatry and Catholicism*. (McGraw-Hill, New York, 1952.)

VAN MELSEN, A. G., **The Philosophy of Nature*. (Duquesne University Press, Pittsburgh, 1953.)

VON WEIZSÄCKER, C. F., *The World View of Physics*. (Routledge, London, 1952.)

WADDINGTON, C. H., *The Scientific Attitude*. (Penguin Books, London, 1941.)

WHITE, A. D., *A History of the Warfare of Science with Theology in Christendom*. (Appleton, New York, 1897.)

WHITEHEAD, A. N., *Science and the Modern World*. (Cambridge University Press, 1926.) Popular and poetic.

WHITROW, G. J., *The Structure of the Universe*. (Hutchinson, London, 1949.)

WHITTAKER, Sir E., **A History of the Theories of Aether and Electricity*. 2 vols. (Nelson, London, 1951; 1953.) For scholars. *Space and Spirit*. (Nelson, London, 1946.) A personal evaluation of traditional arguments for God's existence in the light of modern mathematics.

WILSON, W., *A Hundred Years of Physics*. (Duckworth, London, 1950.)

WIENER, N., **Cybernetics*. (John Wiley, New York, 1948.) Contains a mathematical theory of servo-mechanisms.

WITTGENSTEIN, L., *Philosophical Investigations*. (Blackwell, Oxford, 1953.) Profound and obscure.

YOUNG, G. Z., *Doubt and Certainty in Science*. (Oxford University Press, 1951.)

YZERMANS, Vincent A., *The Unwearied Advocate : Public Addresses of Pope Pius XII*. (St. Cloud Bookshop, 25 Eighth Avenue So., St. Cloud, Minn., 1954.) A collection of 249 public addresses of Pope Pius XII in 3 volumes.

INDEX

367